W9-AXO-128

SCOTT FORESMAN · ADDISON WESLEY

Mathematics

Grade 5

Answer Key

for Reteaching, Practice, Enrichment and Problem Solving

PEARSON

Scott
Foresman

Editorial Offices: Glenview, Illinois • Parsippany, New Jersey • New York, New York

Sales Offices: Parsippany, New Jersey • Duluth, Georgia • Glenview, Illinois
Coppell, Texas • Ontario, California • Mesa, Arizona

ISBN 0-328-04943-3

5 6 7 8 9 10 V084 12 11 10 09 08 07 06 05 04

Name_____

Place Value Through Billions

P 1-1

Write the word form for each number and tell the value of the underlined digit.

1. 34,235,345 **Thirty-four million, two hundred thirty-five thousand, three hundred forty-five; five thousand**

2. 19,673,890,004 **Nineteen billion, six hundred seventy-three million, eight hundred ninety thousand, four; nine billion**

3. Write 2,430,090 in expanded form.
2,000,000 + 400,000 + 30,000 + 90

Write each number in standard form.

4. 80,000,000 + 4,000,000 + 100 + 8 **84,000,108**

5. twenty-nine billion, thirty-two million **29,032,000,000**

6. **Number Sense** What number is 10,000 less than 337,676? **327,676**

Test Prep

7. Which number is 164,502,423 decreased by 100,000?
(A) 164,402,423   B. 164,501,423   C. 164,512,423   D. 264,502,423

8. **Writing in Math** Explain how you would write 423,090,709,000 in word form.
Start at the left and write four hundred twenty-three. Write billion for the comma, ninety, million for the comma, seven hundred nine, and thousand for the comma

Use with Lesson 1-1. **1**

© Pearson Education, Inc. 5

Name_____

Place Value Through Billions

R 1-1

Place-value chart:

Billions period			Millions period			Thousands period			Ones period		
hundred billions	ten billions	billions	hundred millions	ten millions	millions	hundred thousands	ten thousands	thousands	hundreds	tens	ones
6,	3	9	2,	5	8	0,	1	0	1		

Expanded form: 6,000,000,000 + 300,000,000 + 90,000,000 + 2,000,000 + 500,000 + 80,000 + 100 + 1

Standard form: 6,392,580,101

Word form: six billion, three hundred ninety-two million, five hundred eighty thousand, one hundred one

Write the word name for each number and tell the value of the underlined digit.

1. 3,552,308,725 **Three billion, five hundred fifty-two million, three hundred eight thousand, seven hundred twenty-five; 50 million**

2. 843,208,732,833 **Eight hundred forty-three billion, two hundred eight million, seven hundred thirty-two thousand, eight hundred thirty-three; 800 billion**

3. Write 2,000,000,000 + 70,000,000 + 100,000 + 70,000 + 3,000 + 800 + 10 in standard form.
2,070,173,810

4. **Number Sense** What number is 100,000,000 more than 5,438,724,022?
5,538,724,022

Use with Lesson 1-1. **1**

© Pearson Education, Inc. 5

Name_____

Find the Numbers

E 1-1
NUMBER SENSE

Use the number chart to answer the questions. Circle each number you find. You can use only digits that are next to each other to make numbers. Read the rows from left to right. Read the columns from top to bottom.

COLUMNS

	A	C	E	G	I	K	M	O	Q	S
B	3	5	4	3	2	7	1	1	7	1
D	2	4	2	9	7	1	9	2	3	9
F	1	1	6	4	1	3	5	2	1	2
H	1	3	7	2	0	5	9	1	2	5
J	4	2	0	3	6	7	1	7	6	9
L	2	2	6	5	2	9	5	6	9	9
N	2	1	8	5	3	8	6	6	2	2
P	8	1	8	3	8	5	7	3	3	3
R	4	1	6	2	3	8	4	7	5	8
T	5	4	4	3	2	5	9	8	2	5

ROWS

Write the letter of the

1. row that has the four-digit number with the least value. **F**

2. column with the greatest number of digits in counting order. **M**

3. column that has the three-digit number with the greatest value. **S**

4. row with the palindrome with the greatest number of digits. (A palindrome is a number that is the same when read forward or backward. For example, the number 121 is a palindrome.) **J**

5. column with the greatest number of odd numbers in counting order. **K**

6. column with the palindrome with the greatest number of digits. **G**

7. row with the greatest number of digits in reverse counting order. **B**

8. column that has the five-digit number with the least value. **I**

Use with Lesson 1-1. **1**

© Pearson Education, Inc. 5

Name_____

Place Value Through Billions

PS 1-1

Five federal government organizations are active in putting out wildfires. The table shows how much money each organization spent during three different years of fighting wildfires.

Money Spent Fighting Wildfires

	1998	2000	2002
Bureau of Land Management	$63,177,000	$180,567,000	$204,666,000
Bureau of Indian Affairs	$27,366,000	$93,042,000	$109,055,000
Fish and Wildlife Service	$3,800,000	$9,417,000	$15,245,000
National Park Service	$19,183,000	$53,341,000	$66,094,000
USDA Forest Service	$215,000,000	$1,026,000,000	$1,266,274,000
Total	$328,526,000	$1,362,367,000	$1,661,334,000

1. What is the value in dollars of the digit in the greatest place for each year's total?
1998: 300 million; 2000: 1 billion; 2002: 1 billion

2. Write in short-word form the number of dollars the USDA Forest Service spent on putting out wildfires in the year 2000.
1 billion, 26 million dollars

3. Write in expanded form the number of dollars the Fish and Wildlife Service spent on putting out wildfires in 2002.
10,000,000 + 5,000,000 + 200,000 + 40,000 + 5,000

4. **Writing in Math** Explain why the value of a digit depends on its place value.
Sample answer: The place value of a digit in a number tells you what the digit is multiplied by to find its value. If an 8 is in the hundreds place, its value is 8 × 100, or 800.

Use with Lesson 1-1. **1**

© Pearson Education, Inc. 5

Name_____

Comparing and Ordering Whole Numbers

P 1-2

Complete. Write >, <, or = for each ◯ .

1. 23,412 ◯> 23,098

2. 9,000,000 ◯< 9,421,090

Order these numbers from least to greatest.

3. 7,545,999 7,445,999 7,554,000

7,445,999 7,545,999 7,554,000

4. **Number Sense** What digit could be in the ten millions place of a number that is less than 55,000,000 but greater than 25,000,000?

2, 3, 4, or 5

5. Put the trenches in order from the least depth to the greatest depth.

Kermadec Trench,

Philippine Trench,

Tonga Trench,

Mariana Trench

Depths of Major Ocean Trenches

Trench	Depth (in feet)
Philippine Trench	32,995
Mariana Trench	35,840
Kermadec Trench	32,963
Tonga Trench	35,433

Test Prep

6. These numbers are ordered from greatest to least. Which number could be placed in the second position?

2,643,022 1,764,322 927,322

A. 2,743,022 B. 1,927,304 C. 1,443,322 D. 964,322

7. **Writing in Math** Explain why 42,678 is greater than 42,067.

Although the digits in the thousands period are the same, the hundreds digits differ, and since 6 is greater than 0, 42,678 is the greater number.

2 Use with Lesson 1-2.

© Pearson Education, Inc. 5

Name_____

Comparing and Ordering Whole Numbers

R 1-2

Order these numbers from least to greatest: 4,752,213; 5,829,302; 4,234,295; 4,333,209.

Step 1: Write the numbers, lining up places. Begin at the left to find the greatest or least number.

4,752,213
5,829,302
4,234,295
4,333,209

5,829,302 is the greatest.

Step 2: Write the remaining numbers, lining up places. Find the greatest and least of these.

4,752,213   4,234,295
4,234,295   4,333,209
4,333,209

4,752,213 is the greatest of these.

4,234,295 is the least.

Step 3: Write the numbers from least to greatest.

4,234,295
4,333,209
4,752,213
5,829,302

Complete. Write >, <, or = in each ◯ .

1. 7,642 ◯< 7,843

2. 2,858,534 ◯< 2,882,201

Order these numbers from least to greatest.

3. 768,265 769,205 739,802

739,802; 768,265; 769,205

4. Write the areas of each country in order from greatest to least.

28,748; 28,450; 27,830; 27,750

Country	Area in Square Miles
Albania	28,748
Burundi	27,830
Solomon Islands	28,450
Haiti	27,750

2 Use with Lesson 1-2.

© Pearson Education, Inc. 5

Name_____

Pondering Populations

E 1-2
NUMBER SENSE

City A, City B, and City C are close to each other. City A has a population of 210,000. City B has a population that is greater than 200,000 but less than that of City A. City C has less than half the population of City A.

City A	City B	City C
Population: 210,000	Population: >200,000 and <City A	Population: < $\frac{1}{2}$ of City A

1. What number must be in the ten-thousands place of the population of City B?

0

2. What number must City C's population be less than?

105,000

3. What is the greatest population City C could have?

104,999

4. What is the least number of people needed to make the population of City B greater than the population of City A?

2

5. What is the sum of the greatest possible populations of all three cities?

524,998

6. What is the least number of people that could live in City B?

200,001

7. Could City C's population be half of City B's population?

Yes

2 Use with Lesson 1-2.

© Pearson Education, Inc. 5

Name_____

Comparing and Ordering Whole Numbers

PS 1-2

Show Dogs The American Kennel Club keeps a list of purebred dogs registered by their owners. The table shows the four most popular breeds registered with the club in the years 2000 and 2001.

Dogs Registered with the American Kennel Club

Breed	2000	2001
Dachshunds	54,773	50,478
Yorkshire terriers	43,574	42,025
Beagles	52,026	50,419
Labrador retrievers	172,841	165,970

1. In 2000, which breed of dog had the greatest number registered?

Labrador retrievers

2. In 2000, which breed of dog had the least number registered?

Yorkshire terriers

3. Order the breeds from the greatest number to the least number registered in 2001.

Labrador retrievers, dachshunds, beagles, Yorkshire terriers

4. **Writing in Math** When comparing two numbers, should you begin comparing the digits from the right or the left? Why?

Sample answer: You should begin on the left because the place values are the greatest on the left.

2 Use with Lesson 1-2.

© Pearson Education, Inc. 5

© Pearson Education, Inc. 5

Name_____

Place Value Through Thousandths P 1-3

Write the word form for each number and tell the value of the underlined digit.

1. 4.34<u>5</u> **Four and three hundred forty-five thousandths; 0.005**

2. 7.<u>8</u>80 **Seven and eight hundred eighty thousandths; 0.8**

Write each number in standard form.

3. 6 + 0.3 + 0.02 + 0.001 **6.321**

4. seven and five hundred thirty-three thousandths **7.533**

Write two decimals that are equivalent to each number.

5. 0.68 **0.680 and 0.6800**

6. 0.9 **0.90 and 0.900**

7. **Number Sense** Explain why 0.2 and 0.020 are not equivalent.

The first number, 0.2, has a 2 in the tenths place, and the second number, 0.020, has a 0 in the tenths place and a 2 in the hundredths place.

8. Cheri's time in the bobsled race was 1 min, 38.29 sec. Write the word form and the value of the 9 in Cheri's time.

Nine hundredths; 0.09

Test Prep

9. Which is the word form of the underlined digit in 46.<u>5</u>04?

A. 5 ones **B.** 5 tenths C. 5 hundredths D. 5 thousandths

10. **Writing in Math** Write the value for each digit in the number 1.639. **1, 0.6, 0.03, 0.009**

Name_____

Place Value Through Thousandths R 1-3

Here are different ways to represent 1.753.

Place-value chart:

Ones	Tenths	Hundredths	Thousandths
1 .	7	5	3

Expanded form: 1 + 0.7 + 0.05 + 0.003

Standard form: 1.753

Word form: one and seven hundred fifty-three thousandths

The following decimals are equivalent to 0.9.

0.9 = 0.90 and 0.9 = 0.900

Why? Because 9 tenths have 90 hundredths or 900 thousandths.

Write the word name for each number and tell the value of the underlined digit.

1. 6.0<u>2</u> **Six and two hundredths; 2 hundredths**

2. 5.<u>3</u>19 **Five and three hundred nineteen thousandths; 3 tenths**

Write each number in standard form.

3. 7 + 0.7 + 0.04 + 0.005 **7.745**

4. four and five hundred fifty-eight thousandths **4.558**

Write two decimals that are equivalent to each number.

5. 0.80 **0.8; 0.800**

6. 0.300 **0.3; 0.30**

Name_____

Swim Teams E 1-3 DATA

The city pool held an end of the season swimming competition. One of the events was the four-person relay. In this relay, each swimmer swam a different stroke for the same distance. The times in minutes for each team are shown in the table.

Swimming Stroke	Red Team	Yellow Team	Blue Team
Backstroke	1.937	1.652	1.086
Breaststroke	1.521	1.138	2.083
Butterfly	1.937	2.139	1.381
Freestyle	1.214	1.190	1.214

Use the data in the table to answer the questions below.

1. For which stroke did the blue team have a time of 1 + 0.08 + 0.006? **Backstroke**

2. Which team had a time for the freestyle stroke with a 9 in the hundredths place? **Yellow team**

3. For which stroke did the red team have a time with a 5 in the tenths place? **Breaststroke**

4. Which team had a time for the butterfly stroke with a 1 in the thousandths place? **Blue team**

5. For which stroke did two teams have the same time? Which two teams? **Freestyle; red and blue teams**

6. Which team had the same time for two strokes? Which strokes? **Red team; backstroke and butterfly**

7. Which team do you think won the meet? Why? **Blue team; Sample answer: Most of the blue team's times are closer to 1 than to 2.**

Name_____

Place Value Through Thousandths PS 1-3

A men's college swim team keeps records of its best race times in different lengths of races and swim strokes. The best time using a freestyle stroke for 50 m is 22.72 sec. The best time using a backstroke for 100 m is 54.04 sec.

1. Write the time of the 50 m freestyle record in word form.

Twenty-two and seventy-two hundredths

2. Write the time of the 100 m backstroke record in expanded form.

50 + 4 + 0.04

Men's Olympic Swimming Records

Event	Time
100 m freestyle	47.84 seconds
100 m backstroke	53.72 seconds
100 m butterfly	51.96 seconds

3. What is the value of the 8 in the 100 m freestyle record? **8 tenths**

4. What is the place value of the 6 in the 100 m butterfly record? **Hundredths**

5. **Writing in Math** Explain how you write the number 20.158 in word form.

Sample answer: Write "twenty," "and" for the decimal point, and "one hundred fifty-eight thousandths."

Comparing and Ordering Decimals   P 1-4

Write >, <, or = for each ◯ .

1. 5.424 ⟩ 5.343   2. 0.33 = 0.330   3. 9.489 ⟩ 9.479

4. 21.012 ⟩ 21.01   5. 223.21 ⟩ 223.199   6. 5.43 < 5.432

Order these numbers from least to greatest.

7. 8.37, 8.3, 8.219, 8.129   **8.129, 8.219, 8.3, 8.37**

8. 0.012, 0.100, 0.001, 0.101   **0.001, 0.012, 0.100, 0.101**

9. **Number Sense** Name three numbers between 0.33 and 0.34.   **Sample answer: 0.334, 0.335, 0.336**

10. Which runner came in first place?   **Liz**

Half Mile Run

Runner	Time (minutes)
Amanda	8.016
Calvin	7.049
Liz	7.03
Steve	8.16

11. Who ran faster, Amanda or Steve?   **Amanda**

12. Who ran for the longest time?   **Steve**

Test Prep

13. Which number is less than 28.43?

A. 28.435   B. 28.34   C. 28.430   D. 29.43

14. **Writing in Math** Explain why it is not reasonable to say that 4.23 is less than 4.13.

The number 4.23 is greater than 4.13, because there is a 2 in the tenths place and 2 is greater than 1.

Comparing and Ordering Decimals   R 1-4

List the numbers in order from least to greatest: 6.943, 5.229, 6.825, 6.852, 6.779.

Step 1: Write the numbers, lining up places. Begin at the left to find the greatest or least number.	Step 2: Write the remaining numbers, lining up places. Find the greatest and least.	Step 3: Write the numbers from least to greatest.
6.943 5.229 6.825 6.852 6.779 5.229 is the least.	6.943 6.825 6.825 6.852 6.852 6.779 6.779 is the least. 6.852 is greater. 6.943 is the greatest.	5.229 6.779 6.825 6.852 6.943

Complete. Write >, <, or = for each ◯ .

1. 7.539 ⟩ 7.344   2. 9.202 < 9.209   3. 0.75 = 0.750

Order these numbers from least to greatest.

4. 3.898 3.827 3.779   **3.779, 3.827, 3.898**

5. 5.234 5.199 5.002 5.243   **5.002, 5.199, 5.234, 5.243**

Which had the faster speed?

6. Driver A or Driver D   **Driver A**

7. Driver C or Driver A   **Driver C**

Car Racing Winners

Driver	Average Speed (mph)
Driver A	145.155
Driver B	145.827
Driver C	147.956
Driver D	144.809

Dropping Digits   E 1-4
REASONING

Use each digit only once to make the comparisons true.

1. Use 1, 2, and 3.

1.2 5 < 1.3 1

2. Use 8 and 9.

8.1 9 > 8.12

3. Use 0, 4, and 6.

0 .3 4 9 < 0.36 6

4. Use 5 and 7.

46. 7 75 > 46.57 5

5. Use 1, 3, and 8.

8.3 1 < 8.3 3 < 8 .34

6. Use 2, 5, and 9.

9 .128 > 7.3 5 6 > 7. 2 97

7. Use 6, 3, 4, and 1.

4.3 6 1 > 4 .35 > 4.3 2

8. Use 7, 0, 9, and 5.

7. 0 5 < 7 .08 < 7.0 9

Fill in the boxes to make the comparison true. List all possible combinations.

9. Use 6, 7, and 8.

36. 6 4 < 3 7 . 8 4
36. 6 4 < 3 8 . 7 4
36. 7 4 < 3 8 . 6 4
36. 7 4 < 3 6 . 8 4
36. 8 4 < 3 7 . 6 4

10. Use 3, 2, 1, and 0.

3. 2 59 > 2. 1 5 0
3. 2 59 > 2. 0 5 1
2. 3 59 > 2. 1 5 0
2. 3 59 > 2. 0 5 1
2. 1 59 > 2. 0 5 3

Comparing and Ordering Decimals   PS 1-4

Groceries Saraline and her mother went grocery shopping. They bought bread for $2.51, a pineapple for $3.60, a bag of tomatoes for $2.57, and fish for $3.09.

1. Which cost more, the bread or the fish?   **Fish**

2. Which cost more, the bread or the tomatoes?   **Tomatoes**

3. Order the price of each item from least to greatest.

$2.51; $2.57; $3.09; $3.60

College Classes Joseph is taking a number of college classes. A course number identifies each class. Right now he is taking classes 1.31, 1.058, 2.415, 2.412, and 1.06.

4. Which of Joseph's classes has the highest course number?   **2.415**

5. Which of Joseph's classes has the lowest course number?   **1.058**

6. How many classes have course numbers that are greater than 1.50?   **Two classes**

7. **Writing in Math** Is 1.5 greater than or less than 1.05? Explain.

Sample answer: 1.5 is greater than 1.05 because the 1 is in the same place in both numbers, but the 5 is in the tenths place in 1.5 and in the hundredths place in 1.05, and tenths are greater than hundredths.

Name_____

Place-Value Patterns

Tell how many *tens*, *hundreds*, and *thousands* are in each number.

1. 12,000 **12 thousands; 120 hundreds; 1,200 tens**

2. 9,000,000 **9,000 thousands; 90,000 hundreds; 900,000 tens**

What number makes each statement true?

3. $9,000 = 900 \times$ **10**

4. $600,000 = 60 \times$ **10,000**

5. $4 = 0.4 \times$ **10**

6. $60 = 0.6 \times$ **100**

Name each number in two different ways. **Sample answers.**

7. 90,000,000 **90 million or 90,000 thousands**

8. 40,000 **40 thousands or 4,000 tens**

9. **Number Sense** How many thousands are in 5,000,000? **5,000**

10. The volume of Fort Peck Dam is $96,050 \times 1,000$ m³. Suppose the state of Montana decides to increase the volume of the dam. After the improvements, Fort Peck will hold 10 times as many cubic meters. How many cubic meters will Fort Peck hold after the improvements?

960,500,000 m³

Test Prep

11. Which is the correct product for $1,000 \times 0.4$?

A. 4,000   (B.) 400   C. 4.000   D. 0.0004

12. **Writing in Math** Complete the missing information in this sentence:

Twenty-nine **thousand** is equal to $29 \times 1,000$.

Name_____

Place-Value Patterns

You can name the number 30,000 in several different ways.

3 ten thousands (or $3 \times 10,000$)

30 thousands (or $30 \times 1,000$)

300 hundreds (or 300×100)

3,000 tens (or $3,000 \times 10$)

30,000 ones (or $30,000 \times 1$)

Ten Thousands	Thousands	Hundreds	Tens	Ones
3	0	0	0	0
3	**0**	0	0	0
3	**0**	**0**	0	0
3	**0**	**0**	**0**	0
3	**0**	**0**	**0**	**0**

Notice the pattern as you describe 30,000 in terms of ten thousands, thousands, hundreds, tens, and ones. The bold digits show how many ten thousands, thousands, hundreds, tens, and ones there are in 30,000. You can see, for example, that 3 ten thousands is the same as 3,000 tens.

Tell how many tens, hundreds, and thousands are in each number.

1. 50,000 **5,000** tens **500** hundreds **50** thousands

2. 15,000,000 **1,500,000** tens **150,000** hundreds **15,000** thousands

What number makes each statement true?

3. $97,000 = 970 \times$ **100**

4. $8 = 0.8 \times$ **10**

Name_____

How Much Will It Cost?

The average U.S. prices for barley, oats, and wheat for the year 2000 are listed in the table below. Suppose the 2025 prices will be 10 times the 2000 prices, and the 2050 prices will be 100 times the 2000 prices.

1. Complete the table by using the information given above to find the projected crop prices.

Crop Prices—$ per Bushel

Crop	2000	2025	2050
Barley	$2.15	**$21.50**	**$215.00**
Oats	$1.05	**$10.50**	**$105.00**
Wheat	$2.65	**$26.50**	**$265.00**

2. Find the cost of 1,000 bushels of each crop in 2000.

Barley: **$2,150**

Oats: **$1,050**

Wheat: **$2,650**

3. Find the cost of 10 bushels of each crop in 2025.

Barley: **$215**

Oats: **$105**

Wheat: **$265**

4. Find the cost of 100 bushels of each crop for 2050.

Barley: **$21,500**

Oats: **$10,500**

Wheat: **$26,500**

Name_____

Place-Value Patterns

Janine runs a business from her home. Last year she used 21,500 sheets of paper.

1. If Janine uses 10 times as much paper this year as she did last year, how much paper will she use this year?

215,000 sheets

2. A company buys paper from the same manufacturer that Janine does. If the company used 1,000 times as much paper last year as Janine did, how much paper did it use?

21,500,000 sheets

The area of Canada is about 10,000,000 sq km. Of that area, 9,100,000 sq km are land and 900,000 sq km are freshwater.

3. How many thousands of square kilometers of area does Canada have?

10,000 thousands

4. How many hundreds of square kilometers of Canada is freshwater?

9,000 hundreds

5. **Writing in Math** Gina says that you can tell how many tens, hundreds, or thousands are in a number by moving the decimal point. Is she correct? Why or why not?

Yes; Sample answer: Multiplying or dividing by 10 will move the decimal point one place left or right, by 100 two places, and by 1,000 three places.

PROBLEM-SOLVING SKILL   P 1-6
Read and Understand

The day a new manufacturing plant opened, the population of Sunny Grove was 13,731 people. In its first year of operation, 2,950 new residents moved into Sunny Grove. In the second year, double that number moved in. What was the population of Sunny Grove by the end of the second year of the plant's operation?

Sample answers.

1. Tell the problem in your own words. **Before the plant opened, the population was 13,731. The population in Sunny Grove is increasing.**

2. Identify key facts and details. **Year 1 population: 13,731; Year 2 population: 13,731 + 2,950; Year 3 population: 16,681 + 2,950 + 2,950**

3. Tell what the question is asking. **What was the population by the end of the second year?**

4. Show the main idea.

?			
13,731	2,950	2,950	2,950

5. Solve the problem. Write the answer in a complete sentence.
The population was 22,581 people.

PROBLEM-SOLVING SKILL   R 1-6
Read and Understand

Anniversary James's parents celebrated their 25th wedding anniversary in 1999. In what year did they get married?

> Read and Understand

Step 1: What do you know?

• Tell the problem in your own words. James's parents got married during a certain year.

• Identify key details and facts. James's parents had been married for 25 years in 1999.

Step 2: What are you trying to find?

• Tell what the question is asking. You want to know the year that James's parents were married.

• Show the main idea.

1999	
?	25

Use subtraction to find the answer.
1999 − 25 = 1974

Female Athletes In a certain year at Pembrook High School, 24 out of every 500 female students played on the volleyball teams, and 34 played on the soccer teams. If there were 1,000 female students at the high school that year, how many more athletes played on the soccer teams than the volleyball teams?

Sample answers 1–2

1. Identify key facts and details.
There are 34 female soccer players and 24 female volleyball players out of every 500 female students. There are 1,000 female students.

2. Solve the problem. Write your answer in a complete sentence.
68 − 48 = 20; There are 20 more female soccer players than female volleyball players for the 1,000 female students.

Shape Up   E 1-6
VISUAL THINKING

Draw a circle around the figures that are the same.

1.

2.

3.

4.

5.

6.

PROBLEM-SOLVING SKILL   PS 1-6
Read and Understand

Exercise Each summer Mikael changes his workout routine by exercising 190 min more each week. Over the summer months, Mikael exercises a total of 910 min a week. How many minutes a week does he work out when it is not summer?

> Read and Understand

Step 1: What do you know?

1. Tell the problem in your own words.
Mikael works out more in the summer.

2. Identify key facts and details.
Mikael exercises 910 min per week in the summer, 190 min more per week than the rest of the year.

Step 2: What are you trying to find?

3. Tell what the question is asking.
How many minutes a week Mikael works out when it is not summer

4. Show the main idea.

910	
?	190

5. Solve the problem. Write the answer in a complete sentence.
Mikael works out for 720 min each week when it is not summer.

Practice

Name_____

Adding and Subtracting Mentally   P 1-7
Sample answers.

Show how you can add or subtract mentally.

1. 70 + 90 + 30 = _____
$$70 + 90 + 30$$
$$90 + (70 + 30)$$
$$90 + 100 = 190$$

2. 350 − 110 = _____
$$350 - 110$$
$$+ 50 \quad + 50$$
$$\Downarrow \qquad \Downarrow$$
$$400 - 160 = 240$$

National Monuments

Name	State	Acres
George Washington Carver	Missouri	210
Navajo	Arizona	360
Fort Sumter	South Carolina	200
Russell Cave	Alabama	310

3. How many more acres are there at Navajo monument than at George Washington Carver monument?
150 more acres

4. How many acres are there at Fort Sumter and Russell Cave combined?
510 acres

Test Prep

5. Fresh Market bought 56 lb of apples in August from a local orchard. In September, the market purchased an additional 52 lb of apples and 32 lb of strawberries. How many pounds of fruit did the market buy?

   A. 108 lb   **B. 140 lb**   C. 150 lb   D. 240 lb

6. **Writing in Math** Write the definition and give an example of the Commutative Property of Addition. **Sample answer:**
The Commutative Property of Addition says you can add numbers in any order. 30 + 15 + 2 = 15 + 30 + 2

Reteaching

Name_____

Adding and Subtracting Mentally   R 1-7

There are several ways that you can add and subtract numbers mentally to solve a problem.

Commutative Property of Addition

You can add two numbers in any order.

15 + 27 = 27 + 15

Compatible numbers are numbers that are easy to compute mentally.

25 + 93 + 75

25 and 75 are compatible because they are easy to add.

25 + 93 + 75 = (25 + 75) + 93
                   = 100 + 93 = 193

Associative Property of Addition

You can change the groupings of addends.

17 + (13 + 10) = (17 + 13) + 10

With **compensation**, you adjust one number to make computations easier and compensate by changing the other number.

$$320 - 190$$
$$+ 10 \quad + 10$$
$$\Downarrow \qquad \Downarrow$$
$$330 - 200 = 130$$

Add or subtract mentally.

1. 265 + 410 + 335 = **1,010**   2. 885 − 155 = **730**

3. 2,500 + 1,730 + 70 = **4,300**   4. 1,467 − 397 = **1,070**

5. How many more strikeouts did Pitcher A have than Pitcher C?
152 more strikeouts

Strikeout Data

Pitcher	Number of Strikeouts
A	372
B	293
C	220
D	175
E	205

6. How many strikeouts did Pitcher B and Pitcher E have altogether?
498 strikeouts

7. How many strikeouts were recorded by all five pitchers?
1,265 strikeouts

Enrichment

Name_____

Puzzle Squares   E 1-7
NUMBER SENSE

In a puzzle square, the sum of all the numbers in any row, column, or along any diagonal is the same. In the square at the right, every row, column, and diagonal has a sum of 18.

9	4	5
2	6	10
7	8	3

Write the missing number in each puzzle square.

1.
6	**5**	10
11	7	3
4	9	8

2.
14	9	16
15	**13**	11
10	17	12

Look at each number square. Circle the one that is a puzzle square.

3.
3	13	11
7	5	15
17	9	1

5	8	2
10	6	9
3	4	7

11	6	13
12	10	8
7	14	9

Make your own puzzle squares.

4.
2	7	6
9	5	1
4	3	8

5.
1	6	5
8	4	0
3	2	7

Problem Solving

Name_____

Adding and Subtracting Mentally   PS 1-7

Aluminum Cans Jameson, Margie, Julie, and Mark collected cans for recycling to earn money for a service project. The table shows how many cans they collected during the week.

Cans Collected

Jameson	236
Mark	171
Julie	292
Margie	300

1. How many cans did Jameson and Mark collect altogether?
407 cans

2. How many cans did Margie and Julie collect altogether?
592 cans

3. How many more cans did Julie collect than Mark?
121 cans

4. How many more cans did Margie collect than Jameson?
64 cans

5. What is the total number of cans collected by the four students?
999 cans

6. **Writing in Math** Describe two ways that you can add 1,820 + 230 mentally.
Sample answer: You could use compatible numbers by adding 1,800 + 200 = 2,000 and then 20 + 30 = 50; 2,000 + 50 = 2,050. You could use compensation by adjusting 1,820 to 1,800 and compensate by adding 20 to 230 to make it 250; 1,800 + 250 = 2,050.

© Pearson Education, Inc. 5

Name_____

Rounding Whole Numbers and Decimals

P 1-8

Round each number to the place of the underlined digit.

1. 32.6̲0   **32.6**_____

2. 489̲,334,209 **489,000,000**_____

3. 324,̲650   **325,000**_____

4. 32.0̲73   **32.1**_____

5. **Reasoning** Name two different numbers that round to 30 when rounded to the nearest ten.

Sample answer: 29 and 31

In 2000, Italy produced 7,464,000 tons of wheat, and Pakistan produced 21,079,000 tons of wheat. Round each country's wheat production in metric tons to the nearest hundred thousand.

6. Italy **7,500,000 tons**

7. Pakistan **21,100,000 tons**

The price of wheat in 1997 was $3.38 per bushel. In 1998, the price was $2.65 per bushel. Round the price per bushel of wheat for each year to the nearest tenth of a dollar.

8. 1997 **3.4 dollars per bushel**

9. 1998 **2.7 dollars per bushel**

Test Prep

10. Which number rounds to 15,700,000 when rounded to the nearest hundred thousand?

    A. 15,000,000 **B.** 15,579,999 **C.** 15,649,999 **(D.)** 15,659,999

11. **Writing in Math** Write a definition of rounding in your own words.

Sample answer: Rounding helps you adjust a number to make it easier to use.

8   Use with Lesson 1-8.

Name_____

Rounding Whole Numbers and Decimals

R 1-8

Look at the numbers listed below. You can use the number line to tell if 8,237,650 is closer to 8,000,000 or 9,000,000.

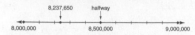

8,237,650 is closer to 8,000,000.

The number line can also help you determine if 7.762 is closer to 7.7 or 7.8.

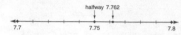

7.762 is closer to 7.8.

Round each number to the place of the underlined digit.

1. 4,7̲25,806

    4,700,000_____

2. 7̲.049

    7_____

3. 165,0̲23,912

    200,000,000_____

4. 18.6̲92

    18.7_____

5. Round the number of connected computers in Year 2 to the nearest ten million.

    40,000,000_____

6. **Number Sense** Marc earned $9.37 per hour working at the library. Round his wage to the nearest ten cents.

    $9.40

Number of Computers Connected to the Internet

Year 1	30,979,376
Year 2	42,199,279
Year 3	63,592,854

8   Use with Lesson 1-8.

Name_____

Cross-Number Puzzle

E 1-8
NUMBER SENSE

Complete the cross-number puzzle. Place the decimal point in each answer in its own square.

Round each number to the place shown.

Across

1. 36.654 to tenths

4. 28.261 to tenths

7. 92,649 to tens

8. 95.227 to hundredths

9. 8,105.473 to hundredths

10. 71.083 to hundredths

12. 14.627 to tenths

13. 59,086 to hundreds

Down

2. 739,126 to thousands

3. 4,561.294 to hundredths

5. 82.957 to tenths

6. 30.768 to hundredths

9. 87,408 to tens

10. 7,507 to tens

11. 8,439 to hundreds

8   Use with Lesson 1-8.

Name_____

Rounding Whole Numbers and Decimals

PS 1-8

Continents The table shows the sizes of the three largest continents on Earth.

Earth's Continents

Continent	Area (sq km)
Asia	44,485,900
Africa	30,269,680
North America	24,235,280

1. Round the area of each continent to the nearest hundred thousand.

Asia: 44,500,000; Africa: 30,300,000; North America: 24,200,000

2. Round the area of each continent to the nearest ten million.

Asia: 40,000,000; Africa: 30,000,000; North America: 20,000,000

Shopping Jeremy has $13.29 in his pocket. He buys a book for $4.99, a stuffed monkey for $3.79, and a box of pencils for $1.49.

3. Round the amount of money Jeremy has to the nearest dollar.

$13.00

4. Round each of Jeremy's purchases to the nearest 10 cents.

$5.00; $3.80; $1.50

5. **Writing in Math** Rock says that 15.452 rounded to the nearest hundredth is 15.44, because the 2 is less than 5. Is he correct? Why or why not?

No; Sample answer: You round down because there is a 2 in the thousandths place, but the 5 in the hundredths place should not be changed to a 4.

Practice

Name_____

Estimating Sums and Differences   P 1-9

Estimate each sum or difference.

Sample answers are given for 1–4.

1. 5,602 − 2,344 __3,300__
2. 7.4 + 3.1 + 9.8 __20__
3. 2,314 + 671 __3,000__
4. 54.23 − 2.39 __52__

5. **Number Sense** Wesley estimated 5.82 − 4.21 to be about 2. Is this an overestimate or an underestimate? Explain.

It is an overestimate because 5.82 was rounded up and 4.21 was rounded down.

Sample answers.

6. Estimate the total precipitation in inches and in days for Asheville and Wichita.

Average Yearly Precipitation of U.S. Cities

City	Inches	Days
Asheville, North Carolina	47.71	124
Wichita, Kansas	28.61	85

About 77 in.; about 210 days

7. In inches and in days, about how much more average yearly precipitation is there in Asheville than in Wichita?

About 20 more in.; about 30 more days

Test Prep

8. Which numbers should you add to estimate the answer to this problem:

87,087 + 98,000?

A. 88,000 + 98,000
B. 87,000 + 98,000
C. 85,000 + 95,000
D. 80,000 + 90,000

9. **Writing in Math** You want to estimate 5.25 − 3.3. Why would using front-end estimation and adjusting tell you more about the answer than rounding?

Sample answer: Front-end estimation and adjusting will tell you if the estimate is more or less than the actual difference.

Use with Lesson 1-9. **9**

Reteaching

Name_____

Estimating Sums and Differences   R 1-9

During one week, Mr. Graham drove a truck to five different towns to make deliveries. About how far did he drive in all?

Mr. Graham's Mileage Log

Cities	Mileage
Mansley to Mt. Hazel	243
Mt. Hazel to Perkins	303
Perkins to Alberton	279
Alberton to Fort Maynard	277
Fort Maynard to Mansley	352

You can round each number to the nearest hundred mile.

$$243 \Rightarrow 200$$
$$303 \Rightarrow 300$$
$$279 \Rightarrow 300$$
$$277 \Rightarrow 300$$
$$+352 \Rightarrow +400$$
$$1,500 \text{ mi}$$

Mr. Graham drove about 1,500 mi.

You can estimate differences in a similar way.

Estimate 7.25 − 4.98.

You can round to the nearest whole number.

$$7.25 \Rightarrow 7$$
$$-4.98 \Rightarrow -5$$
$$2$$

The difference is about 2.

Estimate each sum or difference.

1. 19.7 − 6.9 **About 13**
2. 59 + 43 + 95 **About 200**
3. 582 + 169 + 23 **About 770**
4. 87.99 − 52.46 **About 36**
5. **Estimation** Brigid worked 16.75 hr. Kevin worked 12.50 hr. About how many more hours did Brigid work than Kevin? **About 4 hr**

Use with Lesson 1-9. **9**

Enrichment

Name_____

Fun Raising   E 1-9

DECISION MAKING

The Improve Your Community group needs to raise $600.00 for new playground equipment. The group must choose one of the following fundraising events.

A. The Italian Club held a spaghetti dinner. Each ticket cost $5.00 and the club sold 132 tickets. The expenses were $87.00.

B. The Gardening Club sold plants for their fundraising event. The large plants sold for $8.25 each, the medium plants sold for $6.50 each, and the small plants sold for $5.25 each. The club sold 38 large plants, 31 medium plants, and 52 small plants. The expenses were $129.00.

C. The Theater Club washed cars to raise money last year. It cost $9.00 to wash each car. The club washed 77 cars. The expenses were $103.00.

Sample answers for 1–3.

1. About how much did each fundraising event earn?

Choice A __$650__   Choice B __$780__   Choice C __$720__

2. Estimate how much each fundraising event will earn after expenses.

Choice A __$560__   Choice B __$650__   Choice C __$620__

3. Based on the three fundraising events, which would you suggest the Improve Your Community group choose? Explain.

B; The plant sale makes the most money after expenses, so you would suggest that the group choose this event.

4. If the group wants to choose two of the fundraising events, how many possible combinations are there?

3 combinations: AB, BC, AC

Use with Lesson 1-9. **9**

Problem Solving

Name_____

Estimating Sums and Differences   PS 1-9

Driving Joe is a traveling salesperson. He has started keeping track of the number of miles he drives each week on slips of paper.

	Miles Week 1		Miles Week 2		Miles Week 3		Miles Week 4
M	71	M	93	M	213	M	18u
T	122	T	234	T	114	T	−
W	270	W	−	W	114	W	178
Th	−	Th	−	Th	107	Th	213
F	321	F	397	F	548	F	229
	784		724				809

Sample answers are given for 1–5.

1. Joe wants to estimate how many miles he drove during Weeks 1 and 2. About how many miles did Joe drive during the first two weeks?

About 1,500 mi

2. About how many miles did Joe drive during Weeks 2 and 3 altogether?

About 1,200 mi

3. About how many more miles did Joe drive during Week 2 than Week 3?

About 200 mi

4. About how many miles did Joe travel during Week 4?

About 800 mi

5. About how many miles did Joe travel during all four weeks?

About 2,800 mi

6. **Writing in Math** Explain why in some instances it is better to round up, even if the numbers suggest you should not.

Sample answer: If you have to have enough of something, by rounding up you will be sure that you have enough.

Use with Lesson 1-9. **9**

Name_____

PROBLEM-SOLVING SKILL   P 1-10

Plan and Solve

Yarn Wade and his mother bought four colors of yarn at the craft store. The blue yarn was longer than the green yarn but shorter than the red yarn. The yellow yarn was shorter than the green yarn. Order the colored yarns from the shortest to the longest.

SHORTEST   LONGEST

yellow yarn   **green yarn blue yarn**   red yarn

1. Finish the picture to help solve the problem.

2. What strategy was used to solve the problem?
Make an organized list

3. Write the answer to the problem in a complete sentence.
The order of the colored yarns from shortest to longest is yellow, green, blue, and red.

Basketball Juanita's team is playing in a basketball competition. Each of the seven teams in the competition play all the other teams once. How many games are played in the competition?

4. What strategy did you use to solve this problem?
Sample answer: Make an organized list

5. Give the answer in a complete sentence.
There were 21 games played at the tournament.

Name_____

PROBLEM-SOLVING SKILL   R 1-10

Plan and Solve

Car Sales During March through May, Mr. Matthews sold cars at a dealership. Each month after March, he sold 6 more cars than the previous month. How many cars did he sell during these three months if he sold 8 cars in March?

Here are the steps to follow when you plan and solve a problem.

Step 1: Choose a strategy.	Step 2: Stuck? Don't give up. Try these.	Step 3: Answer the question in the problem.
• Show what you know: Draw a picture, make an organized list, make a table or chart, use objects/act it out.	• Reread the problem. • Tell the problem in your own words.	What strategy can be used to solve the Car Sales problem? A chart can organize the information and make the problem easier to solve.
• Look for a pattern.	• Tell what you know.	
• Try, check, and revise.	• Identify key facts and details.	
• Use logical reasoning.	• Try a different strategy.	
• Solve a simpler problem.	• Retrace your steps.	
• Work backward.		
• Write an equation.		

Mr. Matthews's Car Sales

March	🚗 🚗
April	🚗 🚗 🚗
May	🚗 🚗 🚗 🚗 🚗

Each 🚗 represents 4 cars.

The answer to the problem: Mr. Matthews sold 42 cars in three months.

Reading Lynesia read 2 books during the first week of school. She read 3 books each week after that. How many weeks did it take Lynesia to read 18 books?

1. What strategy might work to solve this problem?
Sample answer: Make an organized list

2. Give the answer to the problem in a complete sentence.
It took seven weeks for Lynesia to read 18 books.

Name_____

Four Food Groups   E 1-10
DECISION MAKING

Frank needs to go grocery shopping. He wants to buy items from each of the four food groups. He has a budget of $10.00. Using the chart at the right, help Frank decide what he should buy.

Fruits and Vegetables		Grains	
Strawberries	$2.99	Bread	$1.99
Apples	$3.99	Bagels	$3.49
Pears	$1.69	Cereal	$4.29
Dairy		**Meat and Fish**	
Milk	$3.29	Turkey	$2.99
Cheese	$1.89	Hamburger	$3.99
Yogurt	$0.79	Tuna	$1.89

1. What is the most Frank can spend on each food group if he spends the same on each?
$2.50

2. If Frank chooses 2 dairy items, can he still buy something from each of the other 3 groups?
Yes; If Frank buys cheese and yogurt, he can still buy 1 item from each of the other groups.

3. Frank remembers that he has fruit already. Show a possible menu for the remaining groups. Tell how much he spent.
Sample answer: cheese: $1.89, bread: $1.99, hamburger: $3.99; Total: $7.87

4. Show one possible menu for Frank. Tell how much he spent.
Sample answer: pears: $1.69, bread: $1.99, milk: $3.29, tuna: $1.89; Total: $8.86

Name_____

PROBLEM-SOLVING SKILL   PS 1-10

Plan and Solve

Ages Jennifer is 4 years older than her sister Jessica. Jessica is 6 years younger than her cousin Jason. Jason is 3 years older than his brother Sam, who is 13. How old is Jennifer?

[Plan and Solve]

Step 1: Choose a strategy.

1. What strategy should you use to solve the problem?
Work backward

Step 2: Stuck? Don't give up. Retrace your own steps.

2. What is something you can do if you get stuck?
You can reread the problem or retrace your steps.

Step 3: Answer the question in the problem.

3. How old is Jennifer?
Jennifer is 14 years old.

4. Every day for the last three weeks Jaecinda has done as many sit-ups as she can. The first week she did 20 sit-ups, the second week she did 27 sit-ups, and the third week she did 34 sit-ups. If she continues at the same pace, how many sit-ups will she do during the fifth week?
Sample answer: If Jaecinda continues at the same pace, by the fifth week she will be able to do 48 sit-ups.

© Pearson Education, Inc. 5

Adding and Subtracting
Whole Numbers

P 1-11

Add or subtract.

1.	29,543	2.	93,210	3.	369,021	4.	893,887
	+ 13,976		− 21,061		− 325,310		+ 22,013
	43,519		**72,149**		**43,711**		**915,900**

5. 971,234 + 55,423 = __**1,026,657**__

6. **Number Sense** Is 4,000 a reasonable estimate for the difference of 9,215 − 5,022? Explain.

Yes, because 9,000 − 5,000 = 4,000.

7. How many people were employed as public officials and natural scientists?

1,319,000 people

People Employed in U.S. by Occupation in 2000	
Occupation	**Workers**
Public officials	753,000
Natural scientists	566,000
University teachers	961,000
Lawyers and judges	926,000

8. How many more people were employed as university teachers than as lawyers and judges?

35,000 more people

Test Prep

9. Which is the difference between 403,951 and 135,211?

A. 200,000   B. 221,365   C. 268,740   D. 539,162

10. **Writing in Math** Issac is adding 59,029 and 55,678. Should his answer be greater than or less than 100,000? Explain how you know.

Greater than 100,000 because an

estimate of 60,000 + 60,000 = 120,000

Adding and Subtracting
Whole Numbers

R 1-11

Find 35,996 + 49,801.

Step 1: Write the numbers, lining up places. Add the ones and then the tens.

```
  35,996
+ 49,801
      97
```

Step 2: Continue adding hundreds, thousands, and ten thousands. Regroup as needed.

```
    11
  35,996
+ 49,801
  85,797
```

So 35,996 + 49,801 = 85,797.

Find 35,996 − 17,902.

Step 1: Write the numbers, lining up places. Subtract the ones, tens, and hundreds.

```
  35,996
− 17,902
     094
```

Step 2: Continue by subtracting thousands. Regroup as needed.

```
    2 15
  35,996
− 17,902
  18,094
```

So 35,996 − 17,902 = 18,094.

Add or subtract.

1.	7,502	2.	64,782	3.	835,029
	+ 9,909		− 33,925		− 26,332
	17,411		**30,857**		**808,697**

4.	85,926	5.	734,588	6.	901,633
	+ 17,938		− 141,672		+ 22,459
	103,864		**592,916**		**924,092**

Myronville School District has 23,081 students, and Saddleton School District has 45,035 students.

7. **Number Sense** How many more students are there in Saddleton than in Myronville?

21,954 more students

Follow the Rules

E 1-11
PATTERNS

Fill in the next three numbers in each pattern. Write what rule makes the pattern true.

1. 255; 355; 455; __**555**__; __**655**__; __**755**__

   Rule: **Add 100**

2. 792; 773; 754; __**735**__; __**716**__; __**697**__

   Rule: **Subtract 19**

3. 1,348; 1,458; 1,568; __**1,678**__; __**1,788**__; __**1,898**__

   Rule: **Add 110**

4. 2,580; 2,520; 2,460; __**2,400**__; __**2,340**__; __**2,280**__

   Rule: **Subtract 60**

5. 882; 844; 806; __**768**__; __**730**__; __**692**__

   Rule: **Subtract 38**

6. 1,573; 1,755; 1,937; __**2,119**__; __**2,301**__; __**2,483**__

   Rule: **Add 182**

7. 3,645; 2,950; 2,255; __**1,560**__; __**865**__; __**170**__

   Rule: **Subtract 695**

8. Write five numbers that follow the rule Add 150. Start at 100.

   100, __**250**__, __**400**__, __**550**__, __**700**__

Adding and Subtracting
Whole Numbers

PS 1-11

Tab Collection For every tab top off an aluminum can that is turned in at an elementary school, the school receives a nickel toward buying computers. The classrooms turned in their tabs by grade. The first grade turned in 2,638 tabs, the second grade turned in 1,472 tabs, the third grade turned in 4,742 tabs, the fourth grade turned in 6,781 tabs, and the fifth grade turned in 8,979 tabs.

1. How many tabs did the first and second grades turn in altogether?

   4,110 tabs

2. How many more tabs did the fourth grade turn in than the third grade?

   2,039 tabs

Classic Cars One type of classic car was first made in 1964. The table shows the number of this type of classic car that was made each year from 1965 through 1970.

Year	Classic Cars Made
1965	559,451
1966	607,568
1967	472,121
1968	317,404
1969	310,454
1970	190,727

3. How many cars were made in 1966 and 1967 altogether?

   1,079,689 cars

4. How many cars were made in 1968 and 1969 altogether?

   627,858 cars

5. How many more cars were made in 1965 than in 1969?

   248,997 cars

6. **Writing in Math** Explain how you found your answer to Exercise 5.

Sample answer: You subtract the

number of cars made in 1969 from the

number of cars made in 1965.

Name_____

Adding Decimals
P 1-12

Add.

| 1. | 58.0
+ 3.6
61.6 | 2. | 40.5
+ 22.3
62.8 | 3. | 34.587
+ 21.098
55.685 | 4. | 43.1000
+ 8.4388
51.5388 |

5. 16.036 + 7.009 = **23.045**   6. 92.30 + 0.32 = **92.62**

7. **Number Sense** Reilly adds 45.3 and 3.21. Should his sum be greater than or less than 48? Tell how you know.

The sum should be greater than 48

because the whole numbers have a sum

of 48 without adding the decimals.

In science class, students weighed different amounts of tin. Carmen weighed 4.361 g, Kim weighed 2.704 g, Simon weighed 5.295 g, and Angelica weighed 8.537 g.

8. How many grams of tin did Carmen and Angelica have combined?

12.898 g of tin

9. How many grams of tin did Kim and Simon have combined?

7.999 g of tin

Test Prep

10. In December the snowfall was 0.03 in. and in January it was 2.1 in. Which was the total snowfall?

A. 3.2 in.   B. 2.40 in.   C. 2.13 in.   D. 0.03 in.

11. **Writing in Math** Explain why it is important to line up decimal numbers by their place value when you add or subtract them. **Sample answer:**
It is important to line up decimals by their

place value so that the answer will be

accurate.

12 Use with Lesson 1-12.

© Pearson Education, Inc. 5

Name_____

Adding Decimals
R 1-12

Miss Solade bought 2.4 lb of ground beef and 1.692 lb of chicken. How many pounds of meat did she buy altogether?

Step 1: Write the numbers. Line up the decimal points. Include the zeros to show place value.

2.400
+ 1.692

Step 2: Add as you would with whole numbers. Bring the decimal point straight down in the answer.

1
2.400
+ 1.692
4.092

Miss Solade bought 4.092 lb of meat.

Add.

1. 2.97 + 0.35 =
3.32

2. 13.88 + 7.694 =
21.574

3. 39.488 + 26.7 =
66.188

4. 88.8 + 4.277 + 78.95 =
172.027

5. **Number Sense** Is 16.7 a reasonable sum for 7.5 + 9.2? Explain.
Yes; 7.5 rounds to 8.0; 9.2 rounds to
9.0; 8.0 + 9.0 = 17.0.

6. How much combined snowfall was there in Milwaukee and Oklahoma City?

105.1 in.

City	Snowfall (inches) in 2000
Milwaukee, WI	87.8
Baltimore, MD	27.2
Oklahoma City, OK	17.3

12 Use with Lesson 1-12.

© Pearson Education, Inc. 5

Name_____

Odd Jobs
E 1-12
DECISION MAKING

Simone does odd jobs in her neighborhood to make money. She decides to make a bar graph to help her see how much money she makes at each job each week. Show each amount on the graph.

1. Simone earns $7.75 each time she washes Mrs. Conlan's car. She washes the car twice a week.

2. Simone helps Mr. Von do his laundry three times each week. She earns $4.00 each time.

3. Simone earns $3.25 per hour when she pulls weeds from Mr. Gahn's garden. She pulls weeds for 4 hours each week.

4. Simone wants to save money to buy a video game system for $200.00. If Simone did all of her jobs each week, how many weeks would she need to work to earn $200.00?

5 weeks

5. Simone is going to join the chess club. She needs to decide which job she should stop doing to make more time for practice. Which job do you think Simone should stop doing? Explain.

Sample answer: Laundry because she

makes the least money helping with laundry

6. Other neighbors asked Simone to wash their cars, help with the laundry, and pull weeds. Simone decides to do one job for several neighbors. Which job do you think she should do? Why?
Sample answer:
Washing cars because she could make

$15.50 from each neighbor by washing cars

12 Use with Lesson 1-12.

© Pearson Education, Inc. 5

Name_____

Adding Decimals
PS 1-12

Fabric Lauren works at a textile mill. She weaves special fabric, which is used to make rugs. On Monday she wove 7.21 yd, on Tuesday she wove 9.653 yd, on Wednesday she wove 6.57 yd, on Thursday she wove 8.56 yd, and on Friday she wove 7.08 yd.

1. How many yards of fabric did Lauren weave from Monday through Wednesday?
23.433 yd

2. How many yards of fabric did Lauren weave during the entire week?
39.073 yd

Earnings This week Jonathan's mother gave him $1.75 for doing the laundry, $2.50 for taking care of her fish, and $1.50 for taking out the trash. He had $4.81 left from his earnings last week, and he found a quarter in the laundry.

3. How much money did Jonathan earn this week?
$5.75

4. How much money does Jonathan have now?
$10.81

5. If Jonathan earns another $3.50 doing chores at two of the neighbors' homes, how much will he have?
$14.31

6. **Writing in Math** Chris says that 2.05 + 1.3 is 2.18. Is he correct? Explain.

Sample answer: No, Chris is not

correct. Chris forgot to line up the

decimal points before adding. The

answer should be 3.35.

12 Use with Lesson 1-12.

© Pearson Education, Inc. 5

Name_____

Subtracting Decimals

P 1-13

Subtract.

1.	2.	3.	4.
92.1 − 32.6	52.7 − 36.9	85.76 − 12.986	32.7 − 2.328
59.5	**15.8**	**72.774**	**30.372**

5. 8.7 − 0.3 = **8.4**   6. 23.3 − 1.32 = **21.98**

7. **Number Sense** Kelly subtracted 2.3 from 20 and got 17.7. Explain why this answer is reasonable.

A good estimate is 20 − 2 = 18, which is close to 17.7.

At a local swim meet, the second place swimmer of the 100 m freestyle had a time of 9.33 sec. The first place swimmer's time was 1.32 sec faster than the second place swimmer. The third place time was 13.65 sec.

8. What was the time for the first place swimmer?   **8.01 sec**

9. What was the difference in time between the second and third place swimmers?   **4.32 sec**

Test Prep

10. Miami's annual precipitation in 2000 was 61.05 in. Albany's was 46.92 in. How much greater was Miami's rainfall than Albany's?

A. 107.97 in.   B. 54.31 in.   C. 14.93 in.   **D.** 14.13 in.

11. **Writing in Math** Explain how to subtract 7.6 from 20.39.

Sample answer: Write the numbers, lining up the decimal points. Write zeros to show place value. Subtract the hundredths, the tenths, and the ones. Place the decimal point in the answer.

Name_____

Subtracting Decimals

R 1-13

Julie ran 2.67 mi and Caitlin ran 1.586 mi. How much farther did Julie run than Caitlin?

Estimate: 2.67 rounds to 3 and 1.586 rounds to 2.

So, 3 − 2 = 1.

Step 1: Write the numbers, lining up the decimal points. Write zeros to show place value.

2.670
− 1.586

Step 2: Subtract the thousandths. Decide if you need to regroup. Regroup 7 hundredths as 6 hundredths and 10 thousandths.

610
2.670
− 1.586
4

Step 3: Subtract the hundredths. Regroup 6 tenths as 5 tenths and 10 + 6 hundredths. Continue subtracting as with whole numbers. Place the decimal in the answer.

51610
2.670
− 1.586
1.084

The difference is close to the estimate so the answer is reasonable.
Check: 1.084 + 1.586 = 2.670
Julie ran 1.084 more miles than Caitlin.

Subtract.

1.	2.	3.
18.6 − 13.8	63.7 − 12.66	8.76 − 4.945
4.8	**51.04**	**3.815**
4.	5.	6.
82.7 − 5.59	43.3 − 12.82	7.28 − 4.928
77.11	**30.48**	**2.352**

7. **Reasonableness** Dylan subtracted 5.6 from 17.28 and got 14.68. Is his answer reasonable? Why or why not?

Sample answer: No; Dylan's answer is not reasonable because 5.6 rounds to 6 and 17.28 rounds to 17. 17 − 6 = 11.

Name_____

Find Those Numbers!

E 1-13
NUMBER SENSE

Fill in the boxes to complete the differences.

1.	2.	3.
1 7 . 7 4 − 9 . 3 6 8 . 3 8	2 . 9 3 − 1 . 6 4 1 . 2 9	1 1 . 4 5 − 7 . 6 8 3 . 7 7
4.	5.	6.
6 . 2 5 − 4 . 3 9 1 . 8 6	3 0 . 4 0 7 − 1 4 . 7 6 5 1 5 . 6 4 2	9 8 . 9 3 7 − 5 2 . 1 0 4 4 6 . 8 3 3
7.	8.	9.
6 2 . 3 3 − 3 4 . 7 1 2 2 7 . 6 1 8	9 4 . 0 6 8 − 3 8 . 7 4 2 5 5 . 3 2 6	6 4 . 7 1 4 − 3 4 . 8 1 2 9 . 9 0 4

Complete the puzzles. Every triangle will be the difference between the rectangle and the oval.

10.	11.	12.
17.64	**29.71**	43.162
5.67	8.42	29.874
11.97	21.29	**13.288**

Name_____

Subtracting Decimals

PS 1-13

County Fair The largest tomato at a county fair weighed 7.29 lb. The largest pumpkin weighed 572.14 lb. The grand champion hog weighed in at 321.09 lb.

1. How much more did the largest pumpkin weigh than the grand champion hog?   **251.05 lb more**

2. How much more did the largest pumpkin weigh than the largest tomato?   **564.85 lb more**

3. How much more did the grand champion hog weigh than the largest tomato?   **313.80 lb more**

At the county fair, tickets for the rides can be bought in sheets of 40 for $10.00, sheets of 100 for $20.00, or each ticket for $0.50.

4. Craig came to the fair with $50.00. He bought a sheet of 100 tickets and bought dinner for $7.81. How much money does Craig have left?   **$22.19**

5. Tyrell came to the fair with $25.00. He spent $13.00 trying to win a prize, and then bought a necklace for $8.69. How much money does Tyrell have left?   **$3.31**

6. **Writing in Math** Explain why you might need to add zeros to the end of a decimal in order to subtract.

Sample answer: If one decimal is being subtracted from another decimal that has fewer places to the right of the decimal point, zeros are added to the right of the first decimal.

Name_____

PROBLEM-SOLVING SKILL   P 1-14

Look Back and Check

Art Collection The Collector's Museum is home to lots of great art. The most valuable item is a painting finished in 1840 called *The Mirror*. Its estimated value is $1,202,450. The piece titled *A Summer Memory* is valued at $100,000 less than the value of *The Mirror*. The entire art collection is estimated to be worth $13,000,000. Overall there are 45 works of art in the museum. What is the total estimated value of the other 43 works of art?

Jacques solved the Art Collection problem. Check his work.

	Jacques
$13,000,000	
$1,202,450	?

$13,000,000 − $1,202,450 = $11,797,550
The 43 works of art are worth $11,797,550.

1. Did Jacques answer the right question? Explain.

Yes; Jacques answered the right question. He is finding the value of the 43 other art works.

2. Is his answer correct? Explain.

No; Jacques's work does not match the information in the problem. He forgot to include the value of *A Summer Memory*.

Solve the problem. Then, look back and check your answer.

3. An empty jar weighs 39 g. A jar that is full of water weighs 207 g. What does the water in the jar weigh?

The water weighs 168 g.

Name_____

PROBLEM-SOLVING SKILL   R 1-14

Look Back and Check

Lunch Cost Anthony bought a pretzel for $0.57 and a box lunch, which cost $3.00. He paid $0.29 for tax. How much did Anthony spend for his lunch? How much change did he get back if he paid with a $5 bill?

Donald's Work

$0.57	$5.00	Anthony spent $3.86 on lunch and received
3.00	− 3.86	$2.14 in change.
+ 0.29	$2.14	
$3.86		

Step 1: Check your answer.
Did Donald answer the right questions? Yes, he found the total cost for the lunch and the amount of change Anthony should get back.

Step 2: Check your work.
Donald could use subtraction and addition to check if his answers are correct. The amount Anthony paid for the lunch is correct, but the amount of change he received should be $1.14 instead of $2.14. Donald forgot to change $5 to $4 when he regrouped the dollars into ten cents.

Order by Age Five students want to line up according to the order of their births. Bradley is the oldest. Jerry's birthday is 5 days after Katie's birthday. Mattison's birthday is on December 31 and is the only birthday in December. Hank's birthday is the closest birthday to Bradley's. In what order would the students line up? Look back and check Colin's work on this problem.

YOUNGEST   OLDEST
Mattison   Hank   Jerry   Katie   Bradley

In order, the students are Bradley, Katie, Jerry, Hank, and Mattison.

1. Is Colin's work correct? Explain.

No; He incorrectly placed Hank's birthday closer to Mattison's instead of Bradley's.

Name_____

Rectangle Search   E 1-14
                                            VISUAL THINKING

1.

How many different rectangles can you find that are formed by the heavy lines?

9 rectangles

2. Name the rectangles.

AGIC; AGHB; BHIC; ADFC; DGIF; ADEB; DGHE; BEFC; EHIF

3. How many small squares are in each of the rectangles?

AGIC: 56; AGHB: 24; BHIC: 32; ADFC: 14; DGIF: 42; ADEB: 6; DGHE: 18; BEFC: 8; EHIF: 24

Name_____

PROBLEM-SOLVING SKILL   PS 1-14

Look Back and Check

Cargo Ship A cargo ship arrives empty in California and loads 42,692 crates. It leaves California and travels to a port in Alaska, where it unloads 27,450 crates. It then goes to a second Alaskan port and unloads another 12,728 crates. When it arrives at the third port, it unloads the rest of the crates. How many crates were unloaded at the third port?

Melissa solved the problem as shown below.

3 12	
42,692	crates loaded
− 27,450	crates unloaded at 1st stop
15,242	crates left after 1st stop
4 123 12	
15,242	crates left after 1st stop
− 12,728	crates unloaded at 2nd stop
2,524	crates left after 2nd stop

Step 1: Have you checked your answer?

1. Was the correct question answered? Explain.

Yes, Melissa answered by finding how many crates were left after the first two stops in Alaska.

Step 2: Have you checked your work?

2. Was Melissa's final answer correct? Explain.

No, 15,242 − 12,728 is not 2,524. Melissa forgot that she had borrowed from the tens place. There were 2,514 crates unloaded at the third port.

Name_____

Champions

At a gymnastics meet, Karl took first place. Karl scored 9.836 on the vault, Yao received a score of 9.772 on the parallel bars, and Quincy scored 9.672 on the vault.

1. How much higher was Karl's vault score than Quincy's vault score? 　**0.164**

2. What information did you not need to answer the question?

   Yao scored 9.772 on the parallel bars.

Four weight lifters competed in the state tournament. Barney lifted 205 kg, Eddie lifted 290 kg, Pierre lifted 305 kg, and Nathan lifted 325 kg.

3. How much more did Eddie lift than Barney? 　**85 kg**

4. How much more did Eddie and Pierre lift combined than Barney and Nathan combined? 　**65 kg**

Six runners competed in a race. Kathryn finished third. Salma finished ahead of Kathryn and Marita. Jackie finished before Lara but after Nikki. List the runners in the order they finished.

5. Draw a picture to help you solve the problem.

   Sample drawing:

   Salma　Marita　Kathryn　Nikki　Jackie　Lara
   ●————●————●————●————●————●

6. Write your answer in a complete sentence.

   Salma, Marita, Kathryn, Nikki, Jackie, Lara is the order in which the runners finished.

© Pearson Education, Inc. 5

Name_____

It's Elemental!

Platinum is a metal element used in chemical equipment, electrical wires, and jewelry. The following data chart shows the demand for platinum in different areas of the world for the years 1998 to 2001. The demand chart shows the areas that use the most platinum in *thousands* of ounces.

Platinum Demand
(in thousands of ounces)

	1998	1999	2000	2001
Europe	910	995	1,150	1,490
Japan	1,795	1,820	1,410	1,250
North America	1,325	1,080	1,225	1,285

Which area had the lesser platinum demand in 2001, Japan or North America?

Step 1: Write the numbers, lining up places. Begin at the left and compare.

1,250,000

1,285,000

Step 2: Find the first place where the digits are different and compare.

1,250,000

1,285,000

Since 5 is less than 8, then 1,250,000 is less than 1,285,000. So, Japan had a lesser platinum demand in 2001.

1. In which year did Japan have a greater platinum demand, 1998 or 1999?

   1999

2. If Europe's platinum demand is 10 times larger in 2011 as in 2001, what will the platinum demand be?

   14,900,000 oz

© Pearson Education, Inc. 5

Name_____

Garbage in the United States

1. The numbers listed below are the kilograms of garbage generated in the United States for 5 years. The amount of garbage generated has increased each year. Complete the table by putting the numbers in order from least to greatest.

   186,545,454,545　110,090,909,091　210,818,181,818
   80,090,909,091　137,818,181,818

2. How much greater is the amount of garbage generated in 1960 and 1970 combined than in 1990?

   3,636,363,637 kg

Garbage in the United States

Year	Kilograms
1960	**80,090,909,091**
1970	**110,090,909,091**
1980	**137,818,181,818**
1990	**186,545,454,545**
2000	**210,818,181,818**

3. Round the kilograms of garbage generated in the United States for each year listed to the nearest billion.

   1960: **80,000,000,000**

   2000: **211,000,000,000**

4. Complete the table by rounding each kilogram of garbage per person per day to the nearest hundredth.

Garbage in the United States—per Person (per Day)

Year	Kilograms	Rounded to the Nearest Hundredth
1960	1.225	**1.23**
1970	1.497	**1.50**
1980	1.678	**1.68**
1990	2.041	**2.04**
2000	2.041	**2.04**

5. How many more kilograms of garbage did each person in the United States generate per day in 2000 than in 1960?

   0.816 kg

© Pearson Education, Inc. 5

Name_____

Trombone

Garrett is renting a trombone for $50.00 a month. He can buy a used trombone for $200.00 from a student who played last year. How long will it take Garrett to spend as much in rental fees as it would cost to buy the used trombone?

Read and Understand

1. How much does it cost to rent a trombone for one month? 　**$50.00**

2. How much does it cost to buy a used trombone? 　**$200.00**

Plan and Solve

3. What strategy will you use? 　**Write an equation**

4. Solve the problem. Write your answer in a complete sentence.

   In four months, Garrett will spend $200 on rental fees.

Look Back and Check

5. Explain how you can check your answer.

   I can multiply $50 × 4 = $200.

Solve Another Problem

6. At the beginning of one week, a large paper company purchased 120,000 boxes of paper. The same week the company sold 92,000 boxes of paper. There were 46,000 boxes of paper left at the end of the week. How many boxes of paper did the company begin the week with?

   18,000 boxes

© Pearson Education, Inc. 5

Name_____

Multiplication Patterns

P 2-1

Find each product. Use patterns and properties to compute mentally.

1. $40 \times 20 =$
800

2. $50 \times 700 =$
35,000

3. $20 \times 2 \times 30 =$
1,200

4. $2 \times 50 \times 30 =$
3,000

5. $250 \times 37 \times 4 =$
37,000

6. $20 \times 65 \times 5 =$
6,500

7. How many calories are in 10 peaches?
350

Calories in Fruit

Fruit (1 piece)	Calories
Apple	80
Orange	60
Peach	35

8. How many calories are in 5 apples?
400

9. Callie ate 3 oranges each day for 10 days. How many calories did all of these oranges have?
1,800

10. Algebra $m \times n = 6,300$. If m and n are 2-digit multiples of 10, what numbers could m and n be?
90 and 70 or 70 and 90

Test Prep

11. Which of the following has a product of 1,600?

A. $4,000 \times 400$ **B.** 4×400 **C.** 400×400 **D.** 40×400

12. Writing in Math Write a definition for the Associative Property of Multiplication in your own words and explain how you would use it to compute $4 \times 27 \times 25$ mentally. **Sample answer:**

Using the Associative Property of Multiplication you can group (4 × 25) and multiply the product by 27 to get 2,700.

16 Use with Lesson 2-1.

Name_____

Multiplication Patterns

R 2-1

Commutative Property of Multiplication	Associative Property of Multiplication
You can multiply two factors in any order.	You can change the grouping of factors.
$15 \times 9 = 9 \times 15$	$(8 \times 20) \times 5 = 8 \times (20 \times 5)$

You can also use patterns to multiply mentally.

Fact: $5 \times 7 = 35$

$50 \times 7 = 350$	$5 \times 70 = 350$
$500 \times 7 = 3,500$	$50 \times 70 = 3,500$
$5,000 \times 7 = 35,000$	$500 \times 70 = 35,000$
$50,000 \times 7 = 350,000$	$5,000 \times 70 = 350,000$

Pattern: Notice that the product is always 35 with the different number of zeros that are in the factors.

Find $30 \times 3 \times 50$.

Use the Associative Property of Multiplication to regroup.

$(30 \times 50) \times 3$

$1,500 \times 3 = 4,500$

Find each product. Use patterns and properties to compute mentally.

1. $80 \times 90 =$ **7,200**

2. $40 \times 800 =$ **32,000**

3. $5 \times 10 \times 20 =$ **1,000**

4. $4 \times 30 \times 25 =$ **3,000**

5. Number Sense You know that $6 \times 7 = 42$. How can you find 60×700?

Sample answer: Basic fact with the number of zeros in the factors altogether; Answer: 42,000

16 Use with Lesson 2-1.

Name_____

Find the Pattern

E 2-1
PATTERNS

Write the next three numbers to continue each pattern.

1. 1; 10; 3; 30; **5** ; **50** ; **7**

2. two; twenty; 2 hundred; 2 thousand; **20 thousand** ; **200 thousand** ; **2 million**

3. 150; 140; 170; 160; **190** ; **180** ; **210**

4. 5; 25; 50; 10; **50** ; **100** ; **15**

5. two; five; ten; three; **five** ; **fifteen** ; **four**

6. 4; 44; 440; 4,400; **44,000** ; **440,000** ; **4,400,000**

7. five million; five hundred thousand; fifty thousand; five thousand; **Five hundred** ; **fifty** ; **five**

8. 2; 22; 222; 2,222; **22,222** ; **222,222** ; **2,222,222**

9. 4; 60; 900; **13,500** ; **202,500** ; **3,037,500**

10. 1,500; 3,720; 5,940; **8,160** ; **10,380** ; **12,600**

11. 1 hundred; 1 million; 2 hundred; 2 million; **3 hundred** ; **3 million** ; **4 hundred**

12. 4; 16; 64; 256; **1,024** ; **4,096** ; **16,384**

13. 20; 80; 320; 1,280; **5,120** ; **20,480** ; **81,920**

14. one; 3 hundred; two; 6 hundred; **three** ; **9 hundred** ; **four**

16 Use with Lesson 2-1.

Name_____

Multiplication Patterns

PS 2-1

New Bats As a gift, a baseball league will receive new bats for each of its teams. Each team will receive 4 new bats.

1. The league now has 8 teams with 5 bats each. What is the total number of bats the league has before the addition of the new bats?
40 bats

2. What will the total number of bats be after the addition of the new bats?
72 bats

The table at the right shows the average number of cans Daniel collected each day during June, July, and August.

Month	Cans per Day
June (30 days)	11
July (31 days)	10
August (31 days)	15

3. How many cans did Daniel collect for the month of June?
330 cans

4. How many cans did Daniel collect for the month of July?
310 cans

5. How many cans did Daniel collect for the month of August?
465 cans

6. Writing in Math Daniel received $2 for every 100 cans he turned in to the recycling center. Explain how you could determine mentally about how much money Daniel made collecting cans for each of the three months.

Sample answer: Round the number of cans collected to the nearest hundred, then multiply the digit in the hundreds place by $2.

16 Use with Lesson 2-1.

Name_____

Estimating Products

P 2-2

Estimate each product. **Sample answers are given for 1–11.**

1. $36 \times 12 \times 9 =$ __3,600__
2. $16 \times 7 \times 34 =$ __6,000__
3. $2 \times 82 \times 26 =$ __4,000__
4. $56 \times 11 \times 2 =$ __1,200__
5. $44 \times 67 \times 7 =$ __28,000__
6. $22 \times 69 \times 4 =$ __5,600__
7. $53 \times 78 \times 21 =$ __78,000__
8. $6 \times 12 \times 42 =$ __2,400__

9. **Number Sense** Give three numbers whose product is about 9,000.

__$99 \times 10 \times 9$__

10. About how much would it cost to buy 4 CD/MP3 players and 3 MP3 players?

About $1,100

Electronics Prices	
CD player	$74.00
MP3 player	$99.00
CD/MP3 player	$199.00
AM/FM radio	$29.00

11. Estimate to decide whether 8 AM/FM radios or 3 CD players cost less. Explain.

Eight AM/FM radios would cost about $240, and 3 CD players would cost about $225. The CD players would cost less.

Test Prep

12. Which is the closest estimate for the product of $2 \times 15 \times 5$?

   A. 1,150   (B.) 150   C. 125   D. 50

13. **Writing in Math** Explain how you know whether an estimate of a product is an overestimate or an underestimate.

Sample answer:
If the numbers are rounded down, it is an underestimate. If the numbers are rounded up, it is an overestimate.

© Pearson Education, Inc. 5

Name_____

Estimating Products

R 2-2

A bus service drives passengers between Milwaukee and Chicago every day. They travel from city to city a total of 8 times each day. The distance between the two cities is 89 mi. In the month of February, there are 28 days. The company's budget allows for 28,000 total miles for February. Is 28,000 mi a reasonable budget mileage amount?

One Way to Estimate

Estimate $28 \times 8 \times 89$.

You can round 89 to 100 and 8 to 10. Then multiply.

$28 \times 10 \times 100 = 280 \times 100 = 28,000$

Because this is an overestimate, there are enough miles.

Another Way to Estimate

Estimate $28 \times 8 \times 89$.

Adjust 28 to 30, 8 to 10, and 89 to 90.

$(30 \times 10) \times 90 = 300 \times 90 = 27,000$

Because all the numbers were adjusted higher, there are enough miles.

28,000 total miles is a reasonable budget amount.

Estimate each product.   **Sample answers:**

1. $42 \times 5 \times 90$ __18,000__
2. $27 \times 98 \times 4$ __10,000__
3. $9 \times 55 \times 10$ __5,500__
4. $22 \times 19 \times 100$ __40,000__

5. **Number Sense** What are two different ways to estimate $9 \times 299 \times 10$?

__$10 \times 300 \times 10 = 30,000; 9 \times 10 \times 300$__
__$= 27,000$__

Mrs. Carter ordered new supplies for Memorial Hospital.

6. About how much will it cost to purchase 48 electronic thermometers?

$1,000

Supplies	
Electronic thermometers	$ 19 each
Pulse monitors	$189 each
Pillows	$ 17 each
Telephones	$ 19 each

7. About how much will it cost to purchase 96 pillows?

$1,700

© Pearson Education, Inc. 5

Name_____

Car Wash

E 2-2
DECISION MAKING

Aaron and five of his classmates are organizing a car wash to raise money for after school activities. They will be able to use some supplies that the school already owns, but they must purchase soap and sponges. The group expects to wash 100 cars. They plan to use 30 sponges.

1. Complete both charts by writing the estimated total cost for each package or container.

Sponges	Cost per Pack	Estimated Total Cost
A. Pack of 5	$5.97	$36.00
B. Pack of 10	$7.95	$24.00
C. Pack of 15	$9.99	$20.00

Soap	Cost per Container	Estimated Total Cost
1. For 5 cars	$0.99	$20.00
2. For 10 cars	$1.52	$15.00
3. For 20 cars	$4.09	$20.00

2. Aaron expects that if they purchase the least expensive sponges, which are not as strong as the others, they will need twice the number of sponges. Write a new estimate for the cost of the least expensive sponges.

$40.00

3. The least expensive soap is also the least effective, and Aaron expects that they will have to use 3 times the amount. Write a new estimate for the cost of the least expensive soap.

$45.00

4. Which packs of sponges and containers of soap should Aaron and his classmates choose? Why?

Sample answer:
Sponges: Pack B; Soap: Container 1 or Container 3; The least expensive options would end up costing more.

© Pearson Education, Inc. 5

Name_____

Estimating Products

PS 2-2

Backpacking A backpacking club is planning a 12-day trip. There are 14 members in the club.

1. Each member of the club eats 2 lb of food each day. Write and solve an expression you could use to overestimate how much food the club should bring.

$12 \times 2 \times 15 = 360$ lb of food

2. Overestimate how many pounds of food would be needed if 4 of the members brought along 1 friend each.

$12 \times 2 \times 20 = 480$ lb of food

3. Estimate the cost of 4 winter coats in 1930.

$120

Item	Cost in 1930
Winter coat	$28
Sewing machine	$24
Gas stove	$21

4. Estimate the cost today of buying 8 sewing machines if each machine costs $285. Estimate the cost today of 9 gas stoves if each stove costs $582.

Sewing machines, $300 \times 8 = $2,400;
Gas stoves, $9 \times $600 = $5,400

5. **Writing in Math** Explain how you estimated the costs in Exercise 4. Was your answer an overestimate or an underestimate?

Sample answer: The prices were rounded up to give an overestimate.

© Pearson Education, Inc. 5

© Pearson Education, Inc. 5

Practice

Name_____

P 2-3

Mental Math:
Using the Distributive Property

Use the Distributive Property to multiply mentally.

1. $5 \times 607 =$ **3,035**
2. $16 \times 102 =$ **1,632**
3. $7 \times 420 =$ **2,940**
4. $265 \times 5 =$ **1,325**
5. $44 \times 60 =$ **2,640**
6. $220 \times 19 =$ **4,180**
7. $45 \times 280 =$ **12,600**
8. $341 \times 32 =$ **10,912**

9. **Number Sense** Fill in the blanks to show how the Distributive Property can be used to find 10×147.

$10 \times (150 - 3) = (10 \times 150) - ($ **10** $\times 3) =$

$1,500 -$ **30** $=$ **1,470**

10. In 1990, there were 1,133 tornadoes in the U.S. If there were the same number of tornadoes for the next 10 years, what would have been the 10-year total?

11,330 tornadoes

11. There were 1,071 tornadoes in the U.S. in 2000. What is the number of tornadoes multiplied by 20?

21,420 tornadoes

Test Prep

12. If $4 \times 312 = (4 \times (300 + n)$, which is the value of n?

A. 4   (B) 12   C. 48   D. 300

13. **Writing in Math** Margaret said that she used the Distributive Property to solve 4×444. Is her answer shown below correct? Explain.

$4 \times 444 = 4 \times (400 + 40 + 4) =$
$(4 \times 400) + (4 \times 40) + (4 \times 4) =$
$1,600 + 160 + 16 = 1,776$

Sample answer: Yes; Margaret correctly used the Distributive Property to solve 4 × 444.

18   Use with Lesson 2-3.

Reteaching

Name_____

R 2-3

Mental Math:
Using the Distributive Property

Mr. Braxton bought 26 boxes of bathroom tissue for his company. Each box contains 6 rolls of tissue. How many rolls of tissue did he order altogether?

You can find 6×26 using the distributive property with addition or subtraction.

Use Addition	Use Addition	Use Subtraction
Split 26 into 20 + 6.	Split 26 into 25 + 1.	Split 26 into 30 − 4.
$6 \times 26 = 6 \times (20 + 6) =$	$6 \times 26 = 6 \times (25 + 1) =$	$6 \times 26 = 6 \times (30 - 4) =$
$(6 \times 20) + (6 \times 6) =$	$(6 \times 25) + (6 \times 1) =$	$(6 \times 30) - (6 \times 4) =$
$120 + 36 =$	$150 + 6 =$	$180 - 24 =$
156	156	156

Use the distributive property to multiply mentally.

1. $8 \times 19 =$ **152**
2. $7 \times 61 =$ **427**
3. $23 \times 101 =$ **2,323**
4. $9 \times 26 =$ **234**
5. $40 \times 17 =$ **680**
6. $5 \times 350 =$ **1,750**

7. There are 16 oz in every pound. How many ounces are there in 5 lb?

$16 \times 5 = (15 \times 5) + (1 \times 5) = 75 + 5 = 80$ oz. Alternate: $16 \times 5 = (20 \times 5) - (4 \times 5) = 100 - 20 = 80$ oz.

8. **Algebra** If $10 \times 198 = (10 \times m) - (10 \times 2)$, what is the value of m?

$m = 200$

18   Use with Lesson 2-3.

Enrichment

Name_____

E 2-3
REASONING

Find the Products

1. Circle the letter of the problem that has the greatest product.

   (a) 85×41 b. 224×13 c. 471×5

2. Write an estimate for each product in Exercise 1.

   a. **3,600**   b. **2,200**   c. **2,500**

3. Find the exact product for each problem in Exercise 1.

   a. **3,485**   b. **2,912**   c. **2,355**

4. Circle the letter of the problem that has a product that is about four times greater than the product of one of the other problems.

   (a) 201×79 b. 509×11 c. 198×20

5. Write an estimate for each product in Exercise 4.

   a. **16,000**   b. **5,000**   c. **4,000**

6. Find the exact product for each problem in Exercise 4.

   a. **15,879**   b. **5,599**   c. **3,960**

7. What are some real-life situations in which you would not want an estimate that is too low or too high? Write one example of each.

Check that students have written one example of an underestimate and one example of an overestimate.

18   Use with Lesson 2-3.

Problem Solving

Name_____

PS 2-3

Mental Math: Using the Distributive Property

Allan drives every day for his business.

Day	Miles
Monday	72
Tuesday	84
Wednesday	84
Thursday	72
Friday	84

1. Use the Distributive Property to mentally determine how many miles Allan drove on Monday and Thursday combined.

   144 mi

2. Use the Distributive Property to mentally determine how many miles Allan drove on Tuesday, Wednesday, and Friday combined.

   252 mi

Measurements Use what you know about the Distributive Property and the table to mentally answer Exercises 3–5.

Area Conversions

1 sq ft = 144 sq in.
1 sq yd = 9 sq ft
1 sq mi = 640 acres

3. How many square feet are there in 72 sq yd?

   648 sq ft

4. How many acres are there in 21 sq mi?

   13,440 acres

5. **Writing in Math** Explain how you used the Distributive Property to solve Exercise 4.

Sample answer: Multiply 20 by 640 because it is easier than multiplying 21 times 640; 20 × 640 = 12,800. Then add 640; 12,800 + 640 = 13,440.

18   Use with Lesson 2-3.

Name_____

Multiplying Whole Numbers

P 2-4

Find each product. Estimate to check that your answer is reasonable.

1. $543 \times 4 =$ **2,172**
2. $254 \times 6 =$ **1,524**
3. $756 \times 6 =$ **4,536**
4. $560 \times 34 =$ **19,040**
5. $424 \times 76 =$ **32,224**
6. $513 \times 13 =$ **6,669**
7. $107 \times 51 =$ **5,457**
8. $816 \times 52 =$ **42,432**

9. $\begin{array}{r} 15 \\ \times\ 29 \end{array}$ **435**
10. $\begin{array}{r} 876 \\ \times\ 4 \end{array}$ **3,504**
11. $\begin{array}{r} 55 \\ \times\ 44 \end{array}$ **2,420**
12. $\begin{array}{r} 89 \\ \times\ 65 \end{array}$ **5,785**
13. $\begin{array}{r} 235 \\ \times\ 32 \end{array}$ **7,520**

14. Show how you can use the distributive property to multiply 22×85.

Sample answer: $(20 \times 80) + (2 \times 5)$

15. Player A's longest home run distance is 484 ft. If Player A hits 45 home runs at his longest distance, what would the total distance be?

21,780 ft

16. Player B's longest home run distance is 500 ft. There are 5,280 ft in 1 mi. How many home runs would Player B need to hit at his longest distance for the total to be greater than 1 mi?

11 home runs

Test Prep

17. Which is a reasonable answer for the product of $96 \times 7 \times 34$?

A. 672   B. 3,264   C. 22,848   D. 28,800

18. **Writing in Math** Why is 2,482 not a reasonable answer for 542×6?

Sample answer: 542×6 is about 3,000; 3,000 is an underestimate, so 2,482 is not a reasonable answer.

Use with Lesson 2-4. **19**

Name_____

Multiplying Whole Numbers

R 2-4

Find 128×23.   Estimate: $100 \times 20 = 2,000$

	Step 1 Multiply the ones. Regroup as needed.	Step 2 Multiply the tens. Regroup as needed.	Step 3 Add the products.
	$\begin{array}{r} 128 \\ \times\ 23 \\ \hline 384 \end{array}$	$\begin{array}{r} 128 \\ \times\ 3 \\ \hline 384 \end{array}$	$\begin{array}{r} 128 \\ \times\ 20 \\ \hline 2,560 \end{array}$

$\begin{array}{r} 128 \\ \times\ 23 \\ \hline 384 \\ + 2,560 \\ \hline 2,944 \end{array}$

Because the answer is close to the estimate, the answer is reasonable.

Find the product. Estimate to check if your answer is reasonable.

Problem	Multiply Ones	Multiply Tens	Add Products
1. $\begin{array}{r} 282 \\ \times\ 19 \\ \hline 2,538 \\ +2,820 \\ \hline \end{array}$ **5,358**	$\begin{array}{r} 282 \\ \times\ 9 \\ \hline 2,538 \end{array}$	$\begin{array}{r} 282 \\ \times\ 10 \\ \hline 2,820 \end{array}$	
2. $\begin{array}{r} 538 \\ \times\ 46 \\ \hline \end{array}$ **24,748**			

3. **Reasonableness** Is 2,750 a reasonable answer for 917×33? Explain.

No; If you round 917 to 900 and 33 to 30, the product is 900×30 or 27,000, so 2,750 is not reasonable.

Use with Lesson 2-4. **19**

Name_____

Take a Drive

E 2-4
NUMBER SENSE

The speed limit on many highways is 55 mi per hour. Use this speed to solve the problems below. Use regrouping and place values when you multiply to solve each exercise.

1. How far would a truck travel in 6 hr? **330 mi**

2. How far would a truck travel in 12 hr? **660 mi**

3. How far would a truck travel in 1 day and 4 hr? (Remember: There are 24 hr in 1 day.) **1,540 mi**

4. How far would a truck travel in 5 days? **6,600 mi**

5. If the speed is 65 mi per hour, how far would a truck travel in 6 hr? **390 mi**

6. How much farther would a truck travel in 12 hr driving 120 mi per hour than in 12 hr driving 65 mi per hour? **660 mi**

7. In construction zones, the speed is reduced to 45 mi per hour. How far would a truck travel in a construction zone if it traveled for $3\frac{1}{2}$ hr? **157.5 mi, or $157\frac{1}{2}$ mi**

8. How much farther would a truck travel in 6 hr driving 65 mi per hour than in 6 hr in a construction zone? **120 mi**

9. Nancy drove her truck on a trip through several states. She drove for 2 hr in a construction zone, 7 hr driving 55 mi per hour, and 5 hr driving 65 mi per hour. How many miles did she drive altogether? **800 mi**

10. Cam drove 162.5 mi at 65 mi per hour, 467.5 mi at 55 mi per hour, and 180 mi at 45 mi per hour. How many hours did he spend driving altogether? **15 hr**

Use with Lesson 2-4. **19**

Name_____

Multiplying Whole Numbers

PS 2-4

Earth Years The table shows the length of a year (in Earth years) for each of the outer planets of our solar system: Jupiter, Saturn, Uranus, Neptune, and Pluto. One Earth year is approximately 365 days, 52 weeks, or 12 months long.

Planet	Length of Year (in Earth years)
Jupiter	12
Saturn	29
Uranus	84
Neptune	165
Pluto	249

1. How many days long is a year on Jupiter? **4,380 days**

2. How many weeks long is a year on Saturn? **1,508 weeks**

3. How many months long is a year on Pluto? **2,988 months**

Savings Account Calvin's mother started a savings account for him when he was born. Every month his mother deposited $25 into his account. She continued depositing $25 every month until he was 18 years old.

4. How much money did Calvin's mother deposit into his account each year? **$300 each year**

5. How much money had Calvin's mother deposited into his savings account by the end of his 18th year? **$5,400 at the end of his 18th year**

6. **Writing in Math** Explain how you solved Exercise 5.

Sample answer: You multiply the amount of money Calvin's mother deposited each year by 18.

Use with Lesson 2-4. **19**

Choose a Calculation Method

P 2-5

Find each product. Tell what computation method you used.

Methods may vary. Sample answers 1–6.

1. $200 \times 50 =$ **10,000; mental math**

2. $57 \times 7 =$ **399; paper and pencil**

3. $34 \times 22 =$ **748; calculator**

4. $60 \times 17 =$ **1,020; mental math**

5. $455 \times 309 =$ **140,595; calculator**

6. $250 \times 200 =$ **50,000; mental math**

7. **Number Sense** Find 77×96. Explain the method you used.

Sample answer: 7,392; Paper and pencil because these numbers are not easy to multiply mentally

8. If Reneé rode her bicycle every day last year for 7 mi each day, how many miles did she ride altogether?

2,555 mi

9. Jason went to school 180 days last year. If he walked 2 mi each way, how many miles did he walk to and from school in all?

720 mi

Test Prep

10. Eli used mental math to solve 6×32. Which answer shows how he could find the correct solution?

A. $(3 \times 3) + (6 \times 2)$

B. $6 \times (9 \times 4)$

C. $(6 \times 30) + (6 \times 2)$

D. $(6 \times 30) + 2$

11. **Writing in Math** Explain why mental math would not be the best way to multiply 309×399.

The numbers are large so it would be easier to use a calculator.

20 Use with Lesson 2-5.

© Pearson Education, Inc. 5

Choose a Computation Method

R 2-5

Use mental math when the numbers are easy to multiply in your head, such as 15×3.

Use paper and pencil when the numbers are not easy to multiply mentally, such as 18×24.

Use a calculator when the numbers are large and you want an exact answer, such as 327×56.

Find each product. Tell what computation method you used.

1. $800 \times 25 =$ **20,000; mental math**

2. $99 \times 71 =$ **7,029; paper and pencil**

3. $243 \times 598 =$ **145,314; calculator**

4. What is the cost of three baseball mitts?

$147; mental math

5. What is the cost of two pairs of in-line skates?

$208; mental math

Sporting Goods Sale	
Item	Price
Baseball mitt	$49
Soccer ball	$32
In-line skates	$104
Softball	$9
Running shoes	$28

6. **Writing in Math** Explain how to use mental math to find the product of 20×49.

Sample answer: $20 \times 49 = 20 \times (50 - 1) = (20 \times 50) - (20 \times 1) = 1,000 - 20 = 980$

20 Use with Lesson 2-5.

© Pearson Education, Inc. 5

Choose a Method

E 2-5
NUMBER SENSE

For each problem, choose a computation method—mental math, paper and pencil, or a calculator—and find the product. Tell which method you used and why. Then explain the advantages. Each method should be used only once.

1. $201 \times 9 =$ **1,809**

Computation method: **Paper and pencil**

Why did you choose this method? **Sample answers: The numbers are simple, but more difficult than mental math.**

Advantages: **It is a good way to check your work.**

2. $741 \times 529 =$ **391,989**

Computation method: **Calculator**

Why did you choose this method? **Sample answers: The numbers were both large.**

Advantages: **It is the fastest way for large numbers.**

3. $3 \times 300 \times 40 =$ **36,000**

Computation method: **Mental math**

Why did you choose this method? **Sample answers: The numbers were simple multiples of ten.**

Advantages: **It is the fastest way for simple numbers.**

20 Use with Lesson 2-5.

© Pearson Education, Inc. 5

Choose a Computation Method

PS 2-5

Appliances The amount of energy used by different appliances is expressed in kilowatt-hours. The estimated annual kilowatt-hours per household for several different appliances are shown.

Appliance	Kilowatt-hours per Year
Blender	15
Toaster	39
Color television	502

Sample methods for 1–3.

1. How many kilowatt-hours would a blender use over 8 years? Tell what computation method you used.

120 kilowatt-hours; mental math

2. How many kilowatt-hours would a toaster use over 8 years? Tell what computation method you used.

312 kilowatt-hours; paper and pencil

3. How many kilowatt-hours would a color television use over 11 years? Tell what computation method you used.

5,522 kilowatt-hours; calculator

Customers at a berry stand can purchase berries that have already been picked, or they can pick the berries themselves. Already-picked strawberries are $3 per basket. U-pick strawberries are $2 per basket. Already-picked blueberries are $5 per basket. U-pick blueberries are $4 per basket.

4. How much would 5 baskets of already-picked strawberries, 5 baskets of already-picked blueberries, 4 baskets of U-pick strawberries, and 3 baskets of U-pick blueberries cost? **$60**

5. **Writing in Math** For Exercise 4, did you use mental math, paper and pencil, or a calculator to determine the answer? Explain your choice.

Sample answer: Paper and pencil; There were too many numbers for mental math.

20 Use with Lesson 2-5.

© Pearson Education, Inc. 5

© Pearson Education, Inc. 5

Name_____

P 2-6

Make an Organized List

Solve each problem. Write the answer in a complete sentence.

1. The mystery first name of a student in class does not begin with A, B, C, D, E, or F. The name's first letter comes before S, T, U, V, and W. The students whose names start with J, K, L, M, and N are not it. All letters from O through Q are not it. X, Y, Z and G, H, I are not it. What is the first letter of the mystery name?

The mystery student's name begins with the letter R.

2. Evan is thinking of a 3-digit odd number that uses the digit 7 twice. The digit in the tens place is less than one. What is the number?

The tens place digit is zero, which goes between the two sevens (707).

3. In the Laser Bowl Tournament, the judges take away 50 points for a gutter ball. Players score 30 points for a red head pin strike, 20 points for a blue pin strike, and 15 points for a green pin strike. Two red head pin strikes in a row earns a one-time bonus of 50 points. How many points would you score if you earned 2 red head pin strikes in a row, 2 blue pin strikes, 0 green pin strikes, and 2 gutter balls?

50 points

4. **Writing in Math** Explain how you completed the list in Exercise 1.

Answers will vary but should discuss how the information from Exercise 1 was used to make a list.

Use with Lesson 2-6. **21**

Name_____

R 2-6

Make an Organized List

Coin Toss Jan and Linda thought of a coin tossing game that uses a quarter. If the coin lands "heads" up, the player receives 10 points. If it lands "tails" up, the player receives 9 points. Each player gets 3 tosses. What scores are possible for one game for one player?

Read and Understand

What do you know? In each round, a player can score either 10 or 9 points. There are 3 rounds.

What are you trying to find? The scores that are possible for one game for one player.

Plan and Solve

What strategy will you use? Strategy: Make an organized list.

Scores per Round	Total Score	
10, 10, 10	30	First, find the combinations
10, 10, 9	29	with a "heads" flip or 10.
10, 9, 9	28	Then, find the combinations
9, 9, 9	27	with a "tails" flip or 9.

Answer: Possible scores are 30, 29, 28, and 27.

Look Back and Check

Is your work correct? Yes, each possible point combination was listed.

1. The sandwich shop sells tuna, egg, and peanut butter sandwiches. You can have your sandwich on whole wheat, rye, or a bagel. How many different sandwiches are possible?

TW, EW, PBW, TR, ER, PBR, TB, EB, PBB; There are 9 different sandwiches.

Use with Lesson 2-6. **21**

Name_____

Mirror Images

E 2-6
VISUAL THINKING

A mirror image of a figure shows the reverse of the original figure. The figures shown at the right are mirror images.

One of the three figures at the right is a mirror image of the figure at the left. Circle the figure that is a mirror image.

1.

2.

3.

4.

5.

Use with Lesson 2-6. **21**

Name_____

PS 2-6

Make an Organized List

Alex and Yvonne are spending the day at Family Fun Park. They have $50 to spend between them. How many combinations of activities can Alex and Yvonne do for under $50?

Family Fun Park	
Activity	**Price**
Water slides	$9
Miniature golf	$5
Mountain bikes	$15

Read and Understand

1. How much will each activity cost for both of them?

$18; $10; $30

Plan and Solve

2. What strategy will you use?

Make an organized list

3. Which combinations will work?

Water slides and miniature golf; miniature golf and mountain bikes; water slides and mountain bikes

4. Write the answer in a complete sentence.

There are 3 combinations of activities that Alex and Yvonne can do for under $50.

Look Back and Check

5. Explain how you can check if your work is correct.

Sample answer: A table or chart could be used.

Use with Lesson 2-6. **21**

Decimal Patterns

P 2-7

Find each product. Use mental math.

1. $0.31 \times 10 =$
3.1

2. $100 \times 7.000 =$
700.0

3. $0.02 \times 1,000 =$
20

4. $1,000 \times 5.1 =$
5,100

5. $45.6 \times 100 =$
4,560

6. $30.3 \times 1,000 =$
30,300

7. $10 \times 102.2 =$
1,022

8. $100 \times 0.312 =$
31.2

9. $10 \times 7.522 =$
75.22

10. $0.002 \times 10 =$
0.02

11. $578.31 \times 100 =$
57,831

12. $9.50 \times 1,000 =$
9,500

13. Which student will enlarge her art to 5 mm if she enlarges it 100 times?
Jess

Student	Art Size
Jade	0.25 mm
Willa	0.24 mm
Jess	0.05 mm
Mae	0.37 mm

14. How many millimeters will Mae's art be if she enlarges it 100 times?
37 mm

15. **Algebra** What is the value of n if $23.2 \times n = 2,320$?
$n = 100$

Test Prep

16. Which is the product of 0.225×100?

   A. 2.25   **(B.)** 22.5   **C.** 225   **D.** 2,250

17. **Writing in Math** Write a word problem using the number sentence $4.23 \times 10 = 42.3$.
Sample answer: Ted has 10 pieces of wood that each measure 4.23 ft. How many feet of wood does Ted have?

Decimal Patterns

R 2-7

You can use patterns to multiply decimals mentally by 10, 100, and 1,000.

Look at what happens to the decimal when you multiply decimals by 10.

Multiplying by 10	What happens to the decimal?
$32.5 \times 10 = 325$	The decimal moves one place to the right.
$5.936 \times 10 = 59.36$	The decimal moves one place to the right.

Now look at multiplying decimals by 100 and 1,000.

Multiplying by 100	What happens to the decimal position?
$32.5 \times 100 = 3,250$	The decimal moves two places to the right.

Multiplying by 1,000	What happens to the decimal position?
$5.9362 \times 1,000 = 5,936.2$	The decimal moves three places to the right.

Find the product. Use mental math.

1. $3.7 \times 10 =$ **37**

2. $1.828 \times 1,000 =$ **1,828**

3. $56 \times 1,000 =$ **56,000**

4. $100 \times 39.9 =$ **3,990**

5. Mr. Williams invests $125 in a stock. After three years, the stock's value is 10 times greater. What is the value of the stock after three years?
$1,250

6. At birth, the length of a snake is 0.087 ft. After three years, the length is 100 times greater than at birth. What is the length of the snake after three years?
8.7 ft

7. **Algebra** What is m if $163.25 \times m = 163,250$?
$m = 1,000$

What a Jump!

E 2-7
ALGEBRA

Use decimal patterns to solve for the variable. If j represents the number of jumps, find the value of j in each of the exercises below.

A woman on the track team at a university in the Midwest recently broke a school record when she jumped 21.04 ft in the long jump.

1. $j \times 21.04 = 210.4$ ft
$j = 10$

2. $j \times 21.04 = 2,104$ ft
$j = 100$

3. $j \times 21.04 = 210,400$ ft
$j = 10,000$

4. $j \times 21.04 = 1,052$ ft
$j = 50$

In the 1996 Summer Olympics a woman from Bulgaria made a high jump of 6.726 ft.

5. $j \times 6.726 = 6,726$ ft
$j = 1,000$

6. $j \times 6.726 = 67.26$ ft
$j = 10$

7. $j \times 6.726 = 672.6$ ft
$j = 100$

8. $j \times 6.726 = 3,363$ ft
$j = 500$

Also in the 1996 Summer Olympics a woman from the Ukraine made a triple jump that totaled 50.295 ft.

9. $j \times 50.295 = 502.95$ ft
$j = 10$

10. $j \times 50.295 = 1,005.9$ ft
$j = 20$

11. $j \times 50.295 = 2,514.75$ ft
$j = 50$

12. $j \times 50.295 = 5,029.5$ ft
$j = 100$

Decimal Patterns

PS 2-7

Speed of Light Light travels at a speed of 300,000 km per second. Because objects are so far apart in space, scientists use the light-year to measure the distances between objects in space. A light-year is the distance light travels in one year. The table below shows the number of light-years between three stars and the Sun.

Star	Distance from Sun (in light-years)
Barnard's Star	5.94
Wolf 359	7.80
Sirius A, B	8.60

1. If a star were 10 times farther away from the Sun than Barnard's Star, how far away would it be?
59.4 light-years

2. If a star were 100 times farther away from the Sun than Wolf 359, how far away would it be?
780 light-years

3. If a star were 1,000 times farther away from the Sun than Sirius A, B, how far away would it be?
8,600 light-years

4. **Writing in Math** Explain the difference between multiplying a decimal by 10 and multiplying the same decimal by 1,000.
Sample answer: When you multiply a decimal by 10, you move the decimal point to the right one place. When you multiply a decimal by 1,000, you move the decimal point to the right three places.

Name_____

Estimating Decimal Products

Estimate each product. **Sample answers for 1–9.**

1. $43 \times 2.1 =$
86

2. $5.40 \times 7 =$
35

3. $2.23 \times 15.9 =$
32

4. $250 \times 5.1 =$
1,250

5. $0.02 \times 96 =$
2

6. $2.65 \times 7.4 =$
21

7. $435.22 \times 2 =$
870

8. $781.93 \times 13 =$
10,000

9. $1.90 \times 526.8 =$
1,060

10. James has $65 to spend at the clothing sale. Does James have enough money to buy one of each item?

Clothing Sale	
Sweater	$19.99
Pants	$29.99
Shirt	$12.99
Socks (1 pair)	$2.99

No, he cannot buy one of each item. He would need about $66.

11. Algebra A reasonable estimate for n is 1,000. Complete the problem to make it true.

$n \times$ __**6.35**__ $= 6,350$

Test Prep

12. Which is a reasonable estimate for 41.3×8.78?

A. 36   **B.** 360   C. 3,600   D. 36,000

13. Writing in Math Explain how you know that 200 is not a reasonable estimate for 19.6×20.

Sample answer: When 19.6 is rounded to 20, then $20 \times 20 = 400$.

Name_____

Estimating Decimal Products

Bonnie wants to buy 3.7 lb of cashews for a recipe. The cashews cost $8.95 per pound. About how much will the cashews cost?

Two Ways for Bonnie to Estimate the Cost of the Cashews

Estimating by rounding	Estimating by using compatible numbers
You can estimate $3.7 \times \$8.95$ by rounding both numbers.	Another way to estimate is to adjust one or both numbers to compatible numbers that are easy to multiply.
3.7 is close to 4. $8.95 is close to $9.	$3.7 \times \$8.95$
$4 \times \$9 = 36$	$3.7 \times \$10$
$3.7 \times \$8.95$ is about $36.	$3.7 \times \$10 = \$37$
So the cashews will cost about $36.	$3.7 \times \$8.95$ is about 37.
This is an overestimate since both numbers were rounded up. The exact answer is less than $36.	So the cashews will cost about $37.

Estimate each product.

1. $6.3 \times \$17.59$
About $120

2. 29×2.002
About 60

3. 88.8×6.908
About 630

4. 7.94×51.25
About 400

5. Number Sense Estimate 6.7×11 using two different ways. Tell how you found each estimate.

By rounding: $7 \times 10 = 70$; by compatible numbers: $6.7 \times 10 = 67$.

6. Which product is greater, 35.34×6.4 or 35.47×6.4? Explain your answer.

The product of 35.47×6.4 is greater because 35.47 is greater than 35.34.

Name_____

Decimal Rules

Write the next three numbers in each decimal pattern. Then write a rule for each pattern. Look out for two-step patterns.

1. 0.1, 0.3, 0.9, __**2.7**__ , __**8.1**__ , __**24.3**__
Rule: **Multiply by 3**

2. 3.4, 4.9, 6.4, __**7.9**__ , __**9.4**__ , __**10.9**__
Rule: **Add 1.5**

3. 0.1051, 1.051, 10.51, __**105.1**__ , __**1,051**__ , __**10,510**__
Rule: **Multiply by 10**

4. 19, 16.7, 14.4, __**12.1**__ , __**9.8**__ , __**7.5**__
Rule: **Subtract 2.3**

5. 500, 100, 20, __**4**__ , __**0.8**__ , __**0.16**__
Rule: **Divide by 5**

6. 1.3, 3.3, 4.5, 6.5, 7.7, __**9.7**__ , __**10.9**__ , __**12.9**__
Rule: **Add 2 then add 1.2**

7. 14.8, 15, 13.2, 13.4, 11.6, __**11.8**__ , __**10**__ , __**10.2**__
Rule: **Add 0.2 then subtract 1.8**

8. 4.8, 9.6, 8.9, 17.8, 17.1, __**34.2**__ , __**33.5**__ , __**67**__
Rule: **Multiply by 2 then subtract 0.7**

Name_____

Estimating Decimal Products

Brenton is making pancakes for his family's breakfast. His measuring spoons and cups are all metric so he must convert the quantities in the recipe. The table below shows the conversions.

1 tsp	= 4.93 mL
1 tbsp	= 14.77 mL
1 c	= 236.64 mL

Sample answers given for 1–4.

1. Brenton must use 2.25 tsp of baking soda and 3 tbsp of melted butter in his pancakes. Estimate to determine about how many milliliters 2.25 tsp and 3 tbsp will be.

About 10 mL (tsp); About 45 mL (tbsp)

2. The recipe calls for 2.25 c of flour. Estimate to determine about how many milliliters 2.25 c will be.

About 480 mL

Marcie is making a new dress for herself. She buys 3.5 yd of white fabric at $4.80 per yard and 2.5 yd of blue fabric at $3.35 per yard.

3. Find an overestimate and an underestimate for the price of the white fabric.

Underestimate: $12; Overestimate: $20

4. Find an overestimate and an underestimate for the price of the blue fabric.

Underestimate: $6; Overestimate: $12

5. Writing in Math Explain how an overestimate and an underestimate can be used to find a reasonable estimate.

Sample answer: They can be averaged to find a reasonable estimate.

© Pearson Education, Inc. 5

Name_____

Multiplying Whole Numbers and Decimals

P 2-9

Find each product.

1.	2.	3.	4.
5.4	3.8	0.55	8.19
$\times\ 3$	$\times\ 4$	$\times\ 8$	$\times\ 5$
16.2	**15.2**	**4.4**	**40.95**

Insert a decimal point in each answer to make the equation true.

5. $5 \times 6.3 = 315$ **31.5**

6. $3.001 \times 9 = 27009$ **27.009**

7. Which desert accumulates the least amount of rain in August?

Mojave

8. If each month in Reno had the same average rainfall as in August, what would the total number of millimeters be after 12 months?

2.28 mm

Average Desert Rainfall in August	
Reno	0.19 mm
Sahara	0.17 mm
Mojave	0.1 mm
Tempe	0.24 mm

Test Prep

9. Algebra If $4n = 3.60$, which is the value of n?

A. 0.09   **B.** 0.9   C. 9   D. 90

Use the desert rainfall table to answer Exercise 10.

10. **Writing in Math** In December, the average rainfall in all of the deserts is 0.89 mm. Use the figures from the table to write a comparison of average desert rainfall in August and December.

Sample answer: In December, the average rainfall is greater than in August, because 0.89 mm > 0.7 mm.

© Pearson Education, Inc. 5

Name_____

Multiplying Whole Numbers and Decimals

R 2-9

A human can walk a long distance at an average rate of 4.2 mi per hour. A high-speed train can travel the same distance 48 times faster. What is the speed of the high-speed train?

Step 1: Estimate, then multiply as with whole numbers.

4.2×48 is about
$4 \times 50 = 200$.

$$\begin{array}{r} 48 \\ \times\ 4.2 \\ \hline 96 \\ 1920 \\ \hline 2016 \end{array}$$

Step 2: Write the decimal point in the product. First, count the number of decimal places in both factors.

$$\begin{array}{r} 48 \leftarrow \text{0 decimal places} \\ \times\ 4.2 \leftarrow \text{1 decimal place} \\ \hline 96 \\ 1920 \\ \hline 201.6 \end{array}$$

Since there is a total of 1 decimal place in the factors, there is 1 decimal place in the product.

Your answer is reasonable. It is close to 200.

1.	2.	3.
6.3	21	0.002
$\times\ 8$	$\times\ 2.5$	$\times\ 4$
50.4	**52.5**	**0.008**

4. $35 \times 5.3 =$ **185.5**

5. $17.6 \times 40 =$ **704**

6. Mrs. Bilda bought six cans of orange juice at a cost of $1.33 per can, including tax. How much change did she get from a $10 bill? **$2.02**

7. **Algebra** If $0.3 \times n = 0.24$, what is the value of n? **$n = 0.8$**

8. **Writing in Math** John is multiplying two factors, each with one decimal place. He says that the product should also have only one decimal place. Is his explanation correct? Explain.

No; The product needs to have two decimal places, the sum of the places in the factors.

© Pearson Education, Inc. 5

Name_____

How Much Faster?

E 2-9
REASONABLENESS

Ryan's Deli makes a sandwich in 1 min. The chart at the right indicates how long it takes other delis to make a sandwich in comparison to Ryan's. For example, Werner's Deli takes 2.2 times as long to make a sandwich as Ryan's. For the exercises below, determine if the statement is reasonable or unreasonable. Explain your answer.

Deli	Time Factor
Werner's	2.2
Main Street	0.6
Two Star	3.74

1. In 10 min, Ryan's Deli will make more than twice as many sandwiches as Werner's Deli.

Reasonable; It takes Werner's more than twice as long to make a sandwich as Ryan's.

2. In 30 min, Main Street Deli will make more than twice as many sandwiches as Ryan's Deli.

Unreasonable; It takes the Main Street Deli more than half as long to make a sandwich as Ryan's.

3. It takes the Two Star Deli under 38 min to make 10 sandwiches.

Reasonable; It takes the Two Star Deli 3.74 min to make 1 sandwich. So, it would take the Two Star Deli 10 × 3.74, or 37.4 min, to make 10 sandwiches.

© Pearson Education, Inc. 5

Name_____

Multiplying Whole Numbers and Decimals

PS 2-9

Life Spans Animals age at different rates. The average life span of several animals is shown.

Average Life Spans	
Domestic dog	12 years
Kangaroo	7 years
Rabbit	5 years

1. What is the average life span of black bears if it is 3.6 times greater than the life span of rabbits? **18 years**

2. What is the average life span of Asian elephants if it is 5.7 times greater than the life span of kangaroos? **39.9 years**

Supply Shopping Kisha is going shopping for back-to-school supplies. She needs 4 three-ring notebooks, 6 folders, 3 highlighting pens in different colors, and 2 pencil boxes.

3. How much will the notebooks cost if they are $3.49 each? **$13.96**

4. How much will the folders cost if they are $1.17 each? **$7.02**

5. Which will cost more, the highlighting pens at $1.23 each or the pencil boxes at $1.32 each?

The highlighting pens will cost more.

6. **Writing in Math** Explain how you know that the product of 8×0.9 is less than 8.

Sample answer: Because 0.9 is less than 1, the product of 8 × 0.9 will be less than 8.

© Pearson Education, Inc. 5

Name_____

Using Grids to Multiply Decimals by Decimals

P 2-10

Write a multiplication sentence that describes the shaded areas of each grid.

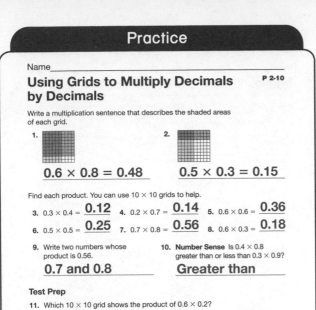

1. $0.6 \times 0.8 = 0.48$

2. $0.5 \times 0.3 = 0.15$

Find each product. You can use 10 × 10 grids to help.

3. $0.3 \times 0.4 =$ __0.12__ 4. $0.2 \times 0.7 =$ __0.14__ 5. $0.6 \times 0.6 =$ __0.36__

6. $0.5 \times 0.5 =$ __0.25__ 7. $0.7 \times 0.8 =$ __0.56__ 8. $0.6 \times 0.3 =$ __0.18__

9. Write two numbers whose product is 0.56.

__0.7 and 0.8__

10. **Number Sense** Is 0.4×0.8 greater than or less than 0.3×0.9?

__Greater than__

Test Prep

11. Which 10 × 10 grid shows the product of 0.6×0.2?

A. B. C. D.

12. **Writing in Math** Explain why 0.2×0.4 equals 0.08 and not 0.8.

Sample answer: By shading 0.2 units with one color on a 10 × 10 grid and 0.4 with another color, 0.08 is the amount shaded by both colors.

© Pearson Education, Inc. 5

Use with Lesson 2-10. **25**

Name_____

Using Grids to Multiply Decimals by Decimals

R 2-10

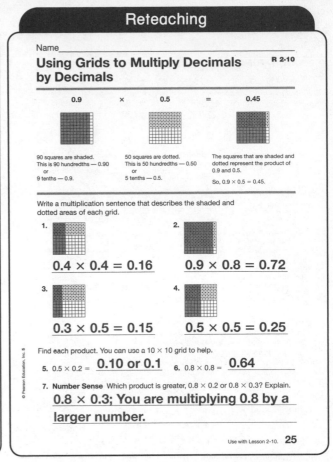

| 0.9 | × | 0.5 | = | 0.45 |

90 squares are shaded. This is 90 hundredths — 0.90 or 9 tenths — 0.9.

50 squares are dotted. This is 50 hundredths — 0.50 or 5 tenths — 0.5.

The squares that are shaded and dotted represent the product of 0.9 and 0.5.

So, $0.9 \times 0.5 = 0.45$.

Write a multiplication sentence that describes the shaded and dotted areas of each grid.

1. $0.4 \times 0.4 = 0.16$

2. $0.9 \times 0.8 = 0.72$

3. $0.3 \times 0.5 = 0.15$

4. $0.5 \times 0.5 = 0.25$

Find each product. You can use a 10 × 10 grid to help.

5. $0.5 \times 0.2 =$ __0.10 or 0.1__ 6. $0.8 \times 0.8 =$ __0.64__

7. **Number Sense** Which product is greater, 0.8×0.2 or 0.8×0.3? Explain.

0.8×0.3; You are multiplying 0.8 by a larger number.

© Pearson Education, Inc. 5

Use with Lesson 2-10. **25**

Name_____

Gridlock

E 2-10
VISUAL THINKING

Matt is a mathematician who creates number grids to represent mathematical equations. He completed four multiplication problems, and his answers were: 0.24, 0.56, 0.35, and 0.49. He also used 10 × 10 grids to represent his answers. In the exercises below, match one of Matt's numeric answers with the number grid shown, and then write the complete equation.

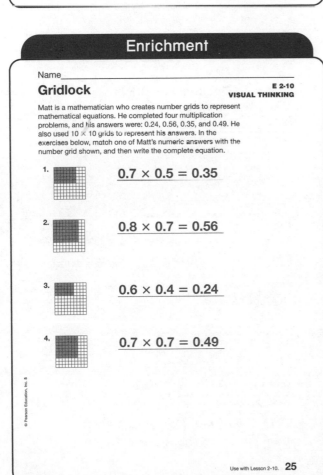

1. $0.7 \times 0.5 = 0.35$

2. $0.8 \times 0.7 = 0.56$

3. $0.6 \times 0.4 = 0.24$

4. $0.7 \times 0.7 = 0.49$

© Pearson Education, Inc. 5

Use with Lesson 2-10. **25**

Name_____

Using Grids to Multiply Decimals by Decimals

PS 2-10

Water Containers Justin has two containers, one that holds 0.8 gal of water and one that holds 0.6 gal of water. He brought the containers to a soccer game he was playing in.

1. One of Justin's teammates drank 4 tenths of the larger container of water. How many gallons did he drink?

__0.32 gal__

2. Justin drank 7 tenths of the smaller container of water. How much water did Justin drink?

__0.42 gal__

Knotted Rope A rope has knots tied at specific intervals along its length. The total length of the rope is 0.9 yd.

3. The first knot is at a spot that is 0.2 of the total length of the rope. Where is the first knot?

__At 0.18 yd__

4. A second knot is located 0.2 of the way past the first knot. Where is the second knot?

__0.36 yd__

5. Where is the halfway point on the rope?

__0.45 yd__

6. **Writing in Math** Tell what the grids and the shaded areas represent.

Sample answer: The grids represent the multiplication sentence $0.7 \times 0.2 = 0.14$.

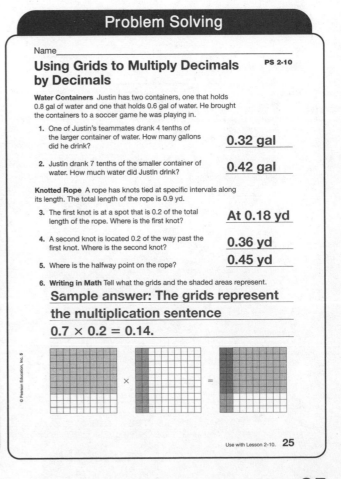

© Pearson Education, Inc. 5

Use with Lesson 2-10. **25**

Name_____

Multiplying Decimals by Decimals P 2-11

Find each product.

1.	2.	3.	4.
3.7	4.4	0.61	1.9
× 0.3	× 0.2	× 6.8	× 0.005
1.11	**0.88**	**4.148**	**0.0095**

5. $0.61 \times 6.8 =$ **4.148**   6. $0.79 \times 0.005 =$ **0.00395**

Insert a decimal point in each answer to make the equation true.

7. $0.2 \times 4.4 = 088$ **0.88**   8. $8.81 \times 5.2 = 45812$ **45.812**

9. **Number Sense** The product of 4.7 and 6.5 equals 30.55.
What is the product of 4.7 and 0.65? 4.7 and 65?
3.055   **305.5**

10. What is the gravity in relation to Earth
that is 3.4 times the gravity of Mercury?
1.258

Relative (to Earth) Surface Gravity	
Planet	Gravity
Mercury	0.37
Neptune	1.22
Pluto	0.06

11. What is the product of the gravity of Pluto
and Neptune?
0.0732

Test Prep

12. How many decimal places are in the product of a number
with decimal places to the thousandths multiplied by a
number with decimal places to the hundredths?

A. 2   B. 3   C. 4   **(D.)** 5

13. **Writing in Math** Explain how you know the number of
decimal places that should be in the product when you
multiply two decimal numbers together.   **Sample answer:**
The total number of decimal places in the
numbers being multiplied is the number
of decimal places in the product.

© Pearson Education, Inc. 5

Name_____

Multiplying Decimals by Decimals R 2-11

Multiplying two decimal numbers is nearly the same as
multiplying two whole numbers. The only difference is deciding
where to place the decimal point in the answer.

Where do you place the decimal point in the answer?

First, multiply as with whole numbers.
Then, count the decimal places in both factors.

0.77 ⟶ 2 decimal places
$\times\ 4.8$ ⟶ 1 decimal place
616
3080
3.696 There are a total of
3 decimal   3 decimal places in the
places   factors, so you need
the same number in
the answer.

When should you add extra zeros to the answer?

0.09 ⟶ 2 decimal places
$\times\ 0.25$ ⟶ 2 decimal places
45
180
225   Since there are 4 decimal
places in the factors, you
need 4 decimal places in
the answer.

0.0225 The product only has
3 decimal places,
so annex 1 zero.

Find each product.

1.	2.	3.
8.7	2.28	92.3
× 0.4	× 0.7	× 0.2
3.48	**1.596**	**18.46**

4. **Estimation** Which is greater, 8.2×0.015 or 8.2×0.15? Explain.
8.2 × 0.15 because 0.15 > 0.015, and
they are both multiplied by 8.2.

5. Noelle found the product of 4.28×0.9. Her answer was
38.52. How do you know her answer was incorrect?
There are 2 decimal places in 4.28 and
1 decimal place in 0.9. There should
be 3 decimal places in the product.
The correct answer is 3.852.

© Pearson Education, Inc. 5

Name_____

Voting Posters E 2-11
DECISION MAKING

The student council is
making posters to
encourage students to vote
in the upcoming election.
The different types, sizes,
and costs of three paper
choices are listed in the
table to the right.

Paper Type	Size	Cost per Sheet
Construction	0.3 m × 0.4 m	$0.73
Posterboard	0.5 m × 0.8 m	$1.29
Craft	0.7 m × 0.9 m	$0.58

1. Find the area of each type of paper by shading the squares
on the grids. Then write the decimal amount shaded. Each
small square stands for 0.01 m².

a. Construction paper   b. Posterboard   c. Craft paper

Area = **0.12 m²**   Area = **0.4 m²**   Area = **0.63 m²**

2. Which type of paper is the best value based on a
comparison of the cost and area? Explain your answer.

The craft paper because it has the greatest
area and the lowest price.

3. Why might the student council choose to use a type of
paper that is not the best value?

Sample answer: The student council might
want a different size, color, or type of paper.

4. Which type of paper should the student council choose to
buy for the posters? Explain your answer.

Sample answer: The posterboard because
it is the strongest and its area is three
times greater than the construction paper.

© Pearson Education, Inc. 5

Name_____

Multiplying Decimals by Decimals PS 2-11

Surface Area The table below shows the surface area of
several items. The area is expressed in square inches.

Item	Surface Area (in square inches)
Sheet of paper ($8\frac{1}{2}$ in. by 11 in.)	93.5
Playing card	7.6
Postage stamps	0.85

1. What is the surface area of 2.5 sheets of paper?   **233.75 sq in.**

2. If postage stamps were 1.25 times larger than
they are now, what would their surface area be?   **1.0625 sq in.**

3. If postage stamps were 1.75 times larger than
they are now, what would their surface area be?   **1.4875 sq in.**

Fruit Connie's mother sends her to the store to buy nectarines
and cherries. The nectarines are $1.50 per pound and the
cherries are $2.60 per pound.

4. Connie buys 4.5 lb of nectarines. How much did she pay?   **$6.75**

5. Connie really likes cherries and wants to buy 2.5 lb with her
own money. She has $5.00 of her own money in her
pocket. Can she buy that many pounds of cherries?
No, Connie would need $6.50.

6. **Writing in Math** Elizabeth says that if you multiply a
decimal with 2 decimal places by a decimal with 3 decimal
places, the product will have 6 decimal places because
$2 \times 3 = 6$. Is she correct? Explain.
Sample answer: No. It will have 5
decimal places because 2 + 3 = 5.

© Pearson Education, Inc. 5

Name_____

Variables and Expressions

P 2-12

1. Write an algebraic expression to represent the cost of a concert ticket, h, with a service charge of $6.75.

$$h + \$6.75$$

2. Write an algebraic expression to represent the cost of m gallons of gasoline if each gallon costs $1.45.

$$m \times \$1.45 \text{ or } \$1.45m$$

Evaluate each expression for $n = 3$ and $n = 6$.

3. $0.2 \times n$ **0.6 1.2**

4. $n - 2.1$ **0.9 3.9**

5. $\frac{12}{n}$ **4 2**

6. $35 + n$ **38 41**

Complete each table.

7.
n	$0.9 + n$
0.5	**1.4**
0.2	**1.1**
0.15	**1.05**
0.1	**1.0**

8.
n	$96 \div n$
1	**96**
2	**48**
3	**32**
4	**24**

9. **Representations** What is another way to write the expression $44n$? $44 \div n$?

$$44 \times n; \ \frac{44}{n}$$

Test Prep

10. Which is the correct product of $n \times 7$ if $n = \$0.25$?

A. $3.25 B. $2.75 C. $2.25 **D.** $1.75

11. **Writing in Math** Write a situation that can be represented by the algebraic expression $3.25d$.

Sample answer: Keri buys d candles at $3.25 each.

Name_____

Variables and Expressions

R 2-12

An algebraic expression is a mathematical phrase that uses variables, numbers, and operations, such as addition and multiplication. Here are some other examples of algebraic expressions.

Addition	Subtraction	Multiplication	Division
$7 + e$	$f - 33$	$5 \times g$ or $5g$	$h \div 2$ or $\frac{h}{2}$

You can evaluate an algebraic expression by replacing the variable with a number, then performing the computation.

Evaluate $a + 7$ if $a = 6.5$.
Replace a with 6.5 in the expression.
$a + 7$
$\Downarrow$
$6.5 + 7 = 13.5$

Evaluate $d \times 9.9$ if $d = 4$.
Replace d with 4 in the expression.
$d \times 9.9$
$\Downarrow$
$4 \times 9.9 = 39.6$

Evaluate each expression for $p = 9$ and $p = 11$.

1. $p - 7 =$ **2; 4**

2. $5.8 + p =$ **14.8; 16.8**

3. $p \times 5 =$ **45; 55**

4. $99 \div p =$ **11; 9**

5. **Representation** What is another way to write the expression $82p$?

$82 \times p$

6. Write an algebraic expression to represent the cost of a dog d with an additional tax of $20.

$d + \$20$

7. **Algebra** Jim is going to give away 7 of the t baseball cards in his collection and wonders how many cards he will have left. Does the algebraic expression $7 - t$ correctly represent this situation? Why or why not?

No; The expression should be $t - 7$ because you need to subtract 7 cards from the total cards in the collection.

Name_____

Prime Time

E 2-12
ALGEBRA

Bill spends time each evening watching television. This amount of time can be represented by the variable t. Use the variable to complete the exercises below.

1. Write an algebraic expression to represent the time Bill's friend Jill spends watching television if she watches 30 min more an evening than Bill.

$t + 30$

2. Write an algebraic expression to represent the time Bill will spend watching television in 8 weeks. (Remember: There are 7 days in 1 week.)

$56t$

3. Bill watches television for 52 min ($t = 52$). Bill's friend Hilda watches half the amount of television that Bill does. Write an algebraic expression to represent this, and solve for the value.

$\frac{t}{2}, \frac{52}{2}$, 26 min

4. Bill spent t min watching television on Monday, 60 min watching television on Tuesday, and 90 min watching television on Wednesday. Wednesday's time can be represented by the variable w. The time Bill spent watching television on Monday was $\frac{1}{2}$ the time spent on Wednesday ($t = \frac{w}{2}$). How much time did Bill spend watching television in those 3 days?

195 min

Name_____

Variables and Expressions

PS 2-12

Shopping Spree Moira is spending the day clothes shopping with her sister, Brianne. The girls plan on using several discount coupons on their shopping spree.

1. Brianne buys a pullover that, when combined with her coupon for x off, brings the total cost down to $38. Write an algebraic expression to represent the original cost of the pullover.

$\$38 + \$x$

2. Moira buys a pair of pants that have a price tag of p. She uses a $3-off coupon to reduce the price. Write an algebraic expression to represent the reduced price of the pants.

$\$p - \$3$

Phone Plan Rick's new long distance phone plan allows him to call anywhere in the country for $0.05 per minute on weekends and evenings and $0.07 per minute on weekdays. Martin's long distance phone plan allows him to call anywhere in the country at any time for $0.08 per minute.

3. Write an expression that represents the cost of an r-minute weekend phone call for Rick and an r-minute weekend phone call for Martin.

Rick: $\$0.05 \times r$; Martin: $\$0.08 \times r$

4. If a weekday phone call for Martin is represented by $\$0.08 \times n$, evaluate for $n = 35$, 45, and 55 min.

$2.80; $3.60; $4.40

5. **Writing in Math** Explain how you would find the length of a $5.00 long-distance phone call that costs $0.10 per minute.

Sample answer: Solve the equation $\$0.10 \times t = \$5.00$; divide $5.00 by $0.10; $t = 50$ min.

PROBLEM-SOLVING SKILL   P 2-13

Translating Words into Expressions

Write each word phrase an as algebraic expression.

1. the product of 5 and n $5n$

2. a height divided by 3 $\frac{h}{3}$ or $h \div 3$

3. $200 less than n $n - \$200$

4. a number of books plus 30 $n + 30$

5. **Number Sense** Explain what the expression $6x$ means.

   Six multiplied by a certain number

6. Dan is 12 in. taller than Jay. Use x for Jay's height. Which expression shows Dan's height, $x + 12$, $x - 12$, or $12x$? $x + 12$

7. There are 60 min in a hour. If there are y hr in a day, what expression shows the number of minutes in a day, $60y$, $60 + y$, or $\frac{y}{60}$? $60y$

8. Write two word phrases for the expression $\frac{t}{30}$.

   Sample answer: The number t divided by 30; the quotient of t and 30

9. **Writing in Math** Explain the difference between the expressions $x - 3$ and $3 - x$.

   Sample answer: The expression $x - 3$ means a number minus 3. The expression $3 - x$ means 3 minus a number.

PROBLEM-SOLVING SKILL   R 2-13

Translating Words into Expressions

You can use the word clues below to write algebraic expressions.

Words or Phrases	Operation	Example	Algebraic Expression
plus sum of more than increased by	addition	15 more than a number	$n + 15$
minus difference less than decreased by	subtraction	a number decreased by 7	$n - 7$
times multiplied by product	multiplication	8 times a number	$8 \times n$, $8 \bullet n$, $8n$
divided by quotient	division	a number divided by 13	$n \div 13$, $\frac{n}{13}$

Write each word phrase as an algebraic expression.

1. 10 less than the number of shoes $n - 10$

2. the quotient of y and 70 $\frac{y}{70}$ or $y \div 70$

3. 15 more than the number of days $n + 15$

4. the product of 14.2 and f $14.2 \times f$

5. **Number Sense** Write two word phrases for $18 + n$.

   Answers should include *more than*, *plus*, *sum*, or *increased by*.

Family Fun

E 2-13
REASONING

Martha has 3 more brothers than she has sisters, and she has 2 sisters. She is half the age of her eldest sister. She is twice the age of her youngest brother. For the exercises below, tell if the statement about Martha's family is true or false and explain why.

1. If Martha's sisters are represented by the variable s, and her brothers are represented by the variable b, the algebraic expression $s \times 3 = b$ represents the number of brothers she has.

   False. $s + 3 = b$ represents the number of brothers.

2. If Martha's youngest brother is represented by the variable y, and Martha's age is represented as a, her youngest brother's age can be represented as $\frac{y}{3} = 2$.

   False. $\frac{a}{2} = y$ is the correct expression.

3. If Martha's oldest sister is represented by the variable k, and Martha's age is represented as a, Martha's age can be represented as $\frac{k}{2} = a$.

   True. $\frac{k}{2} = a$ is the correct expression.

4. If the number of brothers Martha has is represented by the variable b, then the number of sisters she has can be represented as $b + 3$.

   False. $b - 3$ represents the number of sisters Martha has.

5. There are seven children in Martha's family.

   False. Martha has 2 sisters + 3 more brothers than sisters = 5 brothers. 5 + 2 + Martha = 8 children.

PROBLEM-SOLVING SKILL   PS 2-13

Translating Words into Expressions

Bookstore A bookstore is reorganizing its books. All of the books are being removed from their shelves and put in different locations. There are y identical bookcases in the store. Each bookcase holds 78 books.

1. Which expression shows the total number of books that can be stacked on all the bookcases, $y + 78$, $78 \div y$, or $78y$? $78y$

2. Each bookcase has z individual shelves. Which expression shows how many books can be put on each shelf, $78 + z$, $78 \div z$, or $78z$? $78 \div z$

Plant Food Ashanti is giving her houseplants several different kinds of plant food. She reads the labels carefully to make sure she does not give too much or too little to her plants.

3. The label on plant food A says to add one part food supplement to every two parts water. Write an algebraic expression that represents the amount of plant food A that is to be added to an amount w of water. $w \div 2$

4. The label on plant food B says to add 1.25 tsp of food supplement to every cup of water. Write an algebraic expression that represents the amount of plant food B that is to be added to c cups of water. $1.25c$

5. Plant food C is sprinkled around the base of the plant once every d days. Write an algebraic expression that represents the number of times per year plant food C is used. $365 \div d$

6. **Writing in Math** Write what the expression $(2 \times 87) - l$ means.

   Sample answer: The expression means l less than two times eighty-seven.

Name_____

Find a Rule

P 2-14

Find a rule for each table. Write the rule in words.

1.

Input	Output
6	18
24	36
48	60
72	84

Add 12

2.

Input	Output
5	30
9	54
12	72
15	90

Multiply by 6

3.

Input	Output
19	9
54	44
78	68
24	14

Subtract 10

Representations Write a rule with a variable for

4. Exercise 1. $n + 12$

5. Exercise 2. $6n$

6. Find a rule for the table. Write the rule in words.

Multiply the number of roses by 2.

Roses	Cost
12	$24
24	$48
36	$72

7. How much would 72 roses cost?

$144

Test Prep

8. Which is the rule with a variable for the table?

A. Add 78; $n + 78$

B. Multiply by 17; $17n$

C. Multiply by 27; $27n$

D. Add 86; $n + 86$

Input	Output
3	81
5	135
7	189
9	243

9. Writing in Math Explain how you find a rule from a table.

Sample answer: You can multiply to figure out the pattern in the table.

Name_____

Find a Rule

R 2-14

Looking for a pattern in a table can help you find a rule for it.

When you add 3 to each input number, you get the output number.

Input	7	12	19	30
Output	10	15	22	33

$7 + 3 = 10$
$12 + 3 = 15$
$19 + 3 = 22$
$30 + 3 = 33$

The rule for this table is **Add 3.**

How to find a rule for a table:

1. Look at the input numbers. Think about how they relate to the output numbers.

2. Ask yourself what operation and what number have been used to change the input number to the output number.

3. Test it on each pair of numbers in the table. If it works for each pair of numbers, it is the rule.

Write a rule for each table. Write the rule in words.

1.

Input	7	9	11	15
Output	15	17	19	23

Add 8

2.

Input	3	8	9	12
Output	9	24	27	36

Multiply by 3

3.

Input	25	28	30	35
Output	20	23	25	30

Subtract 5

4.

Input	4	8	10	13
Output	36	72	90	117

Multiply by 9

5. Number Sense The rule is **Add 15.** If the input number is 18, what will the output number be?

33

Name_____

Different Rules

E 2-14
PATTERNS

Sample answers are given for rules.

Each input/output table has a different rule. Complete each table below. Then, write a rule to explain each output.

1.

Input	Output
ABC	BCD
DEF	EFG
GHI	**HIJ**
JKL	**KLM**

Rule: **The output is the last 2 input letters with the next alphabetical letter added.**

2.

Input	Output
☆☆	☆☆☆ ☽
☆☆☆	☆☆☆☆ ☽☽
☆☆☆☆	★★★★★ ☽☽☽
☆☆☆☆☆	★★★★★★ ☽☽☽☽

Rule: **Add 1 more star than the number in the input column. Add the number of moons that is 2 less than the number of stars.**

3.

Input	Output
1 nickel	3 pennies
1 dime	3 nickels
1 quarter	**3 dimes**
1 half dollar	**3 quarters**

Rule: **The output is 3 of the next lowest coin.**

Name_____

Find a Rule

PS 2-14

Typing Class Eric took a typing class in school. By the end of the class, he was able to type 65 words per minute with errors and 55 words per minute without errors.

1. Complete the table to show how many words, with errors, Eric types in 1, 2, 3, 4, and 5 min.

Minutes	Words
1	65
2	130
3	195
4	260
5	325

2. Complete the table to show how many words, without errors, Eric types in 1, 2, 3, 4, and 5 min.

Minutes	Words
1	55
2	110
3	165
4	220
5	275

3. What is the rule for the table you made in Exercise 1?

Multiply by 65

4. What is the rule for the table you made in Exercise 2?

Multiply by 55

5. Writing in Math Explain the relationship between a rule and an input/output table.

Sample answer: A rule describes what an input/output table shows.

Name_____

Solving Equations

Solve each equation by using mental math.

1. $a + 3 = 35$ $a = 32$
2. $1 + e = 21$ $e = 20$
3. $3.18n = 31.8$ $n = 10$
4. $\frac{45}{p} = 5$ $p = 9$
5. $7m = 56$ $m = 8$
6. $17x = 51$ $x = 3$

Solve each equation by testing the given values for a variable.

7. $y - 9 = 11$ $y = 20$
   $y = 18, 19,$ or 20

8. $25k = 50$ $k = 2$
   $k = 1, 2,$ or 3

9. $\frac{z}{4} = 12$ $z = 48$
   $z = 48, 49,$ or 50

10. $29 - p = 13$ $p = 16$
    $p = 14, 15,$ or 16

11. **Reasoning** Write an equation that has a solution of $x = 4.3$.
    Sample answer: $\frac{17.2}{x} = 4$

Test Prep

12. Which is the written equation represented by the picture at the right?

    80

    (A) $10k = 80$ **B.** $5k = 80$ **C.** $k = 80$ **D.** $2k = 80$

13. **Writing in Math** Write a description of how mental math can be used to solve the equation $7 = x - 3$.
    Sample answer: Ask yourself what number minus 3 equals 7. The number is 10.

Name_____

Solving Equations

To solve equations, you find the value of the variable that makes the equation true. This value is called the solution. You can use mental math or test different values for the variable.

Use Mental Math

Solve $y - 8 = 14$.

- Ask yourself, "What number minus 8 equals 14?"
- $22 - 8 = 14$ Use mental math.
- $14 = 14$ Check that the equation is true.
- Solution: $y = 22$

Test Different Values for the Variable

Solve $8n = 48$.

- Think of some numbers you can substitute for n, such as 5, 6, and 7.
- Try $n = 5$: $8 \times 5 = 40$ No
  Try $n = 6$: $8 \times 6 = 48$ Yes
  Try $n = 7$: $8 \times 7 = 56$ No
- Solution: $n = 6$

Solve each equation by using mental math.

1. $b + 11 = 19$ $b = 8$
2. $12 \times n = 24$ $n = 2$
3. $62 - c = 42$ $c = 20$
4. $75 \div b = 25$ $b = 3$
5. $144 - f = 124$ $f = 20$
6. $r \times 10 = 140$ $r = 14$

Solve each equation by testing the given values for the variable.

7. $g - 7 = 14$ $g = 21, 24,$ or 28 $g = 21$

8. $11d = 88$ $d = 7, 8,$ or 9 $d = 8$

9. **Reasonableness** Bernie solved $w \div 12 = 12$. He wrote $w = 24$. Is he correct? Explain your answer.
   No; $24 \div 12 = 2$. The correct solution should be $w = 144$, because $144 \div 12 = 12$.

Name_____

Help Stanley

Stanley is learning to solve equations with variables using mental math. Below are equations he has written and his incorrect answers. Help Stanley by writing the correct answers. Then explain what was wrong with Stanley's answers.

1. $f - 132 = 11; f = 153$
   $f = 143$; Stanley added 132 and 11 incorrectly.

2. $77n = 154; n = 77$
   $n = 2$; Stanley added 77 and n instead of multiplying them.

3. $\frac{g}{5.5} = 66; g = 12$
   $g = 363$; Stanley divided 66 by 5.5 instead of multiplying both sides by 5.5.

4. $\frac{99}{3n} = 33; n = 0$
   $n = 1$; Stanley forgot that a number times 0 is 0.

5. $w + 8 = 16; w = 2$
   $w = 8$; Stanley divided 16 by 8 instead of subtracting 8 from 16.

Name_____

Solving Equations

Eggs for Sale The Egg-Rite Hatchery sells fresh eggs. Eggs are collected each morning, packed into egg cartons, and then sold. Each carton holds 12 eggs.

1. One day the hatchery sold 20 cartons of eggs. Write and solve an equation that shows how many eggs were sold. Let e equal the number of eggs sold.
   $20 \times 12 = e; e = 240$ eggs

2. On another day the hatchery sold 276 eggs. Write and solve an equation that shows how many cartons were sold. Let c equal the number of cartons.
   $276 \div c = 12; c = 23$ cartons

Savings Audrey has been saving $20 a month from her allowance for 5 years. She plans to use the money to buy a new computer.

3. There are 12 months in one year. Solve the equation $5 \times 12 = w$ to find the number of months in 5 years.
   $w = 60$ months

4. Using your answer from Exercise 3, write and solve an equation to find how much money Audrey has saved in 5 years. Let m be the amount of money.
   $60 \times \$20 = m; m = \$1,200$ in 5 years

5. **Writing in Math** Explain how a variable is used in an equation.
   Sample answer: A variable is used to represent an unknown value in an equation. By solving the equation, the value of the variable is determined.

Name_____

PROBLEM-SOLVING APPLICATION　　　　　P 2-16

Fast Flights

How Fast Do Birds Fly?

Bird	Speed (miles per hour)
Peregrine falcon	168
Hummingbird	71
Mallard	40.6
Wandering albatross	33.6

1. How fast would a hummingbird be flying if it doubled its maximum speed?

142 mph

2. If a wandering albatross doubled its maximum speed, could it fly as fast as a hummingbird?

No; It would be flying 67.2 mph, but a hummingbird can fly 71 mph.

3. **Estimation** Which bird flies about four times as fast as a mallard?

Peregrine falcon

4. How fast would a wandering albatross be flying if its maximum speed was multiplied by 1.8?

60.48 mph

5. A mallard is flying at a speed of 2.8 mph. If it then flies 1.2 times faster, how fast is it flying?

3.36 mph

6. A certain bird can fly twice as fast as a hummingbird. Write an equation to express this.

$\frac{n}{2} = 71$

© Pearson Education, Inc. 5

Use with Lesson 2-16. **31**

Name_____

PROBLEM-SOLVING APPLICATION　　　　　R 2-16

Let's Eat!

Food	Amount	Calories	Protein (g)	Saturated Fats (g)
Cheddar cheese	1 oz	115	7	6.0
Hard-boiled egg	1	75	6	1.6
Banana	1	105	1	0.2
Raw clams	3 oz	65	11	0.3
Spaghetti and meatballs	1 c	330	19	3.9

How many calories are in 9 oz of raw clams?

There are 65 calories in 3 oz of raw clams. To find the number of calories in 9 oz, multiply by 3.

$$\begin{array}{r} 1 \\ 65 \\ \times\ 3 \\ \hline 195 \end{array}$$

So, there are 195 calories in 9 oz of raw clams.

1. Which contains more grams of protein, 6 oz of raw clams or 3 oz of cheddar cheese?

6 oz of raw clams

2. There are 10 bananas in the bunch. How many total grams of saturated fats are there?

2 g

3. Rhoda ate 3.5 hard-boiled eggs. How many grams of saturated fats did she consume?

5.6 g

4. **Algebra** Write an algebraic expression to represent m calories of bananas.

105m

© Pearson Education, Inc. 5

Use with Lesson 2-16. **31**

Name_____

New Uniforms　　　　　E 2-16
　　　　　NUMBER SENSE

The gymnastics team at Carson Elementary is choosing material for new uniforms. The company making the uniforms has provided four different fabric options.

Option A	Option B	Option C	Option D
$2.99/yd	$3.79/yd	$2.11/yd	$3.49/yd

1. Which fabric option is the most expensive?

Option B

2. Which fabric option is the least expensive?

Option C

The 26 members of the team voted for their favorite fabric options. The line plot shows the results of the vote.

Fabric Votes

3. Which option received the greatest number of votes? The least number of votes?

Option D;

Option B

4. What is the range of the votes?

6

5. The team has planned to spend $7.00 for the fabric for each uniform. Each uniform requires 2 yd of fabric. Can the team use fabric Option B and spend the planned amount?

No, $3.79 + $3.79 = $7.58.

6. Which options can the team use and spend the planned amount?

Options A, C, and D

© Pearson Education, Inc. 5

Use with Lesson 2-16. **31**

Name_____

PROBLEM-SOLVING APPLICATIONS　　　　　PS 2-16

Photo Collection

Amy has three photos that she wants to display on a shelf in her bedroom, with the photos lined up in a row. One photo is of her brother, another is of her sister, and the third is of her parents. In how many ways can she arrange the photos?

Read and Understand

1. What do you know?

There are three photos to be displayed on a shelf.

2. What are you trying to find?

How many ways Amy can arrange the photos

Plan and Solve

3. What strategy will you use?

Make an organized list

4. Write the answer in a complete sentence.

There are 6 ways that Amy can arrange the photos.

Look Back and Check

5. Is your work correct? Explain.

Sample answer: Yes, my work is correct. I have listed every combination for the three photos.

© Pearson Education, Inc. 5

Use with Lesson 2-16. **31**

Name_____

The Meaning of Division

P 3-1

Draw a picture or use objects to show each division situation. Then find the quotient.

1. How many groups of 6 can be formed if there are 36 students in the class?

6 groups of 6

2. In a theater with 108 seats, there are 12 times as many seats as there are rows. How many rows does the theater hold?

9 rows

3. Ann and Bill need to arrange 36 coins from their collection on a page. If they use 4 rows, how many coins will be in each row?

9 coins

Name the operation needed to solve each problem. Then solve.

4. At the airport, 72 people are waiting to board 9 different planes. If an equal number of people board each plane, how many people get on each plane?

Division; 8 people

5. At the halftime show during a football game, a band with 7 people in 8 rows marches out onto the field to entertain the crowd. How many people are in the band?

Multiplication; 56 people

Test Prep

6. A high school volleyball team has 20 members. If there is an equal number of members from each of the 4 grades, how many students from each grade are on the team?

A. 3   B. 4   **C. 5**   D. 6

7. **Writing in Math** If there are 50 students in the fifth grade and the entire grade had to take the same language class, which language would have 10 different classes? Explain.

Russian; 50 ÷ 10 = 5

Language	Class Size
French	7
Italian	6
Russian	5
Spanish	10
German	6

Name_____

The Meaning of Division

R 3-1

To find out how many are in each group when an amount is shared equally, you use a type of division called sharing.

Example:

Suppose there are 22 books being given to a class of 11 students. How many books can each student receive if each student gets the same amount of books?

What you think: 22 separated into equal groups of 11 students.

What you write: 22 ÷ 11 = 2.

Each student can receive 2 books.

Draw a picture or use objects to show each division situation. Then find the quotient.

1. James has 28 pennies. He makes 4 equal groups of pennies. How many pennies are in each group?

Find $28 ÷ 4 = p$. (Hint: Think $4 × p = 28$.)

7 pennies are in each group.

2. There are 4 times as many regular cars as trucks in an auto lot. If the lot has 24 regular cars, how many trucks are in the lot?

Find $24 ÷ 4 = x$.

6 trucks

Name_____

The Backpackers

E 3-1
NUMBER SENSE

Three brothers are going on a backpacking trip in the mountains. They will carry all of their supplies with them in their packs. Their supplies are shown below. If the brothers divide up the supplies equally, how many of each item will each person carry? Fill in the answers on the backpack.

Supplies:

Water Bottles

Sleeping Bags

Food Packets
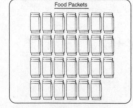

Energy Bars

Each person will carry:

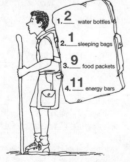

1. **6** water bottles
2. **1** sleeping bags
3. **9** food packets
4. **11** energy bars

Name_____

The Meaning of Division

PS 3-1

1. Cara plans to spend 1 day per week working on her social studies paper, which is due in 4 weeks. If the social studies paper is 8 pages long, how many pages will she write per day until she is finished?

2 pages per day

2. Cara's short story is due in 3 weeks. She plans to spend 4 days per week working on the paper. If the short story is 25 pages long, how many pages will she write per day until she is finished? Will Cara's plan work?

2 pages per day with 1 left over; Cara's plan will work if she writes 1 extra page on one of her planned days.

Salad Dressing Bryan is making salad and two kinds of salad dressing for the weekend picnic. He has decided to make an Italian dressing and a lemon herb dressing.

3. To make 4 batches of Italian dressing, Bryan uses 36 tsp of olive oil. There are 3 tsp in a tablespoon. If Bryan had used a tablespoon to measure the olive oil, how many would he have used to make 4 batches?

12 tbsp

4. To make 2 batches of the lemon herb dressing, Bryan uses 8 c of vinegar. If there are 4 c in 1 qt, how many quarts of vinegar will Bryan use to make the lemon herb dressing?

2 qt

5. **Writing in Math** Explain how Exercise 4 could be made into a multiplication problem.

Sample answer: Multiply the number of cups in 1 qt by the number of quarts to find the total number of cups Bryan needs: $4 × 2 = 8$ c.

Name_____

Division Patterns
P 3-2

Find each quotient. Use mental math.

1. $27 \div 9 =$ **3**   2. $270 \div 9 =$ **30**   3. $2,700 \div 9 =$ **300**

4. $24 \div 4 =$ **6**   5. $240 \div 4 =$ **60**   6. $2,400 \div 4 =$ **600**

7. $720 \div 9 =$ **80**   8. $140 \div 7 =$ **20**   9. $2,100 \div 3 =$ **700**

10. If a bike race covers 120 mi over 6 days and the cyclists ride the same distance each day, how many miles does each cyclist ride each day?   **20 mi**

Use mental math to answer the following questions.

11. If the vehicles are divided evenly between the sections, how many vehicles are in each section?
300 vehicles

Dealership Vehicle Storage	
Sections of vehicles	4
Vehicles for sale	1,200
Rows per section	10

12. If the vehicles are divided evenly between the rows in each section, how many vehicles are in each row?
30 vehicles

13. **Algebra** If $160,000 \div n = 4$, find n.
40,000

Test Prep

14. Find $32,000 \div 8$ mentally.
(A.) 4,000   B. 400   C. 40   D. 4

15. **Writing in Math** Solve the equation $n \times 50 = 5,000$. Explain your solution.
n = 100; **Sample answer: Divide each side by 50.**

Name_____

Division Patterns
R 3-2

You can use math facts and patterns to help you divide mentally.

What is $480 \div 6$?
You already know that $48 \div 6 = 8$.
So, $480 \div 6 = 80$.

What is $60,000 \div 6$?
$60 \div 6 = 10$
So, $60,000 \div 6 = 10,000$.

Find each quotient. Use mental math.

1. $32 \div 8 =$ **4**   2. $320 \div 8 =$ **40**

3. $560 \div 7 =$ **80**   4. $6,400 \div 8 =$ **800**

5. $720 \div 9 =$ **80**   6. $3,500 \div 7 =$ **500**

7. $15,000 \div 3 =$ **5,000**   8. $4,500 \div 5 =$ **900**

9. **Number Sense** Explain how dividing 720 by 9 is like dividing 72 by 9.
You divide 72 by 9. For 720, you add a zero for the ones place.

Newspapers Arlo has a newspaper delivery job. He wants to wrap each of his newspapers in a plastic bag to protect them from the rain. The newspapers are in bundles.

Use mental math to answer the following questions.

Arlo's Newspaper Delivery	
Number of bundles	12
Number of newspapers per bundle	9

10. How many bags will he use for 5 bundles?   **45 bags**

11. How many bags will he use for 7 bundles?   **63 bags**

12. How many bags will he use for all 12 bundles?   **108 bags**

Name_____

Move Those Zeros
E 3-2 PATTERNS

Kerry uses a crane to lower the zeros into the answers below. Cross off each zero after it has been used.

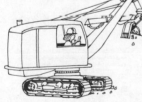

1. $24 \div 6 =$ **4**   7. $560 \div 7 =$ **8 0**

2. $240 \div 6 =$ **4 0**   8. $56 \div 7 =$ **8**

3. $2,400 \div 6 =$ **4 00**   9. $6,300 \div 9 =$ **7 00**

4. $24,000 \div 6 =$ **4 ,000**   10. $63 \div 9 =$ **7**

5. $56,000 \div 7 =$ **8 ,000**   11. $63,000 \div 9 =$ **7 ,000**

6. $5,600 \div 7 =$ **8 00**   12. $630 \div 9 =$ **7 0**

13. How many zeros does Kerry have left over? **2**

14. Write a division problem whose quotient has the same number of zeros that Kerry has left over.
Sample answer: 4,500 ÷ 9 = 500

Name_____

Division Patterns
PS 3-2

Quarter Chain The Park Valley High School students tried to build the longest continuous chain of quarters. The two-day fundraiser raised more than $1,000 for the school.

1. By the end of the two-day fundraiser, there were 6.000 quarters in the chain. If 1 quarter is about 1 inch in diameter, about how many feet long was the chain? (Remember: There are 12 inches in 1 foot.)
About 500 ft

2. How many dollars did the Park Valley High School quarter chain represent?
$1,500

Savings Bond Jack and Martha have decided to cash out a savings bond they received for their marriage 25 years ago. The current value of the bond is $50,000.

3. If Jack and Martha decide to have the value of the bond paid to them in $100 bills, how many bills will they receive?
500 bills

4. How many $20 bills would Jack and Martha receive from the $50,000?
2,500 bills

5. How many $50 bills would Jack and Martha receive?
1,000 bills

6. **Writing in Math** Explain the pattern that helps you solve $40 \div 8$ and $40,000 \div 8$.
Sample answer: 40 divided by 8 is 5. 40,000 is the same as 40 but with three extra zeros to the right. The answer is the same—5 with three extra zeros to the right, or 5,000.

Name_____

Estimating Quotients

P 3-3

Estimate each quotient. Tell which method you used.

Sample answers for 1–8

1. 195 ÷ 4	**50**	**multiplication**
2. 283 ÷ 5	**60**	**rounding**
3. 766 ÷ 8	**90**	**rounding**
4. 179 ÷ 2	**90**	**compatible numbers**
5. $395.20 ÷ 5	**$80**	**rounding**
6. $31.75 ÷ 8	**$4**	**compatible numbers**
7. $247.80 ÷ 5	**$50**	**multiplication**

8. **Reasoning** If you use $63.00 ÷ 9 to estimate $62.59 ÷ 9, is $7.00 greater than or less than the exact answer? Explain.

Greater than; 9 × 7 = 63, which is greater than $62.59.

9. A band playing a 3-night concert earned $321.00. Estimate how much the band earned each night.

About $100 each night

10. At a department store, a woman's total was $284.00 for 7 items. Estimate the cost of each item.

About $40.00

Test Prep

11. Which is the closest estimate for 213 ÷ 4?

(A) 50   B. 40   C. 30   D. 20

12. **Writing in Math** Explain how to estimate 524 ÷ 9.

Sample answer: Round 524 to 500, 9 to 10, and divide: 500 ÷ 10 = 50.

Name_____

Estimating Quotients

R 3-3

There are several ways to adjust whole numbers to estimate quotients.

Example:

There are 216 students. The school has 8 classrooms. How many students will be in each classroom?

Estimate 216 ÷ 8.

Rounding	Compatible Numbers	Multiplication
Round 216 to 200. 200 ÷ 8 = 25 25 students per room is an underestimate because 216 was rounded down to 200.	Substitute 240 for 216, because 24 is a multiple of 8. 24 ÷ 8 = 3 240 ÷ 8 = 30 30 students per class is an overestimate because 216 was rounded up to 240.	Think: 8 times what number is about 216? 8 × 25 = 200 8 × 30 = 240 216 is between 200 and 240. So a good estimate is a little more than 25 and a little less than 30 students per classroom.

Estimate each quotient. Tell what method you used.

Methods will vary.

1. 162 ÷ 4
About 40

2. 925 ÷ 9
About 100

3. $53.54 ÷ 6
About $9.00

4. 5,845 ÷ 9
About 600

5. **Number Sense** If you estimate 342 ÷ 7 by using 350 ÷ 7 = 50, is 50 greater than or less than the exact answer? How did you decide? Is 50 an overestimate or an underestimate?

It is greater because you rounded 342 up to 350. So, 50 is an overestimate.

6. Mr. Delahunt earned $5,985 during a 4-week period at work. About how much did he earn each week?

About $1,500

Name_____

They Have Clues!

E 3-3
ESTIMATION

Each person below has information for you. Use it to write the best estimate from the box for each exercise.

I collected 37 blankets. About how many should each of the 5 homeless shelters get?

Answer Box

$50	5
	7
30	$70

I have $203. About how much money should I give to each of my 4 children to save?

Our team won the tournament. The prize was $562. About how much should each of 8 players get?

1. **7**

2. **$50**

I have 22 pens. About how many should go into each of 4 bins?

There are 7 bird cages at the zoo. About how many of 212 birds will go into each cage?

3. **$70**

4. **5**

5. **30**

Name_____

Estimating Quotients

PS 3-3

Type of Elephant	Weight (kg)
African (male)	5,400–7,200
Indian (male)	3,200

1. Estimate how many tons an African elephant weighs if 889.96 kg equal 1 T.

About 7 tons

2. Using the same information, find about how many tons the Indian elephant weighs.

About 3.5 tons

Food for Wildlife The Rock Creek Wildlife Preserve records the amount of food that is used. The table shows the amount of food used during a 6-month period.

Wildlife Food Used—Jan. to June	
Type of Food	Amount
Millet	289 lb
Sunflower seeds	332 lb
Peanuts	622 lb

3. About how many pounds of sunflower seeds did the preserve use per month?

About 50 lb

4. About how many pounds combined of millet and sunflower seeds did the preserve use in 2 months?

About 200 lb

5. About how many pounds of peanuts did the preserve use in 3 months?

About 300 lb

6. **Writing in Math** Explain why it is easier to estimate quotients when dividing large numbers.

Sample answer: Using compatible numbers makes it easier to mentally divide large numbers.

© Pearson Education, Inc. 5

Practice

Name_____

PROBLEM-SOLVING STRATEGY P 3-4

Look for a Pattern

Look for a pattern. Write the missing numbers, or draw the missing figures.

1. 20, 35, 50, __65__ __80__ __95__

2. 32, 28, 24, __20__ __16__ __12__

3. 4, 12, 20, __28__ __36__ __44__

4. 56, 49, 42, __35__ __28__ __21__

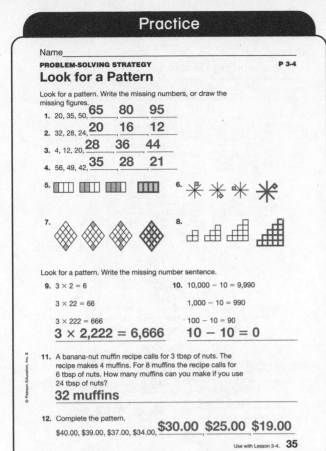

Look for a pattern. Write the missing number sentence.

9. $3 \times 2 = 6$
   $3 \times 22 = 66$
   $3 \times 222 = 666$
   $3 \times 2,222 = 6,666$

10. $10,000 - 10 = 9,990$
    $1,000 - 10 = 990$
    $100 - 10 = 90$
    $10 - 10 = 0$

11. A banana-nut muffin recipe calls for 3 tbsp of nuts. The recipe makes 4 muffins. For 8 muffins the recipe calls for 6 tbsp of nuts. How many muffins can you make if you use 24 tbsp of nuts?

32 muffins

12. Complete the pattern.
    $40.00, $39.00, $37.00, $34.00, __$30.00__ __$25.00__ __$19.00__

Reteaching

Name_____

PROBLEM-SOLVING STRATEGY R 3-4

Look for a Pattern

You can look for a pattern to solve problems.

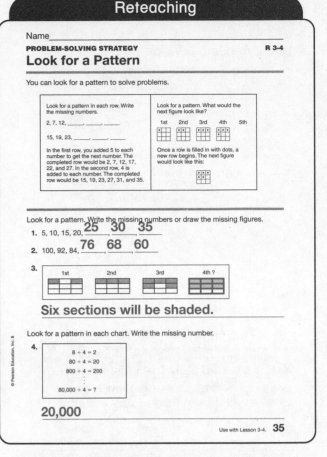

Look for a pattern. Write the missing numbers or draw the missing figures.

1. 5, 10, 15, 20, __25__ __30__ __35__

2. 100, 92, 84, __76__ __68__ __60__

3.

Six sections will be shaded.

Look for a pattern in each chart. Write the missing number.

4.
   $8 \div 4 = 2$
   $80 \div 4 = 20$
   $800 \div 4 = 200$
   $\vdots$
   $80,000 \div 4 = ?$

20,000

Enrichment

Name_____

A Creature of Habit

E 3-4
PATTERNS

Study Karl's weekday schedule. Look for patterns.

Weekday Schedule

Monday	7:00 A.M. Wake up	9:00 A.M.–4:30 P.M. Work at desk			7:15 P.M. Watch television	9:00 P.M. Go to bed
Tuesday	7:00 A.M. Wake up	9:00 A.M.–11:00 A.M. Work at desk	12:30 P.M.–4:30 P.M. Make speech		7:00 P.M. Exercise	9:15 P.M. Go to bed
Wednesday	7:00 A.M. Wake up	9:00 A.M.–10:00 A.M. Work at desk	10 A.M.–12:00 P.M. Meeting	1:00 P.M.–4:30 P.M. Work on computer	7:15 P.M. Read	9:00 P.M. Go to bed
Thursday	7:00 A.M. Wake up	9:00 A.M.–4:30 P.M. Work at desk			7:15 P.M. See a movie	9:30 P.M. Go to bed
Friday	7:00 A.M. Wake up	9:00 A.M.–11:00 A.M. Work at desk	12:30 P.M.–4:00 P.M. Meeting with managers		7:00 P.M. Play games with daughter	9:15 P.M. Go to bed

1. Describe any patterns you noticed.

Sample answer: Karl gets up every day at 7:00 A.M.; He always works at his desk between 9:00 A.M. and 10:00 A.M.; At 7:00 P.M. or 7:15 P.M. he always does a leisure activity; He always goes to bed between 9:00 P.M. and 9:30 P.M.

Problem Solving

Name_____

PROBLEM-SOLVING STRATEGY PS 3-4

Look for a Pattern

Study the picture for number patterns. Then write the missing numbers to complete the pattern.

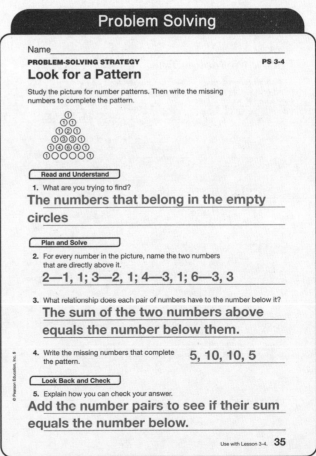

Read and Understand

1. What are you trying to find?

The numbers that belong in the empty circles

Plan and Solve

2. For every number in the picture, name the two numbers that are directly above it.

2—1, 1; 3—2, 1; 4—3, 1; 6—3, 3

3. What relationship does each pair of numbers have to the number below it?

The sum of the two numbers above equals the number below them.

4. Write the missing numbers that complete the pattern.

5, 10, 10, 5

Look Back and Check

5. Explain how you can check your answer.

Add the number pairs to see if their sum equals the number below.

Name_____

Understanding Division
P 3-5

After mowing lawns for one week, John put the money he earned on the table. There were four $100 bills, three $10 bills, and five $1 bills.

1. If John's brother borrowed one of the $100 bills and replaced it with ten $10 bills,

   a. how many $100 bills would there be? **Three $100 bills**

   b. how many $10 bills would there be? **Thirteen $10 bills**

2. If John needed to divide the money evenly with two other workers, how much would each person receive? **$145**

3. If John needed to divide the money evenly with four other workers, how much would each person receive? **$87**

Complete each division problem. You may use play money to help.

4.
```
        3 4
   4 ) 1 3 6
     - 1 2
         1 6
       - 1 6
           0
```

5.
```
        5 4
   3 ) 1 6 2
     - 1 5
         1 2
       - 1 2
           0
```

Test Prep

6. If $644.00 is divided equally between 7 people, how much will each person receive?

   A. $82.00   **B. $92.00**   C. $93.00   D. $103.00

7. **Writing in Math** Write a story problem using two $100 bills, nine $10 bills, and seven $1 bills.

   Sample answer: Karl borrowed $297 from his sister. He pays her $33 each week. How many weeks will it take Karl to pay $297?

© Pearson Education, Inc. 5

Name_____

Understanding Division
R 3-5

Three people want to share $642 equally. How can they divide the money so that each person gets the same amount?

What You Show	What You Think	What You Write
	Share the $100 groups (five $20 bills in each group). Each person gets two $100 groups.	$\begin{array}{r} 2 \\ 3\overline{)642} \end{array}$
	Two $100 groups have been shared. →	−6
	Zero $100 groups are left. →	0
	Share four $10 bills.	$\begin{array}{r} 21 \\ 3\overline{)642} \\ -6\downarrow \end{array}$
	3 of four $10 bills have been shared. →	04
	One $10 bill is left to be shared. →	− 3
	Trade a $10 bill for ten $1 bills.	1
	Share the $1 bills.	$\begin{array}{r} 214 \\ 3\overline{)642} \\ -6 \\ 4 \\ -3\downarrow \end{array}$
	Twelve $1 bills are left. →	12
	Twelve $1 bills have been shared. →	−12
	No $1 bills are left. →	0

Each person gets two $100 groups, one $10 bill, and four $1 bills or $214.

1. Three people share $225 equally. The $20 bills are replaced with twenty $10 bills.

   a. How many $10 bills are there after the $20 bills are replaced? **Twenty-two $10 bills**

   b. How many $10 bills does each person get? **Seven $10 bills**

© Pearson Education, Inc. 5

Name_____

Follow the Money Trail
E 3-5
NUMBER SENSE

Each trail below has money that you collect as you walk. At the end of each trail, the total amount of money is divided by a divisor. You receive the quotient.

1. 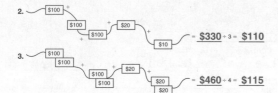 = **$120** ÷ 2 = **$60**

2. = **$330** ÷ 3 = **$110**

3. = **$460** ÷ 4 = **$115**

4.  = **$250** ÷ 5 = **$50**

5. = **$480** ÷ 6 = **$80**

6.  = **$490** ÷ 7 = **$70**

© Pearson Education, Inc. 5

Name_____

Understanding Division
PS 3-5

Ashanti and four of her friends have set up a refreshment stand in their neighborhood. The list shows the prices for a cup of each item sold at the stand.

Refreshment Stand
Lemonade—$0.50 per cup
Strawberries—$1.00 per cup
Blackberries—$1.50 per cup

1. The first weekend, the stand made $26 selling lemonade, $37 selling strawberries, and $42 selling blackberries. How many cups of each item were sold during the first week? What was the total dollar amount sold?

   Lemonade: 52 cups; Strawberries: 37 cups; Blackberries: 28 cups; Total: $105

2. If the total sales are divided equally, how much money will each person get? **$21**

Vacation Spending Jonah is on a 5-day vacation with his parents in San Diego, California. He has been given $150 to spend on souvenirs and $200 to spend on meals and snacks.

3. Jonah would like to spend his souvenir money equally from day to day. How much money will Jonah spend on souvenirs each day? **$30 per day**

4. If Jonah does the same with his meal and snack money, how much money will he spend each day? **$40 per day**

5. **Writing in Math** Explain how the steps in division can be used to show how money is shared.

   Sample answer: The quotient in a division problem represents the number of $100, $10, and $1 bills each person gets.

© Pearson Education, Inc. 5

Practice

Name_____

Dividing Whole Numbers

P 3-6

Find each quotient. Check your answers by multiplying.

1. **293**
2⟌586

2. **188 R1**
3⟌565

3. **143 R3**
5⟌718

4. **149 R3**
4⟌599

5. **128 R2**
5⟌642

6. **59**
6⟌354

7. **23 R3**
9⟌210

8. **115 R7**
8⟌927

The Paez family lives in Louisville, Kentucky, and has decided to take a road trip for their summer vacation.

9. How many miles will the Paez family drive each day if they decide to take 5 days to drive 865 mi to Dallas?

173 mi each day

10. The Paez family decides they want to drive 996 mi to Boston in 6 days. How many miles will they drive each day?

166 mi

Test Prep

11. If a staff of 9 had to clean a hotel with 198 rooms, how many rooms would each person have to clean if they divided the rooms equally?

A. 29　　B. 25　　C. 23　　(D.) 22

12. **Writing in Math** Explain how to check the quotient from a division problem.

Sample answer: You need to multiply the quotient by the divisor and then add the remainder. This should equal the dividend.

Use with Lesson 3-6. **37**

Reteaching

Name_____

Dividing Whole Numbers

R 3-6

Find 882 ÷ 6.

Step 1	Step 2	Step 3
Divide the hundreds. Multiply and subtract.	Bring down the tens. Divide the tens. Multiply and subtract.	Bring down the ones. Divide the ones. Multiply and subtract.
1 6⟌882 −6 2 Divide. 8 ÷ 6 = 1 Multiply. 1 × 6 = 6 Subtract. 8 − 6 = 2 Compare. 2 < 6	14 6⟌882 −6↓ 28 −24 4 Divide. 28 ÷ 6 = 4 Multiply. 4 × 6 = 24 Subtract. 28 − 24 = 4 Compare. 4 < 6	147 6⟌882 −6↓ 28 −24↓ 42 −42 0 Divide. 42 ÷ 6 = 7 Multiply. 7 × 6 = 42 Subtract. 42 − 42 = 0 Compare. 0 < 6

Divide. Check by multiplying.

1. **35 R4**
7⟌249

2. **107 R7**
8⟌863

3. **249 R1**
2⟌499

4. **73**
5⟌365

5. **56**
8⟌448

6. **66**
6⟌396

7. **Number Sense** How can you tell before you divide 425 by 9 that the first digit of the quotient is in the tens place?

9 does not fit into 4.

Use with Lesson 3-6. **37**

Enrichment

Name_____

Is the Bridge Safe?

E 3-6
REASONING

The Davis Construction Company follows certain rules for building safe bridges: The distance between the bridge's supports, called the *span*, must not be more than 100 ft. The chart at the right shows how to classify bridges as very safe, safe, or unsafe. Find the span length of each bridge below. Then tell whether the bridge is very safe, safe, or unsafe.

Bridge Safety Ratings

Length of Span	Rating
0 to 50 ft	very safe
51 to 100 ft	safe
101 ft and up	unsafe

1. Length of bridge: 252 ft

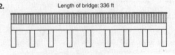

63 ft; Safe

2. Length of bridge: 336 ft

42 ft; Very safe

3. Length of bridge: 266 ft

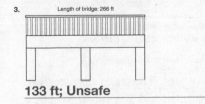

133 ft; Unsafe

Use with Lesson 3-6. **37**

Problem Solving

Name_____

Dividing Whole Numbers

PS 3-6

1. A hamster's heart beats 280 times per minute, and a gray whale's heart beats 8 times per minute. How many times faster does a hamster's heart beat than a gray whale's?

35 times faster

2. A sea otter can hold its breath under water for 5 min, and a bottlenose whale can hold its breath for 120 min. How many times greater is the time a bottlenose whale can hold its breath than the time a sea otter can hold its breath?

24 times longer

Calories Different amounts of calories are burned, or used, by the human body during different activities. The table shows the number of calories burned per minute during different activities by a person who weighs 125 lb.

Calories Burned per Minute

Activity	Calories Burned
Skateboarding	5
Waterskiing	6
Tai chi	4

3. Gizelle burned 615 calories skateboarding. How many minutes did she spend skateboarding?

123 min

4. Carlos spent 140 min waterskiing on Sunday and 70 min practicing tai chi on Monday. How many times more calories did he burn waterskiing?

3 times

5. **Writing in Math** Explain how you can tell when division must be used to solve a number problem.

Sample answer: Division is used to solve a problem when there is a certain amount of something that is divided into specific amounts.

Use with Lesson 3-6. **37**

© Pearson Education, Inc. 5

Name_____

Zeros in the Quotient

P 3-7

Find each quotient. Check your answers by multiplying.

1. $490 \div 7 =$ **70**
2. $326 \div 3 =$ **108 R2**
3. $916 \div 3 =$ **305 R1**
4. $720 \div 2 =$ **360**

5. **470 R1** $2\overline{)941}$
6. **109 R1** $9\overline{)982}$
7. **105 R5** $7\overline{)740}$
8. **140 R3** $5\overline{)703}$

9. If there are 505 seats in an auditorium divided equally into 5 sections, how many seats are in each section? **101 seats**

10. A book company publishes 749 copies of a novel and distributes them to 7 bookstores. If each bookstore were to receive the same amount of novels, how many novels would be sent to each store? **107 novels**

Test Prep

11. In one year Dolores and Tom's 4 children saved $420 by recycling cans. When they divided the money equally, how much money did each child receive?

   A. $50   B. $100   **C. $105**   D. $1,500

12. **Writing in Math** Explain why estimating before you divide $624 \div 6$ helps you place the first digit in the quotient.

   Sample answer: By estimating you will know if the answer will be in the hundreds, tens, or ones.

Name_____

Zeros in the Quotient

R 3-7

Find $823 \div 4$.

Step 1
Estimate. Decide where to place the first digit in the quotient.

$800 \div 4 = 200$
The first digit in the quotient is in the hundreds place.

Step 2
Divide the hundreds.

$\begin{array}{r} 2 \\ 4\overline{)823} \\ -8 \\ \hline 0 \end{array}$ $\begin{array}{l} 8 \div 4 = 2 \\ 2 \times 4 = 8 \\ 8 - 8 = 0 \\ 0 < 4 \end{array}$

Step 3
Bring down the tens. Divide the tens.

$\begin{array}{r} 20 \\ 4\overline{)823} \\ -8\downarrow \\ \hline 02 \end{array}$

There are just 2 tens. You cannot divide 2 tens by 4. Write 0 in the tens place.

Step 4
Bring down the ones. Divide the ones.

$\begin{array}{r} 205 \\ 4\overline{)823} \\ -8\downarrow \\ \hline 023 \\ -20 \\ \hline 3 \end{array}$ $\begin{array}{l} 23 \div 4 = 5 \\ 5 \times 4 = 20 \\ 23 - 20 = 3 \\ 3 < 4 \end{array}$

Find each quotient. Check your answers by multiplying.

1. **80** $8\overline{)640}$
2. **107 R1** $3\overline{)322}$
3. **113 R5** $8\overline{)909}$

4. **15** $15\overline{)225}$
5. **291** $3\overline{)873}$
6. **44 R3** $4\overline{)179}$

7. **Writing in Math** Is $593 \div 6$ a little less than 10, a little more than 10, a little less than 100, or a little more than 100? Explain.

   A little less than 100; $593 \div 6 = 98$ R5, < 100.

Name_____

At the Amusement Park

E 3-7
MENTAL MATH

The chart below shows in seconds how long certain rides at the amusement park take to complete a specific number of revolutions. In the exercises below, estimate first to find how long one revolution will take. Then find the actual time per revolution.

Ride	Number of Revolutions	Time (seconds)
Ferris wheel	5	515
Roller coaster	4	832
Merry-go-round	3	609
Swiss slalom	7	840

1. Ferris wheel **Sample answer:**
   Estimate: 100 sec per revolution
   Actual time per revolution = 103 sec

2. Roller coaster **Sample answer:**
   Estimate: 200 sec per revolution
   Actual time per revolution = 208 sec

3. Merry-go-round **Sample answer:**
   Estimate: 200 sec per revolution
   Actual time per revolution = 203 sec

4. Swiss slalom **Sample answer:**
   Estimate: 100 sec per revolution
   Actual time per revolution = 120 sec

Name_____

Zeros in the Quotient

PS 3-7

1. If it takes Martin 3 hr to travel from Pittsburgh to Memphis, how many miles per hour will he be traveling?
   220 mi per hour

Air Distance from Pittsburgh

Destination City	Miles (One Way)
Memphis	660
Omaha	836

2. Martin's trip from Pittsburgh to Omaha takes 4 hr. How many miles per hour will he be traveling on this trip?
   209 mi per hour

Object or Event	Length, Height, or Distance
Longest home run	618 ft
Length of QE2 ocean liner	963 ft
Height of Saturn rocket	364 ft

3. How many yards is the longest home run? (Hint: There are 3 ft in 1 yd.)   **206 yd**

4. The length of a table-tennis table is 9 ft. How many table-tennis tables can fit end-to-end along the length of the QE2 ocean liner?
   107 table-tennis tables

5. About how many table-tennis tables can fit end-to-end along the distance covered by the Saturn rocket?
   About 40 table-tennis tables

6. **Writing in Math** Explain what the zero represents in the quotient for $648 \div 6$.
   Sample answer: The zero shows that there are no tens in the quotient 108.

© Pearson Education, Inc. 5

Dividing Larger Dividends

P 3-8

Find each quotient. Check your answers by multiplying.

613 R3
1. 6)3,681

1,269 R1
2. 5)6,346

907 R2
3. 8)7,258

387 R3
4. 6)2,325

5. 4,773 ÷ 3 = **1,591**

6. 8,340 ÷ 9 = **926 R6**

7. 5,228 ÷ 7 = **746 R6**

8. 6,574 ÷ 3 = **2,191 R1**

9. Students at Belle School are collecting box tops to get books for their library. Five classes need to collect 7,505 box tops. How many tops must each class collect if the classes collect the same amounts?

1,501 box tops

10. **Estimation** There are 5 days in a school week. How many school weeks will it take a class from Belle School to collect their tops if it takes them 145 days?

29 weeks

Test Prep

11. 1,504 divided by 4 is

A. equal to 40. B. less than 40. C. less than 400. D. more than 400.

12. **Writing in Math** Predict the number of digits in the quotient for 9,010 divided by 8. Explain.

Sample answer: 4 digits in the quotient; Estimating 9,000 ÷ 8 shows that the answer will be in the thousands.

Dividing Larger Dividends

R 3-8

You can divide larger numbers using the same method you used with smaller numbers.

Find 5,776 ÷ 8.

Step 1	Step 2	Step 3	Step 4	Step 5
Estimate first. Use compatible numbers. 5,600 ÷ 8 = 700 The first digit will be in the hundreds place.	Divide the hundreds. Multiply and subtract.	Bring down the tens. Divide the tens. Multiply and subtract.	Bring down the ones. Divide the ones. Multiply and subtract.	Check by multiplying.
	7 8)5,776 −56 1	72 8)5,776 −56↓ 17 −16 1	722 8)5,776 −56↓ 17 −16↓ 16 −16 0	722 × 8 5,776

576 R1
1. 6)3,457

910 R3
2. 8)7,283

2,485 R2
3. 4)9,942

696
4. 2)1,392

5. **Number Sense** In the year 2000, the population of Galax, Virginia, was 6,837. The town covers 8 sq mi. About how many people were there in each square mile?

Sample answer: About 854 people per square mi.

When Must We Flee?

E 3-8
NUMBER SENSE

The town of Janesville sits in the path of Glacier A, which has moved a total of 2,935 ft in 5 years. The town of Donnybrook sits in the path of Glacier B, which has moved a total of 2,352 ft in 8 years. The town of Sunnydale sits in the path of Glacier C, which has moved a total of 2,877 ft in 7 years.

1. How many feet per year did Glacier A move? **587 ft per year**

2. How many feet per year did Glacier B move? **294 ft per year**

3. How many feet per year did Glacier C move? **411 ft per year**

4. In the year 2008, Glacier A will be 1,761 ft away from Janesville. In the year 2006, Glacier B will be 1,764 ft away from Donnybrook. In the year 2005, Glacier C will be 3,288 ft away from Sunnydale. Which town will need to evacuate first? Explain how you found out.

Sample answer: Janesville; Glacier A will reach the town in 3 years, which would be the year 2011. Glacier B will reach Donnybrook in 6 years, which would be the year 2012. Glacier C will reach Sunnydale in 8 years, which would be the year 2013.

Dividing Larger Dividends

PS 3-8

Ms. Fischer's science classes are working on experiments to examine the growth rate of sunflower seedlings in different types of soil.

1. Over the course of 6 days, Ms. Fischer's classes used a total of 1,984 lb of potting soil for their experiments. If 8 teams worked on the project, how many pounds of soil did each team use?

248 lb

2. A total of 2,464 sunflower seeds were used for the experiments. How many seeds did each of the 8 teams use?

308 seeds

The three highest mountain peaks in the world are Mt. Everest, K2, and Mt. Kangchenjunga in the Himalayas. The heights of these peaks are shown in the table.

Mountain	Height	
Everest	29,035 ft	8,850 m
K2	28,250 ft	8,611 m
Kangchenjunga	28,169 ft	8,586 m

3. A climbing team begins their final climb to the peak of Mt. Everest at about 5,000 m. How many meters will they climb each day if it takes them 5 days to complete their climb?

770 m each day

4. A team climbing Kangchenjunga begins their final climb at 21,750 ft. How many feet will they average per day if it takes them 4 days to complete the climb?

1,604 ft R3 per day

5. **Writing in Math** Explain why a zero is not placed in front of the eight in the quotient for 640 ÷ 8.

Sample answer: It is not necessary to have a placeholder for values greater than the 8 in 80.

Name_____

Dividing Money
P 3-9

Find each quotient. Check your answers by multiplying.

1. $9.03 ÷ 7 = **$1.29**

2. $8.24 ÷ 4 = **$2.06**

3. $0.75 ÷ 5 = **$0.15**

4. $17.55 ÷ 5 = **$3.51**

5. **$11.72** 8)$93.76

6. **$3.85** 9)$34.65

7. **$13.45** 7)$94.15

8. **$93.06** 8)$744.48

For 9 and 10, write the dollar amount the farmer received for each pound of potatoes. Then write the year.

Average Potato Prices	
Year	$ per Pound
1940	0.85
1950	1.50
1960	2.00
1970	2.21
1980	6.55
1990	6.08
2000	4.95

9. A farmer received $165.75 for 75 lb of potatoes.

$2.21 **1970**

10. A farmer received $402.05 for 473 lb of potatoes.

$0.85 **1940**

Test Prep

11. Use what you know about patterns and find the missing number. If $25.75 divided by 5 = $5.15, then $257.50 divided by 5 = n.

Ⓐ n = $51.50 **B.** n = $51.55 **C.** n = $515.00 **D.** n = $515.50

12. **Writing in Math** Explain how dividing $6.75 by 9 is like dividing 675 by 9. How is it different?

Sample answer: The steps are the same. One difference is that the decimal point and dollar sign are in the quotient.

© Pearson Education, Inc. 5

Name_____

Dividing Money
R 3-9

Mrs. Hayes bought 8 lb of meat for $17.76, including tax. Find the price per pound for the meat.

Step 1	Step 2	Step 3	Step 4	Step 5
Estimate. Use compatible numbers. $16 ÷ 8 = $2 The first digit in the quotient is the ones digit.	Place the decimal point in the dividend.	Divide the ones.	Bring down the tenths. Divide the tenths. Multiply and subtract.	Bring down the hundredths. Divide the hundredths. Multiply and subtract.

Step 2: 8)17.76

Step 3:
```
   2.
8)17.76
 -16
   1
```

Step 4:
```
   2.2
8)17.76
 -16↓
   17
  -16
    1
```

Step 5:
```
   2.22
8)17.76
 -16
   17
  -16↓
    16
   -16
     0
```

The meat cost $2.22 per pound.

1. **$1.82** 3)$5.46

2. **$4.97** 7)$34.79

3. **$11.68** 8)$93.44

4. **$39.82** 6)$238.92

5. The Mixons went to an amusement park. Each entrance ticket cost $8.50. They also spent $28.90 on food. If there are 4 people in the family, about how much did they spend on each person?

About $15.00 per person

© Pearson Education, Inc. 5

Name_____

The Fancy Restaurant
E 3-9
REASONABLENESS

Three waiters at a restaurant counted their tips at the end of an evening. The amount of money they received along with the number of tables they waited on is listed in the chart. For each exercise, determine if the statement is reasonable or unreasonable. Explain your answer.

Waiter	Number of Tables	Tips
A	6	$72.50
B	5	$67.80
C	7	$69.25

Sample answers are given.

1. Waiter A made over $13.00 per table.

This statement is unreasonable, since 6 × 12 = 72, and Waiter A waited on 6 tables and received only $72.50. Waiter A could therefore not have made over $13.00 per table.

2. Waiter C made less than $10.00 per table.

This statement is reasonable, since 7 × 10 = 70, and Waiter C waited on 7 tables and received $69.25. Waiter C therefore made less than $10.00 per table.

3. Waiter B made between $13.00 and $14.00 per table.

This statement is reasonable, since 5 × 13 = 65 and 5 × 14 = 70, and Waiter B waited on 5 tables and received $67.80. Waiter B therefore made between $13.00 and $14.00 per table.

© Pearson Education, Inc. 5

Name_____

Dividing Money
PS 3-9

Shopping Monica went back-to-school clothes shopping and bought 4 sweaters for a total of $185.00. She also spent a total of $119.85 on 3 pairs of corduroy pants.

1. How much did each sweater cost?

$46.25 each

2. How much did each pair of pants cost?

$39.95 each

Dining Out Some teachers at River Valley High School went out to dinner to celebrate the beginning of the school year. The bill for the 9 faculty members came to $167.40.

3. The group decided to split the dinner bill equally. How much did each person pay?

$18.60 each

4. The group decided to leave a tip of $33.75. How much did each person pay if the tip was divided equally?

$3.75 each

5. After dinner, the group went to a different restaurant for dessert. The total bill was $80.55. If the group decided to split this bill equally, how much did each person pay?

$8.95 each

6. **Writing in Math** Explain how you know where the decimal point goes in the quotient when an amount of money is being divided by a whole number.

Sample answer: When dividing an amount of money by a whole number, the decimal point in the quotient goes directly above its place in the dividend.

© Pearson Education, Inc. **5**

Factors and Divisibility

R 3-10

Find all the factors of each number.

1. 36   **1, 2, 3, 4, 6, 9, 12, 18, 36**

2. 27   **1, 3, 9, 27**

3. 30   **1, 2, 3, 5, 6, 10, 15, 30**

4. 75   **1, 3, 5, 15, 25, 75**

5. 90   **1, 2, 3, 5, 6, 9, 10, 15, 18, 30, 45, 90**

6. 84   **1, 2, 3, 4, 6, 7, 12, 14, 21, 28, 42, 84**

Number Sense A number is divisible by 4 if the last two digits are divisible by 4. Write yes on the line if the number is divisible by 4 and no if it is not.

7. 324   **Yes**

8. 634   **No**

9. 172   **Yes**

10. A class of 80 students is graduating from elementary school. The teachers need help figuring out how to line up the students for the ceremony. One row of 80 students would be too long. What other ways could the students be arranged for the ceremony?

2 rows of 40, 4 rows of 20, 5 rows of 16, 8 rows of 10

11. A number is divisible by another number when the **remainder** is 0.

Test Prep

12. What factor pair is missing for 45 if you already know 1 and 45, 5 and 9?

A. 7 and 6   B. 8 and 6   (C) 3 and 15   D. 4 and 12

13. **Writing in Math** Explain how to find all the factor pairs of 40.

Sample answer:

Follow the rules for divisibility of 2, 3, 4, 5, 6, 9, and 10, and check if the number is divisible by 7 and 8.

Use with Lesson 3-10. **41**

Factors and Divisibility

R 3-10

A number is divisible by:	Example:
2 → If the number is even.	16, 20, 300, 568
3 → If the sum of the digits of the number is divisible by 3.	99 $9 + 9 = 18$ $18 \div 3 = 6$
4 → If the last two digits are divisible by 4.	1,024 $24 \div 4 = 6$
5 → If the last digit is 0 or 5.	30; 105; 645; 10,100
6 → If the number is divisible by BOTH 2 and 3.	996 $9 + 9 + 6 = 24$ $24 \div 3 = 8$ Divisible by 3. Even number, so divisible by 2.
9 → If the sum of the digits is divisible by 9.	9,585 $9 + 5 + 8 + 5 = 27$ $27 \div 9 = 3$
10 → If the last digit is 0.	200; 1,000; 46,000

1. Is 4,400 divisible by 10? How do you know?

Yes, because the last digit is 0.

2. Is 234 divisible by 9? How do you know?

Yes, because the sum of the digits is divisible by 9.

Find all the factors of each number.

3. 12   **1, 2, 3, 4, 6, and 12**

4. 35   **1, 5, 7, and 35**

5. 45   **1, 3, 5, 9, 15, and 45**

6. 49   **1, 7, and 49**

7. **Writing in Math** Explain how to find all the factors of 72. List all the factors.

Try each number from 1 through 9. List the factor pairs. 1, 2, 3, 4, 6, 8, 9, 12, 18, 24, 36, and 72

Use with Lesson 3-10. **41**

What's the Secret Word?

E 3-10
NUMBER SENSE

1. Shade each square that has a number divisible by either 2, 3, 5, or 9.

114	69	35	73	80	81	95	87	55	100	27	163	155	210	30	143	38	432	12	67	21	505	48
18	17	13	83	9	121	4	151	45	11	37	133	41	63	89	119	54	167	51	131	234	20	88
50	140	22	77	124	25	16	91	56	169	79	113	193	222	43	149	90	179	702	61	171	31	902
66	10	50	139	33	155	90	173	303	127	191	323	49	82	187	359	88	181	99	103	261	804	71
75	107	53	161	69	60	137	65	161	24	105	120	157	431	64	47	433	78	26	708	97	225	101	164

2. What word is spelled by the shaded boxes?

Factor

3. Shade each square that has a number divisible by either 4, 6, or 10.

289	16	356	40	23	41	50	204	48	471	119	24	252	10	67	263	522	246	20	111	18	300	116
17	308	231	28	65	47	36	81	78	51	57	117	462	273	251	119	330	77	40	25	80	87	39
113	132	264	88	143	171	56	284	84	363	411	511	210	279	91	85	72	73	318	43	288	270	108
61	100	57	491	89	53	608	31	66	37	337	251	30	119	311	71	30	54	87	113	37	199	380
519	252	211	63	171	419	180	27	20	71	83	180	60	492	69	21	132	67	312	209	120	672	92

4. What word is spelled by the shaded boxes?

Pairs

Use with Lesson 3-10. **41**

Factors and Divisibility

PS 3-10

Jordan is trying to figure out how to arrange the plants in her vegetable garden. She is planting cabbage and string bean seedlings.

1. Jordan has 24 string bean seedlings. How many different planting arrangements are possible for the string beans?

Eight different arrangements are possible.

2. There are 28 cabbage plants. How many different planting arrangements are possible for the cabbages?

Six different arrangements are possible.

Mr. Baldwin is planning the testing schedule for his classes. For the month of April, he would like to space his tests out evenly. (Remember: There are 30 days in April.)

3. Mr. Baldwin plans to give 5 science tests. How many days apart will each science test be?   **6 days apart**

4. There are 2 social studies tests to be given during the month. How many days apart will these tests be given?   **15 days apart**

5. If Mr. Baldwin gives 3 math tests, how many days apart will they be given?   **10 days apart**

6. **Writing in Math** Explain why the answers for Exercises 3–5 would be different for the month of March. (Hint: How many days are in March?)

Sample answer: The month of March has 31 days. There are no numbers that can be divided into 31 evenly, except for itself and 1.

Use with Lesson 3-10. **41**

Practice

Name_____

Prime and Composite Numbers   P 3-11

Write whether each number is prime or composite.

1. 21 **Composite**   2. 36 **Composite**   3. 31 **Prime**

4. 87 **Composite**   5. 62 **Composite**   6. 23 **Prime**

Use factor trees to find the prime factorization of each number.

7. 44 **2 × 2 × 11**   8. 63 **3 × 3 × 7**

9. 13 **1 × 13**   10. 54 **2 × 3 × 3 × 3**

11. **Number Sense** Audrey says that the prime factorization of 42 is 21 × 2. Is she correct? If not, tell why.

Sample answer: Audrey is not correct. Since 21 can be divided by 7 or 3, 21 is not prime.

12. Is 4,564,282 prime or composite? Explain how you determined your answer.

Composite; It ends with an even number, so it is divisible by 2.

Test Prep

13. Which of the following is a prime number?

A. 105   B. 27   C. 19   D. 9

14. **Writing in Math** Does it matter what two factors you select to complete a factor tree? Explain.

No, because the prime numbers will be the result of the factoring.

42   Use with Lesson 3-11.

© Pearson Education, Inc. 5

Reteaching

Name_____

Prime and Composite Numbers   R 3-11

Numbers such as 2, 3, 5, 7, and 11 are prime numbers. A prime number has *only* two factors, itself and 1. A whole number greater than 1 that has *more than* two factors is called a composite number.

3 is an example of a prime number. Its only factors are 1 and 3.

○○○   1 × 3 = 3

8 is a composite number. Its factors are 1, 2, 4, and 8.

○○○○○○○○   1 × 8 = 8

○○○○
○○○○   2 × 4 = 8

How to use a factor tree.

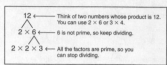

12 ← Think of two numbers whose product is 12. You can use 2 × 6 or 3 × 4.

2 × 6 ← 6 is not prime, so keep dividing.

2 × 2 × 3 ← All the factors are prime, so you can stop dividing.

Write whether each number is prime or composite.

1. 17 **Prime**   2. 47 **Prime**

3. 68 **Composite**   4. 266 **Composite**

Find the prime factors of each number.

5. 28 **Prime factors: 2, 2, 7**

6. 24 **Prime factors: 2, 2, 2, 3**

7. **Number Sense** The prime factorization of a number is 2 × 3 × 3. What is the number?   **18**

42   Use with Lesson 3-11.

© Pearson Education, Inc. 5

Enrichment

Name_____

Guess Me!   E 3-11
     NUMBER SENSE

Answer each riddle below.

1. I am a number between 50 and 60. One of my factors is 28. What number am I?   **56**

2. My four factors add up to 48, and I am between the numbers 30 and 40. What number am I?   **33**

3. I am the only number between 41 and 49 that has 5 as a factor. What number am I?   **45**

4. My prime factors are 2, 3, and 5, and I am a number between 58 and 68. What number am I?   **60**

5. I have only one rectangular array, and I am between the numbers 12 and 16. What number am I?   **13**

6. I have only two factors, 1 and myself. What kind of number am I?   **Prime number**

7. I am the only number between 22 and 30 that has 7 as a factor. What number am I?   **28**

8. I am a number under 10. My factors add up to 13. What number am I?   **9**

9. I am a number between 80 and 90. Each of my factors is the same number. What number am I?   **81**

42   Use with Lesson 3-11.

© Pearson Education, Inc. 5

Problem Solving

Name_____

Prime and Composite Numbers   PS 3-11

River Lengths The approximate length of four major rivers is given in the table to the right.

River	Approximate Length (miles)
Missouri	2,315
Yukon	1,979
Tocantins	1,677
Don	1,223

1. For which of the rivers would it be possible for towns to be located at equal distances along the river's length?

The Missouri and Tocantins Rivers

2. For which of the rivers would it not be possible for towns to be located at equal distances along the river's length? Explain.

Because their lengths are prime numbers, the Don and Yukon Rivers cannot be divided into equal lengths.

3. By what distance would towns be separated if they were located at equal lengths along the Missouri River or the Tocantins River?

Missouri River, 5 mi apart; Tocantins River, 3 mi apart

4. **Writing in Math** Explain how you found which river lengths were prime and which were not.

Sample answer: The numbers 1,979 and 1,223 were found to be prime by dividing each number by prime numbers starting with 2 and stopping at 29.

42   Use with Lesson 3-11.

© Pearson Education, Inc. 5

Name_____

PROBLEM-SOLVING SKILL   P 3-12
Interpreting Remainders

A fifth-grade project was to make something representative of the United States and send it to an address outside the United States. The shipping prices for weight are at the right.

Shipping Prices	
Pounds	**Price**
1–5	$3.00
6–10	$7.00
11–15	$10.00
16–20	$15.00
More than 20	$20.00

1. One group of students pooled their money together before shipping their projects. Four students came up with $24.00. Three out of the 4 packages fell into the same weight category. Which size packages could the students afford to ship?

$24.00 divided by 3 = 7 R3. Therefore, 3 packages fell into the 6 to 10 lb category and 1 package fell into the 1 to 5 lb category.

Another group of students wanted to have the same size boxes for shipping. This group had a total of $30.00.

2. If all 4 students have the same size package, what weight group will their packages fall into?

$30.00 divided by 4 = 7 R2. Therefore, all 4 packages fell into the 6 to 10 lb category.

3. After they have paid for their packages, how much money will be left over?   **$2.00**

4. If divided equally, how much money will each person get back?

$0.50 ($2.00 divided by 4 = $0.50)

Name_____

PROBLEM-SOLVING SKILL   R 3-12
Interpreting Remainders

Elron has 159 CDs. He is going to purchase CD cases for the CDs. Each case holds 12 CDs.

Question 1	Question 2	Question 3
How many cases will he need to hold all of his CDs?	How many cases will be filled?	How many extra CDs are in the case that is not filled?
Plan and Solve	**Plan and Solve**	**Plan and Solve**
159 ÷ 12 = 13 R3	159 ÷ 12 = 13 R3	159 ÷ 12 = 13 R3
14 cases are needed.	13 cases will be filled.	There are 3 extra CDs in the case that is not filled.
Look Back and Solve	**Look Back and Solve**	**Look Back and Solve**
One more case is needed for the 3 extra CDs. So, 13 + 1 = 14 cases are needed.	13 cases will have 12 CDs. An additional one will have less than 12.	The remainder of 3 tells us there are 3 extra CDs.

1. Sadee has 139 quarters. She wants to put them in paper rolls. Each roll holds 20 quarters.

   a. How many rolls will be completely filled?   **6 rolls**

   b. How many quarters will be in the unfilled roll?   **19 quarters**

2. Bukka has 983 paperback books. He wants to put his paperback books on storage shelves. Each shelf can hold 50 paperback books.

   a. How many shelves will be completely filled?   **19 shelves**

   b. How many paperback books will be on the shelf that is not completely filled?   **33 books**

Name_____

The U.S. House and Senate   E 3-12
                                                      REASONING

There are 435 representatives in the U.S. House of Representatives and 100 senators in the U.S. Senate. Use this information to complete the exercises below.

1. If all the members of the U.S. House of Representatives boarded 7 buses, and 1 representative was left without a seat, how many seats would each bus have? Explain how you know.

   62 seats, because 435 ÷ 7 = 62 R1.

2. The members of the House of Representatives attended a luncheon. They were seated at tables with 16 chairs each. However, when everyone sat down, 3 members were left standing. How many tables were at the luncheon? Explain how you know.

   27, because 435 ÷ 16 = 27 R3.

3. Suppose the senators voted to give themselves a pay raise of a total of $214,000. Tell how you can calculate how much each senator gets, using mental math, and why there is no remainder.

   $2,140. $214,000 has a factor of 10, so it is not a prime number, and to divide by 100, you can remove 2 zeros from the dividend for a total of $2,140.

4. If the members of the U.S. House of Representatives and the U.S. Senate all boarded an ocean liner with 4 people to a stateroom, how many staterooms would they fill? How many would be left over? Explain how you know.

   They would fill 133 staterooms with 3 people left over: 435 + 100 = 535, and 535 ÷ 4 = 133 R3.

Name_____

PROBLEM-SOLVING SKILL   PS 3-12
Interpreting Remainders

Olympic Mountain Hike Ten hikers set out on a route that covers 51 mi through the Olympic Mountains of Washington. Each hiker is carrying a 30 lb backpack. If they hike 4 mi per day, how many days will it take the hikers to complete the route?

Read and Understand

1. What is the total mileage of the route?   **51 mi**

2. How many miles will the hikers travel per day?   **4 mi per day**

3. What are you trying to find?

   How many days it will take to complete the route

Plan and Solve

4. Write and solve a number sentence.

   51 mi ÷ 4 mi per day = 12 days R3

5. Write the answer in a complete sentence.

   It will take the hikers 12 days plus part of another day to finish the route.

Look Back and Check

6. Explain what the remainder of 3 represents.

   The remainder of 3 represents the number of miles the hikers must hike on the 13th day.

Name_____

Order of Operations

P 3-13

Use the order of operations to evaluate each expression.

1. $4 \times 4 + 3 =$ **19**
2. $3 + 6 \times 2 \div 3 =$ **7**
3. $24 - (8 \div 2) + 6 =$ **26**
4. $(15 - 11) \times (25 \div 5) =$ **20**
5. $26 - 4 \times 5 + 2 =$ **8**
6. $15 \times (7 - 7) + (5 \times 2) =$ **10**
7. $(8 \div 4) \times (7 \times 0) =$ **0**
8. $5 \times (6 - 3) + 10 \div (8 - 3) =$ **17**

9. **Number Sense** Which is a true statement,
$5 \times 4 + 1 = 25$ or $3 + 7 \times 2 = 17$? $3 + 7 \times 2 = 17$

Insert parentheses to make each statement true.

10. $25 \div 5 - 4 = 25$ $25 \div (5 - 4) = 25$
11. $7 \times 4 - 4 \div 2 = 26$ $7 \times 4 - (4 \div 2) = 26$
12. $3 + 5 \times 2 - 10 = 6$ $(3 + 5) \times 2 - 10 = 6$

13. Insert parentheses in the expression $6 + 10 \times 2$ so that:

    a. the expression equals 32. $(6 + 10) \times 2$

    b. the expression equals $(12 + 1) \times 2$. $6 + (10 \times 2)$

Test Prep

14. Solve $(25 - 7) \times 2 \div 4 + 2$.

    A. 6   B. 11   C. 5   D. 18

15. **Writing in Math** Write two order of operation problems.
Then trade with a classmate and solve the problems.

    Sample answer: $2 \times 6 + 3 - (8 \div 8)$;
    $(9 + 20) - (24 \div 2) - 6$; 14; 11

Name_____

Order of Operations

R 3-13

Order of Operations	Example
First, do the operations inside the parentheses.	$36 - (3 + 2) \times 5$
Then, multiply and divide from left to right.	$36 - \quad 5 \times 5$
Finally, add and subtract from left to right.	$36 - \quad 25 = 11$

How to insert parentheses to make a statement true:

$7 + 2 \times 3 = 27$

By placing parentheses around $7 + 2$, you
would do this operation first:

$(7 + 2) \times 3 = 27$
$9 \times 3 = 27$

Use the order of operations to evaluate each expression.

1. $2 + 3 \times 5 =$ **17**
2. $5 \times (2 + 7) =$ **45**
3. $6 + 2 \times 2 \times (1 + 1) =$ **14**
4. $10 \times 4 - (9 + 11) =$ **20**

Insert parentheses to make each statement true.

5. $17 - 8 - 5 = 14$ $17 - (8 - 5) = 14$
6. $88 \div 2 + 6 - 7 = 4$ $88 \div (2 + 6) - 7 = 4$

7. **Number Sense** Felix bought 3 bags of oranges with 12
oranges per bag and 5 bags of apples with 10 apples per
bag. Write an expression with sets of parentheses for the
total amount of fruit that Felix bought.

    $(3 \times 12) + (5 \times 10)$

Name_____

Parentheses Please

E 3-13
NUMBER SENSE

You have a total of five sets of parentheses to use. Insert the
parentheses where needed to make the number sentences below
true. Three of the number sentences do not need parentheses.

( ) ( ) ( ) ( ) ( )

1. $5 \times (3 + 2) - (2 + 5) \times 3 = 4$

2. $2 \times 2 \times 2 + 3 \div 3 \times 5 = 13$

3. $(4 + 3) \times 4 - 3 = 25$

4. $(3 \times 6) - 2 + (2 \times 5) = 6$

5. $10 \div 2 - 3 + 1 = 3$

6. $(1.3 + 2.6) \times 2 - 5 = 2.8$

7. $56 \div 8 + (3 + 2) \times 2 = 17$

8. $(7 \times 4) + 3 \times 6 + 5 - 1 = 50$

Name_____

Order of Operations

PS 3-13

Emilio and Steven are buying flowers for their
mothers. The table shows the price of each
type of flower.

Amaryllis—$4 each
Baby's breath—$1 bunch
Carnation—$2 for 2
Rose—$3 each
Sunflower—$3 each

1. Emilio selects 2 amaryllis flowers,
2 carnations, and 2 bunches of baby's
breath for his bouquet. Write an expression
with parentheses to represent the cost of
Emilio's bouquet.

    $(\$4 \times 2) + \$2 + (\$1 \times 2)$

2. Steven selects 1 sunflower, 1 carnation, and 2 roses for
his bouquet. The sunflower is discounted $1 because it
is slightly smaller than the other sunflowers. Write an
expression with parentheses to represent the cost of
Steven's bouquet.

    $(\$3 - \$1) + (\$2 \div 2) + (\$3 \times 2)$

Mrs. Campbell is organizing the textbooks in her classroom.
She starts by stacking all of the textbooks according to subject.

3. After stacking, Mrs. Campbell has 4 stacks of 10 science
books, 3 stacks of 8 history books, and 6 stacks of
5 mathematics books. Write an expression to represent
the total number of books.

    $(4 \times 10) + (3 \times 8) + (6 \times 5)$

4. Mr. Barber, another teacher, takes 3 science
books. Write an expression to represent the
total number of Mrs. Campbell's science
books and the books taken by Mr. Barber. $(4 \times 10) - 3$

5. **Writing in Math** Explain how the expression in Exercise 4
would be different if no parentheses were used.

    The expression would not be different
    because you would still multiply before
    subtracting.

Practice

Name_____

Graphing Ordered Pairs

P 3-14

Name the point that is located by each ordered pair.

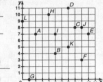
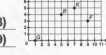

1. (9, 3) **F**   2. (1, 0) **G**

3. (7, 5) **K**   4. (5, 7) **I**

Write the ordered pair for each point.

5. D **(7, 11)**   6. C **(8, 8)**

7. E **(10, 7)**   8. L **(0, 9)**

Graph each point on the grid to the right.
Label each point.

9. M(3, 4)   10. Z(6, 5)

11. T(0, 9)   12. X(4, 4)

13. P(3, 0)   14. A(2, 8)

15. H(7, 7)   16. B(2, 9)

17. J(3, 7)   18. L(1, 6)

Test Prep

19. Which is the ordered pair for a point 7 units to the right of
the y-axis and 8 units above the x-axis?

   A. (8,7)   **B.** (7,8)   C. (1,7)   D. (1,8)

20. **Writing in Math** Why are (4, 6) and (6, 4) not at the same
point on a grid?
**Sample answer: The first number tells
how far to move to the right from 0, and
the second number tells how far to go up.**

Use with Lesson 3-14. **45**

Reteaching

Name_____

Graphing Ordered Pairs

R 3-14

How to locate a point on a grid.

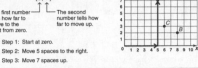

The ordered pair (5, 7) describes
the location of point A.

(5, 7)

The first number
tells how far to
move to the
right from zero.

The second
number tells how
far to move up.

Step 1: Start at zero.
Step 2: Move 5 spaces to the right.
Step 3: Move 7 spaces up.

The ordered pair for point B is (8, 2).

The ordered pair for point C is (6, 3).

Name the point that is located by each
ordered pair.

1. (7, 1) **E**   2. (2, 6) **H**

3. (0, 8) **C**   4. (4, 3) **G**

Write the ordered pair for each point.

5. F **(7, 6)**   6. B **(1, 4)**   7. D **(2, 1)**   8. A **(8, 4)**

Graph each point on the grid at the right.
Label each point.

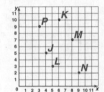

9. J(3, 5)   10. K(5, 10)

11. L(4, 3)   12. M(7, 7)

13. N(8, 2)   14. P(2, 9)

Use with Lesson 3-14. **45**

Enrichment

Name_____

Submarines

E 3-14
REASONING

An admiral in the navy has given the location of six submarines
somewhere in the Atlantic Ocean by indicating each submarine's
coordinates on a grid. In the exercises below, tell whether the
admiral's coordinates are correct. If they are not correct, give the
correct coordinates.

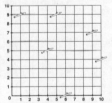

1. The admiral says there is a submarine at (0, 6).
Incorrect; (6, 0)

2. The admiral says there is a submarine at (9, 7).
Correct

3. The admiral says there is a submarine at (10, 4).
Correct

4. The admiral says there is a submarine 4 units above (5, 1).
Incorrect; (1, 9)

5. The admiral says there is a submarine 3 units to the right of (2, 8).
Incorrect; (5, 9)

6. The admiral says there is a submarine 2 units to the left of (6, 5).
Correct

Use with Lesson 3-14. **45**

Problem Solving

Name_____

Graphing Ordered Pairs

PS 3-14

Rachel's Room Rachel's bedroom is shown on the grid. The positions of the
windows, the door, the closet, and her bed are represented by ordered pairs.

1. What pairs of coordinates describe the position of each of
the two windows on the grid?
**West window: (2, 5), (2, 6), (2, 7); South
window: (4, 2), (5, 2), (6, 2), (7, 2)**

2. What pairs of coordinates describe the four corners of Rachel's bed?
(6, 5), (9, 5), (6, 8), (9, 8)

3. Rachel would like to put a nightstand next to her bed on
the side closest to the south window. What four pairs of
coordinates show where the nightstand should be placed?
Sample answer: (9, 3), (9, 4), (8, 3), (8, 4)

4. **Writing in Math** Explain how coordinates on a grid can
describe a line that is twice as long as another line.
**Sample answer: The coordinates
of a shorter line could be, for example,
(2, 2) and (2, 4). The coordinates of the
longer line would be (2, 2) and (2, 6).**

Use with Lesson 3-14. **45**

© Pearson Education, Inc. 5

Name_____

Rules, Tables, and Graphs

Create a table of values for each rule. Use at least four values for *x*.

1. Multiply by 3, then add 2: $3x + 2$ **2.** Divide by 3, then add 1: $x \div 3 + 1$

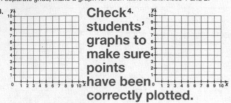

x	3x + 2
1	5
2	8
3	11
4	14

Sample answers for 1–4

x	$\frac{x}{3}$ + 1
3	2
6	3
9	4
12	5

On separate grids, make a graph for each table in Exercises 1 and 2.

3. **4.**

Check students' graphs to make sure points have been correctly plotted.

Test Prep

5. Which of the following coordinates does not belong in the table of values for the rule: Multiply by 2, then add 1: $2x + 1$.

A. (2, 5)   **B.** (3, 6)   C. (4, 9)   D. (0, 1)

6. **Writing in Math** Make a table of values for the following rule: Multiply by 3, then subtract 2. Explain.

Set up the expression $3x - 2$

x	3x − 2
1	1
2	4
3	7

Name_____

Rules, Tables, and Graphs

How to make a table of values from a rule:

Rule in words: Multiply by 4, then add 2.

Rule using a variable: $4n + 2$.

Step 1

Draw a table.
Write in the rule.

n	4n + 2
1	
2	
3	
4	
5	

Select five values for *n* and write them in the table.

Step 2

Evaluate the expression $4n + 2$ using 1, 2, 3, 4, and 5 for *n*.

n	4n + 2
1	6
2	10
3	14
4	18
5	22

← For n = 1, 4n + 2 = 4 × 1 + 2 = 6
← For n = 2, 4n + 2 = 4 × 2 + 2 = 10
← For n = 3, 4n + 2 = 4 × 3 + 2 = 14
← For n = 4, 4n + 2 = 4 × 4 + 2 = 18
← For n = 5, 4n + 2 = 4 × 5 + 2 = 22

Write the answer in the right column of the chart.

Create a table of values for each rule. Use at least four values for *n*.

1. Subtract 9: $n - 9$

Sample answer:

n	n − 9
9	0
10	1
11	2
15	6

2. Multiply by 2, then add 1: $(n \times 2) + 1$

Sample answer:

n	(n × 2) + 1
1	3
2	5
5	11
10	21

3. **Writing in Math** Write this rule in words: $8v + 7$.

Multiply by 8, then add 7.

Name_____

Which Plan Is Best?

Steve is deciding how to invest his money. His financial advisor has given him three graphs of plans that show what each investment would earn. Each graph is based on a rule, such as multiply by 3. This means that if Steve invests $7, the investment would multiply that amount by 3, giving him $21.

In 1–3, determine the rule for each graph. Then decide which plan Steve should invest with.

1. **Investment A**

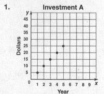

Rule: Multiply by 5

2. **Investment B**

Rule: Multiply by 7, subtract 6

3. **Investment C**

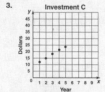

Rule: Multiply by 3, add 9

4. In which investment should Steve place his money?

Investment B

Name_____

Rules, Tables, and Graphs

Playing Guitar Karl's favorite activity is playing guitar. He plays guitar every day for 3 times the amount of time he spends reading.

1. Write a rule to show that the time spent playing guitar is 3 times the time spent reading.

Multiply by 3

2. Complete the table of values for the rule. Then complete the graph for your table of values.

g	3g
5 min	15 min
10 min	30 min
15 min	45 min
20 min	60 min
25 min	75 min
30 min	90 min

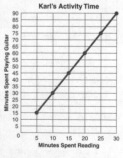

Karl's Activity Time

3. **Writing in Math** Explain why it is easier to understand information presented in a table by graphing it.

Sample answer: By graphing information, it is easier to see increases, decreases, or other changes that take place over time.

Name_____

PROBLEM-SOLVING APPLICATION   P 3-16

Hit Parade

Motown Records is one of the most famous African American owned music companies. During the 1960s and 1970s, Motown artists wrote, recorded, and produced a large number of No. 1 rhythm-and-blues songs and records.

Smokey Robinson was one of Motown's most famous songwriters, singers, producers, and musicians.

1. If Smokey Robinson wrote a total of 176 songs in an 8-year period, how many songs did he write per year?

   22 songs per year

2. **Writing in Math** Smokey Robinson wrote about 24 No. 1 hits for Motown artists. Explain how you know that the numbers 3 and 4 are both factors of 24.

   3: the sum of the digits, 2 + 4, is divisible by 3; 4: the last (and only) 2 digits are divisible by 4, since 24 ÷ 4 = 6.

3. If you paid $53.94 for 6 Smokey Robinson CDs, how much did you pay for each CD?   **$8.99**

Stevie Wonder is another famous original Motown songwriter and recording artist.

4. Nine of Stevie Wonder's CDs have a total of 107 songs. About how many songs are on each CD?

   About 11 songs per CD

5. Robbie bought 7 Stevie Wonder CDs. 4 CDs cost $8.00 each. 2 CDs cost $9.00 each. 1 CD costs $7.00. He gave the cashier $70.00. To calculate his change, Robbie correctly wrote the following equation: Change = 70 − 4 × 8 − (2 × 9 + 7). How much change did he get?   **$13.00**

© Pearson Education, Inc. 5

Name_____

PROBLEM-SOLVING APPLICATION   R 3-16

Writers

During a 9-year period, Jack London wrote 135 short stories. About how many short stories did he write each year?

First estimate. Use compatible numbers.

$150 ÷ 10 = 15$

Then divide using these steps:

Step 1	Step 2
Divide the tens.	Bring down the ones.
The first digit of the quotient will go in the tens place.	Divide the ones.
$\begin{array}{r} 1 \\ 9\overline{)135} \\ -9 \\ \hline 4 \end{array}$	$\begin{array}{r} 15 \\ 9\overline{)135} \\ -9\downarrow \\ \hline 45 \\ -45 \\ \hline 0 \end{array}$
Multiply 1 × 9, then subtract.	Multiply 5 × 9, then subtract.

London wrote about 15 short stories each year for 9 years.

1. Mark Twain is another famous American author. *The Complete Short Stories of Mark Twain* contains all of Twain's short stories. The last 5 stories are printed on a total of 153 pages. About how long is each story?

   Each story is about 30 pages long.

2. **Writing in Math** Explain the meaning of the remainder in Exercise 1.

   The remainder (of 3) means 3 more pages. So the answer is that each story is slightly longer than 30 pages.

© Pearson Education, Inc. 5

Name_____

Find Me, I'm Different   E 3-16
                                                VISUAL THINKING

Examine each group of figures. Which one does not belong? Tell why it does not belong.

1.

   a.   b.   c.   d.

   C; No polygon inside

2.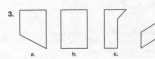

   a.   b.   c.   d.

   A; Not cut in half perfectly

3.

   a.   b.   c.   d.

   C; Not four-sided

4.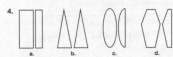

   a.   b.   c.   d.

   B; Second shape not half of first shape

© Pearson Education, Inc. 5

Name_____

PROBLEM-SOLVING APPLICATIONS   PS 3-16

Planting Trees

The Longbow Forestry Service is replacing trees that were harvested during a recent deforestation project. They have 762 fir trees and 751 spruce trees to replant on 6 hillsides. The service would like to plant equal numbers of trees on each hillside. How many fir trees and how many spruce trees will the forestry service plant on each hillside?

Read and Understand

1. What are you trying to find?

   The number of firs and the number of spruces to be planted on each hillside

Plan and Solve

2. Write and solve a number sentence for the number of each kind of tree to be replanted.

   762 ÷ 6 = 127 fir trees; 751 ÷ 6 = 125 R1 spruce trees

3. Write the answer in a complete sentence.

   127 firs will be planted on each of 6 hillsides and 125 spruces will be planted on each of 6 hillsides with 1 tree left over.

Look Back and Check

4. Explain how you can check your answer.

   Multiply: 127 × 6 = 762 fir trees; 125 × 6 = 750 + 1 left over = 751 spruce trees

© Pearson Education, Inc. 5

Name_____

Dividing by Multiples of 10

P 4-1

Find each quotient. Use mental math.

1. 480 ÷ 60 = **8**   2. 8,100 ÷ 90 = **90**

3. 32,000 ÷ 40 = **800**   4. 15,000 ÷ 30 = **500**

5. 4,900 ÷ 70 = **70**   6. 16,000 ÷ 40 = **400**

Solve for *n*.

7. *n* ÷ 20 = 60   8. *n* + (400 ÷ 20) = 27   9. 420 ÷ *n* = 70

n = 1,200   **n = 7**   **n = 6**

The vegetable farm is planning the summer harvest layout.

10. How many plants will be harvested from each section?

3,000 plants

Vegetable Farm Layout
Plants harvested: 60,000
Sections: 20
Rows in each section: 30

11. How many plants will grow in each row?

100 plants

Test Prep

12. Using the data above, determine how many plants would be harvested in each row if 30,000 plants were harvested and only 10 sections were used.

A. 10   **B.** 100   C. 1,000   D. 10,000

13. **Writing in Math** Explain the steps you took to figure out your answer for Exercise 12.

Sample answer: 30,000 ÷ 10 = 3,000; 3,000 is divided by 30 to find that 100 plants would be harvested in each row.

48   Use with Lesson 4-1.

Name_____

Dividing by Multiples of 10

R 4-1

You can use basic facts and patterns to divide mentally.

Using basic facts	Using patterns
What is 350 ÷ 70?	What is 5,400 ÷ 60?
Think: 350 ÷ 70 is the same as 35 tens ÷ 7 tens.	5,400 ÷ 60 is the same as 540 ÷ 6.
35 ÷ 7 = 5	54 ÷ 6 = 9, so 540 ÷ 60 = 9.
So, 350 ÷ 70 = 5.	So, 5,400 ÷ 60 = 90.

Find each quotient. Use mental math.

1. 280 ÷ 70 = **4**   2. 320 ÷ 40 = **8**

3. 360 ÷ 60 = **6**   4. 7,200 ÷ 80 = **90**

5. 9,000 ÷ 30 = **300**   6. 4,800 ÷ 80 = **60**

7. 2,000 ÷ 40 = **50**   8. 5,600 ÷ 70 = **80**

9. **Number Sense** How is dividing 250 by 50 the same as dividing 2,500 by 500?

Sample answers:

You get the same result, 5. This is because 250 ÷ 50 is like dividing 25 tens by 5 tens, and 2,500 ÷ 500 is like dividing 25 hundreds by 5 hundreds. In both cases, the answer is 5.

10. **Writing in Math** Explain how you can mentally determine that 35,000 ÷ 70 = 500.

You can think of 35,000 as 3,500 tens and 70 as 7 tens. So, 3,500 ÷ 7 = 500.

48   Use with Lesson 4-1.

Name_____

Blimp Rides

E 4-1
MENTAL MATH

Blimps are huge airships. Today they may float over huge public events for the purpose of advertising or for taking aerial photographs. In earlier times, blimps were called *zeppelins* and were used for air travel. Use mental math and the numbers in the blimps to help answer Exercises 1–4.

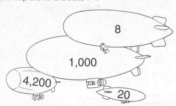

1. 400 people rode on 20 blimps.   **20 people per blimp**

2. 320 people rode on 40 blimps.   **8 people per blimp**

3. If 60 blimps each had 70 people on board, how many people would be riding on the blimps?

4,200 people

4. If 25 blimps each had 40 people on board, how many people would be riding on the blimps?

1,000 people

5. Use one of the numbers in the blimps and write an original division problem that can be solved by mental math.

Sample answer:

4,200 people rode in 7 blimps. How many people rode in each blimp? 4,200 ÷ 7 = 600 people

48   Use with Lesson 4-1.

Name_____

Dividing by Multiples of 10

PS 4-1

Library Books The school library is filled with specially made book cabinets. Each cabinet has 10 shelves. Each shelf can hold 40 books.

1. How many shelves are needed to fit 1,440 books?   **36 shelves**

2. How many cabinets are needed to fit 2,400 books?   **6 cabinets**

3. The students have checked out 360 books. How many shelves are needed when the books are returned?   **9 shelves**

Bakery A bakery made muffins that were sold to both grocery stores and restaurants. The muffins that were sold to the grocery store were packed 50 muffins to a box. The muffins that were sold to restaurants were packed 20 muffins to a box.

4. If 4,000 muffins were sold to a grocery store, how many boxes would there be?   **80 boxes**

5. If 1,000 muffins were sold to a restaurant, how many boxes would there be?   **50 boxes**

6. On a day the bakery made 3,000 muffins, 50 grocery store-sized boxes were packed. The remaining muffins were packed in restaurant-sized boxes. How many restaurant-sized boxes were packed?

25 restaurant-sized boxes

7. **Writing in Math** How many minutes equal 54,000 seconds? Explain how you used mental math to solve this problem.

Sample answer: Using mental math, 54,000 ÷ 60 is the same as 5,400 tens ÷ 6 tens = 900 min.

48   Use with Lesson 4-1.

© Pearson Education, Inc. 5

Practice

Name_____

Estimating with Two-Digit Divisors   P 4-2

Estimate each quotient. Tell which method you used.   **Methods will vary.**

1. 269 ÷ 33   **9; compatible numbers**

2. 158 ÷ 52   **3; compatible numbers**

3. $910 ÷ 85   **$10; rounding**

4. $250 ÷ 48   **$5; rounding**

5. 200 ÷ 29   **7; compatible numbers**

6. 1,950 ÷ 94   **20; rounding**

The Town Traveling Club has 19 members. Estimate each member's share of each trip expense.

7. transportation $195
About $10

8. jet ski rentals $635
About $30

9. food $385
About $20

10. Estimate the total expense for each member of the Town Traveling Club.
About $60

Test Prep

11. Which is a reasonable estimate for 378 ÷ 87?

A. 1   B. 3   (C) 4   D. 7

12. **Writing in Math** Which quotient is greater? Explain how you know without finding the answer.

$37.68 ÷ 15 or $35.25 ÷ 15

$37.68 ÷ 15 is greater; Sample answer: A greater dividend will give a greater quotient.

Use with Lesson 4-2. **49**

Reteaching

Name_____

Estimating with Two-Digit Divisors   R 4-2

There are different ways to estimate quotients.

Estimating with compatible numbers:	Estimating using rounding and multiplication:	Estimating with decimals and money:
Estimate 1,750 ÷ 32. Substitute 1,800 for 1,750 and 30 for 32. 1,800 ÷ 30 = 60 So, a good estimate is about 60.	Estimate 1,750 ÷ 32. 32 × ? is about 1,750. Round 32 to 30. Round 1,750 to 1,800. 30 × 60 = 1,800 So, a good estimate is about 60.	Estimate $78.60 ÷ 41. Round $78.60 to $80. Round 41 to 40. $80 ÷ 40 = 2 When estimating with money, it is good to find an overestimate. Round the dividend up and the divisor down.

Estimate each quotient. Tell which method you used.

1. 298 ÷ 25   **About 10 (rounding)**

2. 5,391 ÷ 77   **About 70 (compatible)**

3. 24,303 ÷ 12   **About 2,000 (compatible)**

4. 43.44 ÷ 85   **About 0.5 (compatible)**

5. $63.75 ÷ 59   **About $1.00 (decimals and $)**

6. 397.86 ÷ 31   **About 13 (compatible)**

At Elmer Elementary School, fifth-grade students are saving money for a summer trip to Washington, D.C.

7. About how many times more money has Percy saved than James?
As much as 3 times

8. About how many times more money has Bertha saved than Emily?
As much as 2 times

Student	Amount Saved
Percy	$125
Emily	$80
George	$202
James	$41
Bertha	$159

Use with Lesson 4-2. **49**

Enrichment

Name_____

Orbiting Estimates   E 4-2   ESTIMATION

Mercury makes a complete orbit around the Sun in 88 days. Mars makes a complete orbit around the Sun in 687 days. In the exercises below, use compatible numbers and multiplication to find the estimates.

1. How many orbits around the Sun will Mercury make in 1,060 days? Show your work.

Sample answer: Estimate $\frac{1,060}{88}$. Substitute 1,080 for 1,060, substitute 90 for 88. $\frac{1,080}{90}$ = 12. Estimate is about 12 times. Actual is 12.04

2. Now use a different operation to estimate for the same problem. Show your work.

Sample answer: 88 × ? = 1,060. Round 88 to 90. 90 × 12 = 1,280. Estimate is about 12 times.

3. Estimate the number of days it will take Mars to complete 12 orbits. Show your work.

Sample answer: Estimate 12 × 687. Substitute 10 for 12. 10 × 687 = 6,870. Estimate is about 6,870 days. Actual answer is 8,244 days.

Use with Lesson 4-2. **49**

Problem Solving

Name_____

Estimating with Two-Digit Divisors   PS 4-2

A public library held a used book sale. At the sale the books were placed onto tables according to the type of book. For Exercises 1–2, round to the nearest ten to estimate. The library sold 359 children's books and 912 magazines.

1. About how many children's books were placed on each of 13 tables?
About 36 books

2. About how many magazines were placed on each of 16 tables?
About 45 magazines

Planets The length of a day is different on each planet. It is determined by the speed at which the planet rotates on its axis. The length of a day on each planet, measured in Earth hours, is shown on the chart.

Planet	Length of Day (measured in Earth hours)
Mercury	1,408
Venus	5,833
Earth	24
Mars	25
Jupiter	10
Saturn	11
Uranus	17
Neptune	16
Pluto	153

3. The length of a day on Pluto is about how many times the length of a day on Saturn?
About 15 times

4. The length of a day on Venus is about how many times the length of a day on Uranus?
About 300 times

5. **Writing in Math** What compatible numbers would you use to compare the length of a day on Mercury to the length of a day on Neptune? Explain.
Sample answer: 1,600 for Mercury and 16 for Neptune; 1,600 ÷ 16 = 10

Use with Lesson 4-2. **49**

Name_____

Try, Check, and Revise

Solve. Write your answer in a sentence.

1. Bryan needs to build a fence around his rectangular vegetable garden. The length will be 2 ft longer than the width. If he uses 16 ft of fencing, what will be the length and width?

   The length is 5 ft and the width is 3 ft.

2. Bryan plans on building a larger garden next year. He would like to keep the length the same but extend the width of his garden so that it is square. If Bryan extends the width to make a square, how much fencing will he need to surround the garden?

   Bryan will need 20 ft of fencing.

3. The school district has 294 basketballs to distribute to 36 different teams in the intramural basketball league. If the basketballs are equally distributed, how many basketballs can each team have for practice? How many basketballs will be remaining?

   Each team will get 8 basketballs;
   There will be 6 basketballs remaining.

4. Hannah is 8 in. taller than her brother Quinn. If Quinn stood on Hannah's shoulders they would be 80 in. tall. How tall is Quinn?

   Quinn is 36 in. tall.

5. The area of a rectangle is 50 ft. The length is two times the width. What are the length and the width? (Hint: The area of a rectangle is $l \times w$.)

   The length is 10 ft and the width is 5 ft.

Name_____

Try, Check, and Revise

Heights David is 10 in. taller than his sister Katie. The sum of their heights is 104 in. What is each of their heights?

Read and Understand

Step 1: What do you know?	Step 2: What are you trying to find?
• Tell the problem in your own words.	• Tell what the question is asking.
When you add David's and Katie's heights, they total 104 in.	You want to know the height of each person.
• Identify key facts and details.	• Show the main idea.
David is 10 in. taller than Katie.	David's height + Katie's height = 104 inches

Plan and Solve

Step 3: What strategy will you use?   Strategy: Try, Check, and Revise

Try: David = 50 in., Katie = 40 in.

Check: 50 + 40 = 90

Revise: 90 is too low. Their heights must equal 104. Increase each height.

Try: David 57 in., Katie 47 in.

Check: 57 + 47 = 104

Answer: David is 57 in., Katie is 47 in.

Mr. Caine filled a large container with 129 qt of water. (4 qt = 1 gal) He wants to pour the water into gallon containers. He does this without spilling any water. How many gallon containers will be needed?

1. Identify key facts and details.

   4 qt = 1 gal

2. Solve the problem. Write the answer in a complete sentence.

   33 gal containers will be needed.

Name_____

Tree House

The Lopez family plans to build a tree house in the big elm tree in their backyard. They want the floor of the tree house to be a rectangle 3 ft longer than it is wide. They also want the floor of the tree house to be 42 ft around. Below are three diagrams of the tree house floor.

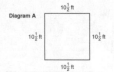

Diagram A — $10\frac{1}{2}$ ft, $10\frac{1}{2}$ ft, $10\frac{1}{2}$ ft, $10\frac{1}{2}$ ft

Diagram B — 12 ft, 9 ft, 9 ft, 12 ft

Diagram C — 11 ft, 10 ft, 10 ft, 11 ft

1. What is the measurement around the floor for each diagram?

   A. **42** ft   B. **42** ft

   C. **42** ft

2. Is Diagram A correct? What is right or wrong with it?

   Sample answer: No; All the sides are the same measurement.

3. Is Diagram B correct? What is right or wrong with it?

   Sample answer: Yes, because the width is 9 ft and the length is 12 ft, which is a difference of 3 ft.

4. Is Diagram C correct? What is right or wrong with it?

   Sample answer: No; The difference in length and width is only 1 ft.

Name_____

Try, Check, and Revise

Library Volunteers Student volunteers reshelve books in the library at the end of each school day. On Tuesday, Allen and Bonnie both reshelved the same number of books. Kara reshelved 20 more books than Bonnie did. Together, the three volunteers reshelved 260 books. How many books did each volunteer place on the shelves?

Read and Understand

1. What is the total number of books the students reshelved?   **260 books**

2. How many students volunteered at the library?   **3 students**

Plan and Solve

3. What is a reasonable first try for solving the problem?   **Sample answer: Estimate 270 books divided by 3 students is 90; 90 + 90 + (90 + 20) = 290**

4. Does the answer fit the information given in the problem?   **Sample answer: No, 90 is too high a number.**

5. Revise your first answer to make a reasonable second try.   **Sample answer: Try a lower number divisible by 3: 240 ÷ 3 = 80; 80 + 80 + (80 + 20) = 260**

6. Does your answer now fit with the information in the problem?   **Yes**

Look Back and Check

7. What other strategy could be used to solve this problem?

   Sample answer: Write an equation

Name_____

Dividing Whole Numbers by Two-Digits P 4-4

Complete. Find each missing remainder or quotient.

1. $37\overline{)120}$ 3 R $\boxed{9}$

2. $39\overline{)342}$ $\boxed{8}$ R30

3. $14\overline{)413}$ 29 R $\boxed{7}$

Find each quotient. Check by multiplying.

4. $25\overline{)768}$ **30 R18**

5. $34\overline{)264}$ **7 R26**

6. $19\overline{)401}$ **21 R2**

7. $62\overline{)338}$ **5 R28**

8. $599 \div 37 =$ __**16 R7**__

9. $9{,}227 \div 83 =$ **111 R14**

10. The school student council sponsored a Switch Day where students were able to switch classes every 20 min. The students are in school for 7 hr. If each student switched the same number of times, how many times did each student get to visit another classroom? (Hint: There are 60 min in 1 hr.) **21 times**

11. 456 students participated in Switch Day. The students raised money for a charity so that the principal would approve of the day. If the total amount of money raised was $912 and each student brought in the same amount of money, how much did each student raise? **$2.00**

Test Prep

12. Which is $458 \div 73$?

A. 5 R19   B. 5 R20   C. 6 R19   (D.) 6 R20

13. **Writing in Math** If you have a two-digit divisor and a three-digit dividend, does the quotient always have the same number of digits? Explain.

Sample answer: No, the quotient can have one or two digits.

Use with Lesson 4-4. **51**

© Pearson Education, Inc. 5

Name_____

Dividing Whole Numbers by Two-Digit Divisors R 4-4

Find $437 \div 39$.

	What You Think	What You Write
Step 1 Estimate. Decide where to place the first digit in the quotient. $437 \div 39$ is about $440 \div 40$ or 11.	Start dividing tens.	
Step 2 Divide the tens. Multiply and subtract.	1 group of 39 or $1 \times 39 = 39$. This leaves 4 left over.	$\begin{array}{r} 1 \\ 39\overline{)437} \\ -39 \\ \hline 4 \end{array}$
Step 3 Divide the ones. Multiply and subtract.	1 group of 39 or $1 \times 39 = 39$. This leaves 8 left over.	$\begin{array}{r} 11 \\ 39\overline{)437} \\ -39 \\ \hline 47 \\ -39 \\ \hline 8 \end{array}$
Step 4 Compare and write the answer.	Since $39 > 8$, I do not have to divide again.	$437 \div 39 = 11$ R8

Complete.

1. $77\overline{)283}$ 3 R $\boxed{52}$

2. $49\overline{)197}$ 4 R $\boxed{1}$

3. $58\overline{)418}$ $\boxed{7}$ R12

Find each quotient. Check by multiplying.

4. $18\overline{)179}$ **9 R17**

5. $94\overline{)835}$ **8 R83**

6. $67\overline{)356}$ **5 R21**

Use with Lesson 4-4. **51**

© Pearson Education, Inc. 5

Name_____

Park Areas E 4-4 DATA

The chart at the right shows the area, in square miles, of four parks. In the exercises below, write your answers in square miles.

State	Area (square miles)
A	656
B	269
C	164
D	147

1. If you divided Park A into 32 equal parts, how large would each part be? How large would the remaining area be?

Each section would be 20 sq mi with a remaining section of 16 sq mi.

2. If you divided Park B into 53 equal parts, how large would each part be? How large would the remaining area be?

Each section would be 5 sq mi with a remaining section of 4 sq mi.

3. If you divided Park C into 16 equal parts, how large would each part be? How large would the remaining area be?

Each section would be 10 sq mi with a remaining section of 4 sq mi.

4. Complete the pictograph after choosing a picture to represent 32 sq mi. Be sure to represent any remaining area reasonably.

$\square$ = 32 sq mi   **Sample answer:**

Park A	☐☐☐☐☐☐☐☐☐☐☐☐☐☐☐☐☐☐☐☐☐
Park B	☐☐☐☐☐☐☐☐☐
Park C	☐☐☐☐☐☐
Park D	☐☐☐☐☐

Use with Lesson 4-4. **51**

© Pearson Education, Inc. 5

Name_____

Dividing Whole Numbers by Two-Digit Divisors PS 4-4

A small roadside stand sold apple juice in 64 oz cartons.

1. On Thursday, 515 oz of apple juice were produced. How many 64 oz cartons were filled? How many ounces were left over?

8 cartons; 3 oz

2. On Friday, the same amount of apple juice was produced as on Thursday, but the farmer sold it in 16 oz cartons. How many 16 oz cartons were filled? How many ounces were left over?

32 cartons; 3 oz

A shipment of school supplies has arrived at Rosedale School. The supplies are to be shared equally among the school's 18 classrooms.

School Supply List
Pencils – 144 boxes
Pens – 89 boxes
Notebooks – 126 boxes
Folders – 60 boxes

4. Can any of the items in the shipment be shared equally among the classrooms with none left over? If so, which items and how many for each classroom?

8 boxes of pencils; 7 boxes of notebooks

5. How many boxes of pens can be distributed to each classroom? Are there any left over? If so, how many?

4 boxes of pens; 17 boxes left over

6. **Writing in Math** How many boxes of folders would each of the 18 classrooms receive? What is your suggestion for the most even distribution of the remaining boxes? Explain.

3 boxes of folders; Sample answer: Three classrooms could share one of the six remaining boxes.

Use with Lesson 4-4. **51**

© Pearson Education, Inc. 5

Name_____

Dividing Larger Numbers

P 4-5

Find each quotient. Check your answers by multiplying.

119 R17	**122 R4**	**364 R5**	**104 R23**
1. 53)6,324	2. 52)6,348	3. 86)31,309	4. 33)3,455

5. $17,496 \div 91 =$ **192 R24**   6. $25,214 \div 47 =$ **536 R22**

7. $2,312 \div 26 =$ **88 R24**   8. $4,895 \div 83 =$ **58 R81**

The Humphrey family decided to fly from San Francisco, California, to Tokyo, Japan. There were 3 stops along the way.

9. It took the Humphrey family 6 hr to travel from San Francisco to New York. How many kilometers did they travel per hour?

Distances by Plane	
San Francisco to New York	4,140 km
New York to Rome	6,907 km
Rome to New Delhi	5,929 km
New Delhi to Tokyo	5,857 km

690 km per hour

10. During the flight from New Delhi to Tokyo, the children played some games. If they switched games every 575 km, how many games did they play?

10 games

Test Prep

11. Use the data from Exercises 9–10. When the family arrived in New Delhi from Rome, the youngest son asked the pilot how fast he was flying the plane. The pilot told him about 847 km per hour. How many hours did it take the family to fly from Rome to New Delhi?

A. 5 hr   B. 6 hr   C. 7 hr   D. 8 hr

12. **Writing in Math** Write a word problem that would require you to use $5,621 \div 23$.

Check students' problems.

© Pearson Education, Inc. 5

Name_____

Dividing Larger Numbers

R 4-5

Find $899 \div 19$.

Step 1	Step 2	Step 3	Step 4
Estimate. Decide where to place the first digit in the quotient. $899 \div 19$ is about $900 \div 20 = 45$ or 4 tens, 5 ones. Start dividing tens.	Divide the tens. Multiply and subtract. 4 19)899 −76 13 Multiply: $4 \times 19 = 76$ Subtract: $89 − 76 = 13$ Compare: $13 < 19$	Bring down the ones. Divide the ones. Multiply and subtract. 47 19)899 −76↓ 139 −133 6 Multiply: $7 \times 19 = 133$ Subtract: $139 − 133 = 6$ Compare: $6 < 19$	Check: 47 ×19 423 47 893 + 6 899 So, $899 \div 19 = 47$ R6.

Find each quotient. Check your answer by multiplying.

79 R4	**63 R5**	**51 R11**
1. 48)3,796	2. 41)2,588	3. 85)4,346

159 R19	**87 R25**	**55 R9**
4. 47)7,492	5. 94)8,203	6. 43)2,374

© Pearson Education, Inc. 5

Name_____

Scrapbook Spacing

E 4-5
VISUAL THINKING

The pages in a scrapbook are arranged so that each letter represents either a picture or a measurement of space. Use the information below the chart to find the measurements for each page.

1. What are the measurements for c, d, and e?

$c = 1$ in.

$d = 5$ in.

$e = 9$ in.

Album page: 30 in. × 24 in.
A = 9 in. × 14 in.
B = 8 in. × 6 in.

2. If you removed picture B from the page, how much space would there be between the two remaining pictures?

10 in.

3. What are the measurements for f, g, and h?

$f = 1$ in.

$g = 2$ in.

$h = 7$ in.

Album page: 25 in. × 17 in.
T = 7 in. × 3 in.

4. If another picture with dimensions 2 in. by 7 in. were centered in the h space, what would be the measurements of space on the sides?

$2\frac{1}{2}$ in. and 2 in.

© Pearson Education, Inc. 5

Name_____

Dividing Larger Numbers

PS 4-5

Vacation Steve's family is thinking of taking a vacation. They have not decided where they will go, but they do know they will drive to their destination. Steve lives in Buffalo, New York. The distance to some of the possible vacation destinations is listed below.

Driving Distance	
From Buffalo, New York to:	
Indianapolis	510 mi
Miami	1,445 mi
Detroit	252 mi
Seattle	2,596 mi
Washington, D.C.	386 mi

1. Steve's mom and dad plan to drive an average speed of 60 mi per hour on the trip. At that rate, which cities on the list could be reached in 20 hr of driving, or less?

Indianapolis, Detroit, Washington, D.C.

2. At the same driving rate, which cities on the list could be reached in more than 20 hr, but less than 30 hr of driving?

Miami

3. **Writing in Math** Is there any city on the list that would require more than 30 hr of driving at 60 mi per hour? At that rate, how many hours of driving would it take? Explain how you know that the quotient (number of hours) would begin in the tens column.

Seattle would take over 43 hr of driving.

Sample answer: I knew that the first digit in the quotient would be in the tens column because the distance of 2,596 can be estimated at 2,400. 2,400 ÷ 60 = 40, or 4 tens.

© Pearson Education, Inc. 5

Practice

Name_____

Dividing: Choose a Computation Method   P 4-6

Divide and check. Tell which computation method you used.

1. $40\overline{)24,000}$ **600**
2. $40\overline{)6,440}$ **161**
3. $22\overline{)4,818}$ **219**
4. $46\overline{)9,936}$ **216**

Computation methods may vary.

5. $37,800 \div 90 = $ **420**

6. $18,000 \div 30 = $ **600**

7. $24,000 \div 60 = $ **400**

8. $350,000 \div 35 = $ **10,000**

The summer-sale paper was delivered to everyone in the neighborhood.

9. Toni and Bill saw the sale paper and thought they could share the cost of the speed boat with their 4 brothers and sisters. If they divide the cost equally, how much will each person pay?

Summer Sale	Speed boat $18,000
	Pontoon boat $9,672
	Jet ski $2,100

$3,000

Test Prep

10. Use the data from Exercise 9. Four different families decided to share the cost of the pontoon boat. There would be a total of 8 people sharing the cost of the boat. How much did each person have to pay?

A. $2,418.00   **(B)** $1,209.00   **C.** $806.00   **D.** $604.50

11. Writing in Math Describe when it is helpful to use a calculator in dividing. When is it better to use another method?

Sample answer: It is helpful when the numbers are not divisible by 10. It is better to use one of the other methods when the numbers are divisible by 10.

Use with Lesson 4-6. **53**

Reteaching

Name_____

Dividing: Choose a Computation Method   R 4-6

You can divide using mental math, paper and pencil, or a calculator.

	Find $50,000 \div 10$.	Find $58,560 \div 80$.	Find $93,279 \div 37$.
What You Think	This is easy to do in my head, so I will use **mental math**.	Both numbers are multiples of 10, so $58,560 \div 80$ is the same as $5,856 \div 8$. One digit divisors are easy to do with **paper and pencil**.	There are no basic facts or zeros, so using a **calculator** is the easiest way to find the quotient.
What You Do	$50,000 \div 10$ is the same as $5,000 \div 1$. Since $50 \div 10 = 5$, $5,000 \div 10$ must be 500. So, $50,000 \div 10 = 5,000$.	$\begin{array}{r} 732 \\ 8\overline{)5,856} \\ -56 \\ \hline 25 \\ -24 \\ \hline 16 \end{array}$ So, $58,560 \div 80 = 732$.	93279 ÷ 37 =  **2521.054** So, $93,279 \div 37$ is a little greater than 2,521.

Divide and check. Tell what computation method you used.

1. $25\overline{)500}$ **20**
2. $100\overline{)3,000}$ **30**
3. $82\overline{)735}$ **8 R79**

Sample methods given.

Mental math	**Mental math**	**Paper and pencil**
129	**10 R9**	**2,000**
4. $50\overline{)6,450}$	**5.** $85\overline{)859}$	**6.** $16\overline{)32,000}$

Mental math	**Calculator**	**Mental math**

Use with Lesson 4-6. **53**

Enrichment

Name_____

Diamonds Are Forever   E 4-6 ALGEBRA

In the exercises below, solve for the value of each variable. Cross out the correct answer in the answer box. The number that is left answers the question in Exercise 5.

1. $73 \times f = 3,942$ $f = $ **54**

2. $g \times 45 = 900$ $g = $ **20**

3. $8 \times y = 1,848$ $y = $ **231**

4. $s \times 52 = 2,756$ $s = $ **53**

Answer Box 1

54	20
231	53
10	

5. Question: A diamond is the hardest naturally occurring substance. The Moh's scale is the measure of hardness. What is a diamond's measure on the Moh's scale?   **10**

Answer Box 2

60	81
9	
57	355

6. $20 \times a = 1,200$ $a = $ **60**

7. $b \times 80 = 6,480$ $b = $ **81**

8. $53 \times c = 477$ $c = $ **9**

9. $d \times 16 = 5,680$ $d = $ **355**

10. Question: The finished cut diamond in the picture is called "brilliant" because it has how many facets (cut sides)?   **57**

Use with Lesson 4-6. **53**

Problem Solving

Name_____

Dividing: Choose a Computation Method   PS 4-6

Largest Lakes Information about the 8 largest lakes in the world is listed in the chart.

Lake	Area (Square Miles)
Caspian Sea	152,239
Superior	31,820
Victoria	26,828
Huron	23,010
Michigan	22,400
Aral	13,000
Tanganyika	12,700
Baikal	12,162

1. The Caspian Sea is about how many times larger than Lake Superior?

About 5 times

2. Which lake is about twice as large as Lake Aral?

Lake Victoria

3. Which lake is closest to 12.5 times smaller than the Caspian Sea?

Lake Baikal

4. Which lake is about 7 times larger than Lake Michigan?

The Caspian Sea

5. Writing in Math Explain what calculation method you would use to find $240 \div 60$.

Sample answer: You would use mental math to solve this problem because $240 \div 60$ is the same as $24 \div 6 = 4$.

Use with Lesson 4-6. **53**

Name_____

Dividing with Zeros in the Quotient   P 4-7

Find each quotient. Check your answers by multiplying.

1. $60\overline{)6,360}$ **106**
2. $84\overline{)8,750}$ **104 R14**
3. $14\overline{)9,828}$ **702**
4. $57\overline{)36,485}$ **640 R5**

5. $12,925 \div 19 =$ **680 R5**
6. $22,348 \div 37 =$ **604**
7. $9,523 \div 28 =$ **340 R3**
8. $16,451 \div 81 =$ **203 R8**

9. If 75 players hit 7,950 baseballs at the batting cages, how many hits were there for each player?   **106 hits**

Find each quotient.

10. $3,030 \div 30 =$ **101**   11. $4,242 \div 42 =$ **101**   12. $5,050 \div 50 =$ **101**

13. **Number Sense** Explain the reason for the pattern in the quotients in Exercises 10–12.

Sample answer: The pattern in the dividend is that it is a repeat of the divisor.

Test Prep

14. Which is $17,889 \div 88$?

   A. 203   **B.** 203 R25   C. 204 R1   D. 205

15. **Writing in Math** Write a problem with a two-digit divisor, a five-digit dividend, and a quotient of 308. Explain how you did it.

Sample answer: 10,164 ÷ 33 = 308; I multiplied 308 by a two-digit divisor that is greater than 32.

54 Use with Lesson 4-7.

Name_____

Dividing with Zeros in the Quotient   R 4-7

Sometimes when you bring down the next digit in dividing, you get a number less than the divisor. You need to place a zero in the quotient and bring down the next digit.

Step 1	Step 2	Step 3
Find 9,286 ÷ 89. Estimate. Decide where to place the first digit in the quotient. Think: 9,000 ÷ 90 = 100. Start dividing hundreds.	Divide hundreds. Multiply, subtract, and bring down. $\begin{array}{r} 10 \\ 89\overline{)9,286} \\ -89 \\ \hline 38 \end{array}$ Since 38 < 89, you cannot divide. Write a zero in the quotient. Bring down the next digit.	Continue to divide. $\begin{array}{r} 104 \\ 89\overline{)9,286} \\ -89 \\ \hline 38 \\ -0 \\ \hline 386 \\ -356 \\ \hline 30 \end{array}$ So, 9,286 ÷ 89 = 104 R30.

Find each quotient. Check your answer by multiplying.

1. $59\overline{)641}$ **10 R51**
2. $32\overline{)3,354}$ **104 R26**
3. $53\overline{)5,777}$ **109**

4. $58\overline{)6,326}$ **109 R4**
5. $79\overline{)8,299}$ **105 R4**
6. $49\overline{)5,358}$ **109 R17**

7. **Number Sense** Is $5,309 \div 26$ greater than 20, less than 20, greater than 200, or less than 200?

Greater than 200

54 Use with Lesson 4-7.

Name_____

Teacher for a Day   E 4-7
NUMBER SENSE

You have been selected to be the teacher for a day. You are teaching division to your students. In the exercises below, explain how you can tell that each student has made an error. Then provide the correct quotient and remainder, if any.

1. Julie has written $4,411 \div 22 = 220$.

Sample answer: There must be a zero in the tens place. Q = 200, R = 11

2. Jorge has written $7,128 \div 36 = 202$.

Sample answer: There must be a one in the hundreds place. Q = 198

3. Jack has written $11,716 \div 58 = 212$.

Sample answer: There must be a zero in the tens place. Q = 202

4. Jamie has written $2,244 \div 22 = 120$. **Sample answer: There must be a zero in the ones place instead of the tens place. Q = 102**

Here are two divisibility rules to teach your students:
• A number is divisible by **8** if the last 3 digits are divisible by 8.
• A number is divisible by **9** if the sum of its digits is divisible by 9.

Are the following numbers divisible by 8 or 9, or both?

5. 202,008 **8**
6. 30,030,003 **9**
7. 45,600 **8**
8. 2,160 **9, 8**

54 Use with Lesson 4-7.

Name_____

Dividing with Zeros in the Quotient   PS 4-7

Pet Food We R Pets, a large pet store, orders dog and cat food in large shipments. Then the store bags and sells the pet food to its customers.

1. A shipment of 6,150 lb of dog food was divided into 30 lb bags. How many 30 lb bags were filled?   **205 bags**

2. A shipment of 1,962 lb of cat food was divided into 18 lb bags. How many 18 lb bags could be filled?   **109 bags**

3. A shipment of 4,320 lb of dog food was divided into 16 lb bags. How many 16 lb bags could be filled?   **270 bags**

Recycling When the Northridge recycling center opened, many families brought their items for recycling.

4. The paper-recycling bin can hold 45 lb of paper. Every time 45 lb of paper were placed in the bin, it had to be emptied. If 4,770 lb of paper were recycled in the first week, how many times was the paper bin emptied?   **106 times**

5. The glass-recycling bin can hold 250 lb of glass. Every time 250 lb of glass were placed in the bin, it had to be emptied. If 27,450 lb of glass were recycled at Northridge, how many times was the glass bin emptied? How many more pounds need to be added before it is emptied again?

109 times; 50 lb

6. **Writing in Math** The plastics-recycling bin can hold 55 lb of plastic. Every time 55 lb of plastic were placed in the bin, it had to be emptied. If 11,275 lb of plastic were recycled in the first week, how many times was the plastics bin emptied? Explain how you found out there was a zero in the quotient.

205 times; Sample answer: In the tens place of the quotient, 27 cannot be divided by 55, so a 0 is in the quotient.

54 Use with Lesson 4-7.

© Pearson Education, Inc. 5

Name_____

PROBLEM-SOLVING SKILL   P 4-8

Multiple-Step Problems

Write and answer the hidden question or questions in each problem and then solve the problem. Write your answer in a complete sentence.

Storewide Sale	
Jeans	$29.95 for 1 pair OR 2 pairs for $55.00
T-shirts	$9.95 for 1 OR 3 T-shirts for $25.00

1. Sue bought 2 pairs of jeans and a belt that cost $6.95. The tax on the items was $5.85. Sue paid the cashier $70.00. How much money did Sue receive in change?

What was the total cost of Sue's items?

$67.80; Sue will receive $2.20 in change.

2. A recreation department purchased 12 T-shirts for day camp. The department does not have to pay sales tax. It paid with a $100.00 bill. How much change did it receive?

What was the cost for 12 T-shirts? $100.00;

The department will not receive any

change in return because it is paying the

exact amount.

3. When Mrs. Johnson saw the sale, she decided to get clothes for each child in her family. She bought each of her 6 children a pair of jeans and a T-shirt. She paid $14.35 in sales tax. How much was Mrs. Johnson's total bill?

How much did the jeans cost? $165;

How much did the T-shirts cost? $50;

The total bill was $229.35.

4. **Writing in Math** Write a two-step problem about buying something at the mall that has a hidden question. Tell what the hidden question is and solve your problem. Use $8.95 somewhere in your equation. Write your answer in a complete sentence.

Check students' problems.

Name_____

PROBLEM-SOLVING SKILL   R 4-8

Multiple-Step Problems

Law Firm Mr. Barnett earned about $98,000 last year at his law firm. He had to pay about $19,000 in taxes. He also had to pay about $6,000 for office supplies. About how much did he make each month?

Read and Understand

Step 1: What do you know?

$98,000 was Mr. Barnett's income. He had to pay $19,000 and $6,000.

Step 2: What are you trying to find?

How much money he earned each month

Plan and Solve

To solve problems that involve multiple steps, ask yourself what hidden questions are in the problem.

- Hidden question 1: What were Mr. Barnett's total expenses?

  $19,000 + $6,000 = $25,000

- Hidden question 2: How much did he earn after expenses?

  $98,000 − $25,000 = $73,000

$73,000 ÷ 12 is about $6,000. So, Mr. Barnett made about $6,000 each month.

Write and answer the hidden question or questions and then solve the problem.

1. Leslie bought 3 posters that were priced at $9.98 each, including tax. The store had a special sale that day. For each 3 posters you buy, you get the third one for half price. Leslie gave the cashier $30.00. How much change did she receive?

Hidden question 1: How much does she

pay for the third poster at half price?

$4.99. Hidden question 2: How much does

she pay for 3 posters? $24.95. She

received $30 − $24.95, or $5.05, in

change.

Name_____

Smart Shoppers

E 4-8 DECISION MAKING

Mr. Murphy owns a fruit stand in the city. People buy fruit all day long as they pass by. Help the customers spend their money wisely.

Murphy's Fruit Stand	
Fruit	Price
Bananas	$ 0.40 each or $1.98 for a bunch of 8
Apples	$0.50 each or $3.99 for a bag of 10
Grapes	$1.99 for 1 lb or $3.49 for 2 lb

1. One customer bought two 2 lb bunches of grapes. How much did she save by buying these instead of four 1 lb bunches?

$0.98

2. Another customer bought 6 bananas, 9 apples, and 1 pound of grapes. Based on the money he spent, identify an example of how he could purchase more fruit for less money.

Sample answer: The customer spent

$8.89. For that amount, he could buy a

bag of 10 apples, a pound of grapes, and a

bunch of 8 bananas as well as 1 more

apple and 1 more banana or 2 bananas.

3. You have $10.00 to spend at Murphy's Fruit Stand. Give one example of how you could get the best value for the money. Tell what you would buy and how much money you have left over.

Sample answer: I could buy a bunch

of 8 bananas, a bag of 10 apples, and

2 lb of grapes. I would spend $9.46

and have $0.54 left over or I could buy

1 more banana and have $0.14 left.

Name_____

PROBLEM-SOLVING SKILL   PS 4-8

Multiple-Step Problems

In a typical 7-day week, the Staten Island Ferry takes 648 trips. There are 64 trips each weekend day. The remaining trips are equally divided between the weekdays. How many trips does the Staten Island Ferry make each weekday?

Read and Understand

1. What are you trying to find?

The number of trips the ferry makes

each weekday

Plan and Solve

2. What is one of the hidden questions?

Sample answer: What is the total number

of trips made on the weekends?

3. What is the answer to the hidden question?

There are 128 trips on the weekends.

4. Write the answer to the problem in a complete sentence.

The ferry makes 104 trips each weekday.

Look Back and Check

5. Explain why your answer is logical.

An estimate is 650 − 100 = 550 ÷ 5 =

110, which is close to the answer.

Name_____

Dividing Decimals by 10, 100, and 1,000

P 4-9

Find each quotient. Use mental math.

1. 86.6 ÷ 10 = __8.66__   **2.** 192.5 ÷ 100 = __1.925__

3. 1.99 ÷ 100 = __0.0199__   **4.** 0.87 ÷ 10 = __0.087__

5. 228.55 ÷ 1,000 = __0.22855__   **6.** 0.834 ÷ 100 = __0.00834__

7. 943.35 ÷ 1,000 = __0.94335__   **8.** 1.25 ÷ 10 = __0.125__

Algebra Write 10, 100, or 1,000 for each n.

9. 78.34 ÷ n = 0.7834   **10.** 0.32 ÷ n = 0.032   **11.** (75.34 − 25.34) ÷ n = 5

__n = 100__   __n = 10__   __n = 10__

12. There are 145 children taking swimming lessons at the pool. If 10 children will be assigned to each instructor, how many instructors need to be hired?

__15 instructors__

13. The instructors must pass a test before getting the job. The instructors must swim 2 mi. If it takes Jane 5 min every half mile, how long should it take her to finish?

__20 min__

Test Prep

14. Ronald ran 534.3 mi in 100 days. If he ran an equal distance each day, how many miles did he run per day?

A. 5   **B.** 5.13   **C.** 5.343   **D.** 6.201

15. Writing in Math Carlos says that 17.43 ÷ 100 is the same as 174.3 × 0.01. Is he correct? Explain.

No, he is not correct. 17.43 ÷ 100 is 0.1743 and 174.3 × 0.01 is 1.743.

Name_____

Dividing Decimals by 10, 100, and 1,000

R 4-9

Understanding place value makes it easy to divide decimals by 10, 100, and 1,000.

Dividing a number by 10 moves the decimal point one place to the left.

Example: 317 ÷ 10 = 31.7

Dividing a number by 100 moves the decimal point two places to the left.

Example: 317 ÷ 100 = 3.17

Dividing a number by 1,000 moves the decimal point three places to the left.

Example: 317 ÷ 1,000 = 0.317

Find each quotient. Use mental math.

1. 87.3 ÷ 10 = __8.73__   **2.** 56.2 ÷ 100 = __0.562__

3. 77.78 ÷ 100 = __0.7778__   **4.** 275 ÷ 100 = __2.75__

5. 38.93 ÷ 1,000 = __0.03893__   **6.** 128.75 ÷ 10 = __12.875__

7. 66.28 ÷ 1,000 = __0.06628__   **8.** 1.85 ÷ 1,000 = __0.00185__

9. Writing in Math 87.5 divided by 100 is the same as 87.5 multiplied by what decimal? Explain your answer.

$$87.5 ÷ 100 = \frac{87.5}{100} = (87.5)\left(\frac{1}{100}\right) = (87.5)(0.01)$$

Algebra Write 10, 100, or 1,000 for each n.

10. 14.7 ÷ n = 0.147   __100__

11. 6.4 ÷ n = 0.64   __10__

12. 325.67 ÷ n = 0.32567   __1,000__

Name_____

Descending Decimals

E 4-9
PATTERNS

Help the hiker descend Math Mountain by solving the decimal problems.

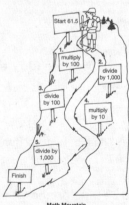

Math Mountain

1. __6,150__
2. __6.15__
3. __0.0615__
4. __0.615__
5. __0.000615__   You have reached the finish!

Name_____

Dividing Decimals by 10, 100, and 1,000

PS 4-9

Swim Races The Jefferson High School swim team posted its records on a sign in the gymnasium.

Swim Team Records
50 yd freestyle — 20.17 sec
100 yd freestyle — 47.83 sec
100 yd butterfly — 53.49 sec

1. What was the speed per yard of the swimmer with the butterfly-stroke record?

__0.5349 sec__

2. What was the speed per yard of the swimmer with the 100 yd freestyle record?

__0.4783 sec__

3. If the 50 yd freestyle record-holder could swim the 100 yd race in exactly double his 50 yd time, what would his speed per yard be?

__0.4034 sec__

Spring Fundraiser Ten students formed the school fundraising committee. The committee planned several events for the spring.

4. One of the events, the spring relay race, raised $2,190.80. How much was raised per committee member?

__$219.08 per committee member__

5. For another event, the committee members worked on a bake sale. The bake sale raised $345.60. How much was raised per worker?   __$34.56__

6. Writing in Math For the spring formal fundraiser, the committee was increased to 50 members. Each member worked 2 hr. The event raised $1,267.00. How much money was raised per hour of work? Explain how and why you moved the decimal point.

$12.67; Since there were 100 hr of work, move the decimal 2 places. It was moved to the left because the number had to be smaller than the original.

Name_____

Dividing Money by Two-Digit Divisors

P 4-10

Find each quotient. Check your answers by multiplying. (Round to the nearest cent, if necessary.)

$0.81
1. 11)$8.91

$0.72
2. 61)$43.92

$7.02
3. 12)$84.24

$0.15
4. 28)$4.20

5. $87.08 ÷ 82 = **$1.06**

6. $93.49 ÷ 59 = **$1.58**

7. $17.83 ÷ 5 = **$3.57**

8. $114.38 ÷ 19 = **$6.02**

Number Sense Decide if each quotient is greater than or less than $1.00.

9. $76.65 ÷ 73   **Greater than $1.00**

10. $9.30 ÷ 62   **Less than $1.00**

11. **Estimation** Is the quotient you get when you divide $550.81 by 70 closer to $0.80, $8.00, or $80.00?   **$8.00**

Test Prep

12. If 6 people split a dinner bill of $180.30, how much will each person pay?

(A) $30.05   **B.** $30.15   **C.** $30.50   **D.** $30.55

13. **Writing in Math** Explain why $46.50 ÷ 30 could not be $15.00.

Sample answer: When using estimation you see that $60.00 divided by 30 would be in the ones column and $15.00 would be too large.

Use with Lesson 4-10. **57**

Name_____

Dividing Money by Two-Digit Divisors

R 4-10

You buy a 22 oz box of granola for $2.86. How much do you pay per ounce?

Step 1	Step 2	Step 3
Write the decimal point in the quotient directly above the decimal point in the dividend. 22)$2.86	22 is greater than 2, so place a zero above the 2. 0. 22)$2.86 Start dividing tenths. 0.1 22)$2.86 −2 2 6	Bring down the hundredths. Continue dividing. 0.13 22)$2.86 −2 2 66 −66 0 You paid $0.13 for 1 oz of granola.

Find each quotient. Check your answers by multiplying.

$0.67
1. 13)$8.71

$0.62
2. 59)$36.58

$1.93
3. 87)$167.91

Decide if each quotient is greater than or less than $1.00.

4. 7)$11.55

5. 11)$8.25

6. 16)$17.95

More than $1.00   **Less than $1.00**   **More than $1.00**

7. **Writing in Math** Suppose 2.1 lb of ham costs $6.30. Is it reasonable to state that the price per pound of ham is $3.00? Why or why not?

Yes. $6.30 is about $6.00. 2.1 is about 2. So $6.00 ÷ 2 = $3.00.

Use with Lesson 4-10. **57**

Name_____

On the Highway

E 4-10
NUMBER SENSE

Each car listed in the table has a different cost per mile according to the amount of fuel and maintenance it needs. Use the clues to put the cars in order from the least expensive per mile to the most expensive per mile.

Type of Car	Cost per Mile
Economy	$0.34
Sedan	$0.43
SUV	$0.75
Off-road vehicle	$1.18

CLUES

1. The driver of the economy car has spent $49.98 driving 147 mi.

$49.98 ÷ 147 = $0.34 per mile

2. The driver of the off-road vehicle has spent $0.42 less to drive 42 mi than it took the economy car to drive 147 mi.

$49.98 − $0.42 = $49.56 ÷ 42 = $1.18 per mile

3. The SUV and the economy driver each had $75.00 to spend. The economy car went 20 mi more than twice as far on the same money. (Round to nearest 10 mi.)

220 mi traveled by the economy car on $75; Distance SUV traveled is 100 miles: $75 ÷ 100 = $0.75 per mile

4. It would cost the sedan driver $37.50 less than the off-road vehicle driver to travel 50 mi.

$1.18 × 50 = $59, $59 − $37.50 = $21.50, $21.50 ÷ 50 = $0.43 per mile

Use with Lesson 4-10. **57**

Name_____

Dividing Money by Two-Digit Divisors

PS 4-10

Buying Gas The price of a gallon of gas often changes. Hector kept a record of how much gas he bought and the total cost.

1. On March 5, Hector bought 10 gal of gas for $23.22. What was the cost of each gallon of gas?   **$1.29**

2. On March 12, Hector bought 20 gal of gas for $25.00. Was the cost per gallon greater than or less than the price per gallon on March 5?

$1.25; less than

3. On March 19, Hector bought 12 gal of gas for $16.68. What was the cost of each gallon of gas?   **$1.39**

Out for Dinner A group of 13 friends went out for dinner. They decided to share the bill equally.

4. The total bill was $168.35. What was each friend's share?   **$12.95**

5. After the friends figured a tip, the total amount came to $194.35. What was each friend's share, including tip?   **$14.95**

6. Because it was Jessica's birthday, the friends decided to treat her and divided the bill 12 ways. To the nearest penny, what would each friend's share of the bill and tip be if only 12 friends contributed?   **$16.20**

7. **Writing in Math** Eight CDs cost $79.92. Each CD was the same price. What is the cost of each CD? Explain why your answer is logical.

$9.99; The answer is logical because an estimated cost of $80 divided by 8 would be $10 and that is very close to the actual answer.

Use with Lesson 4-10. **57**

Name_____

Dividing Decimals by Whole Numbers

P 4-11

Find each quotient. Check by multiplying.

5.3
1. 13)68.9

11.78
2. 35)412.3

0.16
3. 90)14.4

0.89
4. 60)53.4

5. $123.08 \div 34 =$ **3.62**

6. $0.57 \div 30 =$ **0.019**

7. $562.86 \div 59 =$ **9.54**

8. $24.4 \div 80 =$ **0.305**

9. If a package of granola bars with 12 bars costs $3.48, how much does each granola bar cost? **$0.29**

10. John paid $7.99 for 3 boxes of cereal. The tax was $1.69. Excluding tax, how much did John pay for each box of cereal if they all were the same price? **$2.10**

Test Prep

11. $64.82 \div 11$ is

A. a little more than 6.   B. a little less than 6.

C. a little more than 60.   D. a little less than 60.

12. **Writing in Math** Explain how to divide 0.12 by 8.

Sample answer: Write zeros in the ones and hundredths places. Add a zero to the dividend and continue dividing. The quotient is 0.015.

© Pearson Education, Inc. 5

Name_____

Dividing Decimals by Whole Numbers

R 4-11

Dividing decimals by whole numbers	Dividing decimals by multiples of 10, 100, and 1,000
Find $1.64 \div 4$.	
Step 1: Place the decimal point in the quotient above the decimal point in the dividend.	$36 \div 90 = 0.4$
Step 2: Divide the same way you would with whole numbers.	$3.6 \div 90 = 0.04$
	$0.36 \div 90 = 0.004$

```
  0.41     Answer: 0.41
4)1.64     Check: 0.41 × 4 = 1.64
 -16
   04
 -  4
    0
```

Notice the pattern. When you move the decimal one place to the left and then divide by the same number, you move the decimal point in the previous answer one more place to the left. To do this, you often have to add zeros as decimal place holders.

Find each quotient. Check by multiplying.

0.45
1. 14)6.3

0.03
2. 77)2.31

0.028
3. 89)2.492

Choose the best estimate for each.

4. $34.61 \div 16$

A. 2.2   B. 0.22   C. 20.2

5. $16.3 \div 17$

A. 1   B. 0.1   C. 0.01

6. $59.4 \div 65$

A. 0.9   B. 9.1   C. 0.09

7. **Reasonableness** Is $61.5 \div 15$ a little less than 4, a little more than 4, a little less than 40, or a little more than 40?

A little more than 4

© Pearson Education, Inc. 5

Name_____

Meet the Scores

E 4-11
REASONING

In gymnastics an athlete's individual score for an event is the average score of several judges. The chart below shows the total scores that Randy received for his performance in a recent meet.

Randy's Olympic Score Chart

Event	Number of Judges	Total Score	Average
Balance beam	9	65.70	**7.3**
Parallel bars	8	52.16	**6.52**
Floor exercise	7	38.01	**5.43**
Rings	8	73.76	**9.22**

1. Calculate to find the average score for each event. Then write the average scores in the chart.

2. The highest and lowest score are often "tossed" before determining the final score. If the highest score for the balance beam was 8.2 and the lowest score was 5.5, what was Randy's new average?

7.43; 65.70 − (8.2 + 5.5) = 52 ÷ 7 (2 fewer scores) = 7.429

3. Randy believes he can greatly improve his score on the floor exercise. If there are 7 judges for the next meet, what would his total score have to be to average 8.5 on the floor exercise? Check your answer with a division statement.

59.5; 7 × 8.5 = 59.5; check 59.5 ÷ 7 = 8.5

© Pearson Education, Inc. 5

Name_____

Dividing Decimals by Whole Numbers

PS 4-11

Ms. Jenkins's class of 22 students worked together to gather facts about the history of their town. They did library research and interviews with older residents to find their information.

1. Each student wrote an equal amount for the final report. If the entire report was 16.5 pages when printed, what decimal part of a page was contributed by each student?

0.75 of a page

2. There were 7.7 hr of interviews that were recorded. Each student recorded for an equal amount of time. Did each student tape more or less than a full hour? What decimal part of an hour did each student tape?

Less than a full hour; 0.35

The 17 students in wood shop class planned their first project very carefully. The teacher prepared the wood that was needed for the entire class to make coat racks.

3. There was a total length of 105.4 ft of wood for the entire class. In decimal terms, how much lumber did each student get for his or her project? **6.2 ft**

4. Each student used wooden pegs to make hooks for the coat rack. The pegs were cut from a 212.5 in. length of dowel. Each student received 5 pegs. What was the length of each individual peg? **2.5 in.**

5. **Writing in Math** Hannah said that if she was given a 5.2-in. dowel rod to make 4 pegs, each would be 13 in. long. Explain Hannah's error. What is the correct answer?

Hannah has misplaced the decimal point. The correct answer is 1.3 in.

© Pearson Education, Inc. **5**

Name_____

Listen to This

The Federal Communications Commission (FCC) reported that there were 12,615 radio stations in the United States in 1999.

1. The FCC reported that there were 4,783 AM radio stations in the United States in 1999. Round 4,783 to the nearest hundred.

4,800 AM stations

2. Use that number to determine the average number of AM radio stations per state in the United States. (Hint: There are 50 states in the United States.)

96 AM stations per state

3. There were 5,766 FM radio stations in the United States in 1999. Find the average number of FM radio stations per state in the United States. Round your answer to the nearest one.

115 FM stations per state

4. In a 30-year period between 1970 and 2000, 6,108 new radio stations were started in the United States. If the number of radio stations started was the same each year, about how many radio stations were started per year?

About 200 stations per year

5. During a 20 hr broadcast day, the average United States radio station broadcasts about 280 min of commercials. About how many minutes of commercials are broadcast each hour? (Remember: There are 60 min in 1 hr.)

About 14 min per hour

Name_____

Cable TV

In the year 2000, the number of American homes that had cable television was 68,544,000. What is $68,544,000 \div 10$?

Remember, to divide a number by 10, you can move the decimal point one place to the left.

68,544,000.

So, $68,544,000 \div 10 = 6,854,400$.

Cable Television There were 10,929 cable television systems in the United States in the year 2000.

Find each quotient. Use mental math.

1. $10,929 \div 10 =$
1,092.9

2. $10,929 \div 100 =$
109.29

3. $10,929 \div 1,000 =$
10.929

4. The Jameson Cable Television Company is housed in a building that takes up 9,400 sq yd. Suppose the building is divided into 25 separate departments. How big is each department?

376 sq yd

5. The company sold a total of 15 cable TV systems for $9,285. How much does each system cost?

$619

Name_____

Pyramids of Nine

Nines have an unusual number pattern when they are multiplied. Try to discover the pattern rather than actually multiplying.

1. Fill in the NINE pyramid.

$$9 \times 9 = 81$$
$$99 \times 99 = 9,801$$
$$999 \times 999 = 99,801$$
$$9,999 \times 9,999 = \text{ } \textbf{99,980,001}$$
$$99,999 \times 99,999 = \text{ } \textbf{9,999,800,001}$$
$$999,999 \times 999,999 = \text{ } \textbf{999,998,000,001}$$
$$9,999,999 \times 9,999,999 = \text{ } \textbf{99,999,980,000,001}$$

2. Write the pattern in complete sentences.

Sample answer: Reading left to right— The number of 9s in the answer is one less than the factor in the problem, followed by an 8, followed by the same number of 0s as 9s followed by a 1.

3. What would be the product for ten 9s × ten 9s?
99,999,999,980,000,000,001

Name_____

Take Me Out to the Ball Game

Three friends went to see their favorite baseball team play. Each one bought a ticket to the game, a snack, a drink, and a program. Together, the snack, the drink, and the program cost as much as the ticket to the game. The three friends spent a total of $98.04 altogether. How much did the ticket to the game cost?

Read and Understand

1. How much did the three friends spend in total?
$98.04

2. What are you trying to find?
Cost of the ticket

Plan and Solve

3. What is one hidden question in the problem?
What did each friend spend?   **Sample answer:**

4. Write the answer to the hidden question above.
Each friend spent $32.68.   **Sample answer:**

5. Solve the problem and write your answer in a complete sentence.
The ticket to the game cost $16.34.   **Sample answer:**

Look Back and Check

6. Is your answer reasonable?
Yes; An estimate is $15 × 6 = $90, which is close to the total cost.

Name_____

Collecting Data from a Survey

P 5-1

Identify each statement as either a fact or an opinion.

1. Dogs are the best pets to own.   **Opinion**
2. Nine students received As on their tests.   **Fact**
3. Five students live 3 blocks from school.   **Fact**
4. Three people is a good number for a team.   **Opinion**
5. Spaghetti is the tastiest meal.   **Opinion**

Music Bought in Class B

```
                          x
                          x       x
        x      x          x       x
        x      x          x       x
        x      x     x    x       x
      Rock   R & B  Classical Alternative Country
                  CDs Bought
```

6. If the entire class responded to the survey, how many students are in the class?   **18 students**

7. What information was collected about music?

The type of music CDs students buy most often

Test Prep

8. Use the line plot above. Which type of CDs did students buy most often?

   (A) Alternative   **B.** Classical   **C.** Country   **D.** Rock

9. **Writing in Math** Write a survey question that might gather the following information.

   In one school there are 6 sets of twins, 2 sets of triplets, and 1 set of quadruplets.

   Sample answer: Are you one of a set of twins, triplets, or quadruplets?

Name_____

Collecting Data from a Survey

R 5-1

You ask survey questions to gather information called data. Data can be facts or opinions.

A fact is actual information. Here are some facts:
   Cars use gasoline.
   Cats have whiskers.

An opinion is what a person likes or dislikes. Here are some opinions:
   Steak is the tastiest food.
   Football is a better sport than soccer.

Data that are gathered can be shown in a line plot or frequency table.

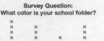

Survey Question:
What color is your school folder?

```
   x       x
   x       x
   x       x
   x       x        x       x
  Red    Blue    Green   Yellow
          Folder Color
```

Survey Question:
What is your favorite animal?

Favorite Animals	
Animal	Number
Pig	3
Elephant	9
Ram	4

Identify each statement as a fact or an opinion.

1. The racetrack is 1.5 mi long.   **Fact**
2. The president is doing a good job with foreign policy. **Opinion**

Write a survey question that might gather the following information.

Sample answers:

3. The favorite day of the week of 4 people is Friday.

   Which day of the week is your favorite?

4. How many people responded to the favorite sports survey?

   11 people

Favorite Sports	
Sport	Number
Soccer	7
Football	3
Track	1

5. **Writing in Math** Describe how you might pick a sample of 50 minivan owners that represents the minivan owners of your state.

   Choose from 4 regions of the state.

Name_____

What's the Question?

E 5-1
REASONING

The data for these exercises was gathered by students who asked people three different survey questions. What questions do you think were asked? Write two questions for each set of data.

1.
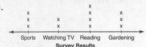

```
        x              x
  x     x      x       x
  x     x      x       x
Sports Watching TV Reading Gardening
          Survey Results
```

Sample answers: How do you spend your time after school? What leisure activities do you enjoy?

2.

Food	Number
Peanuts	18
Eggs	7
Dairy products	12
Sweets	9

Sample answers: What foods are you allergic to? What is your favorite food?

3.
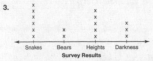

```
  x
  x            x
  x            x
  x            x       x
  x     x      x       x
  x     x      x       x
Snakes Bears Heights Darkness
         Survey Results
```

Sample answers: What are you afraid of? What are some dangerous things?

Name_____

Collecting Data from a Survey

PS 5-1

Amusement Park Carl took a survey of his eighth-grade class for his project. The survey results are shown on a line plot.

Favorite Amusement Park Ride

```
               x          x
        x      x          x
  x     x      x          x
  x     x      x          x
  x     x      x          x
  x     x      x          x
 Roller  Ferris      Merry-
 Coaster Wheel      Go-Round
```

1. What question might Carl have asked in order to get this information?

   Sample answer: Of the roller coaster, Ferris wheel, and merry-go-round, which ride is your favorite?

2. How many people responded to this survey?   **20 people**

3. Is the survey question about a fact or an opinion?   **Opinion**

4. Write a survey question to gather information on how much time people spend listening to the radio.

   Sample answer: In an average week, how many hours do you spend listening to the radio?

5. **Writing in Math** Most of Carl's survey was the result of asking his school friends. Does his survey represent all the people who would go on amusement park rides?

   Sample answer: No, people of all ages go on amusement park rides.

Name_____

Bar Graphs

P 5-2

The data at the right shows the number of students who bought lunch the first week of school during the 1999–2000 and 2000–2001 school years. The data has been rounded to the nearest ten.

Students Buying Lunch

Days	1999–2000	2000–2001
Mon.	90	140
Tue.	60	70
Wed.	120	160
Thur.	130	140
Fri.	100	120

1. Which data would have the shortest bar on a graph?

   Tuesday of the 1999–2000 school year

2. Complete the graph to the right.

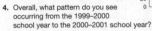

3. During which school year did the most students buy lunches? How many more?

   2000–2001; 130 more students

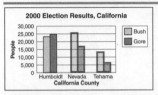

4. Overall, what pattern do you see occurring from the 1999–2000 school year to the 2000–2001 school year?

   More students bought lunch in the 2000–2001 school year.

Test Prep

5. Use the graph above. On which day of the week was an average of 100 lunches sold?

   A. Tuesday   B. Wednesday   C. Thursday   (D.) Friday

6. **Writing in Math** Is a data file needed to make a bar graph? Explain.

   Yes, information is needed to make the bar graph.

Use with Lesson 5-2. **61**

Name_____

Bar Graphs

R 5-2

How to make a bar graph

Step 1 Decide on a scale and its intervals. Draw the graph. Label the axes.

Step 2 Write a key for the two bars.

Step 3 Graph the data by drawing bars of the correct length or height.

Step 4 Title your graph.

Conference Baseball Champions

High School	Freshmen	Varsity
Smith	2	4
Phillips	3	3
Dominican	5	2

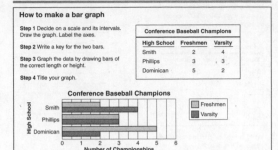

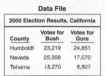

Data File

2000 Election Results, California

County	Votes for Bush	Votes for Gore
Humboldt	23,219	24,851
Nevada	25,998	17,670
Tehama	13,270	6,507

1. Complete the graph. Write a sentence about the data represented.

   Sample answer: Bush had more votes in two of the three counties.

2. **Representations** Explain why you need to use a double bar graph and not a single bar graph to represent this data.

   Sample answer: You need a double bar graph because you are graphing information for each county for two different candidates.

Use with Lesson 5-2. **61**

Name_____

Ms. Wilson Is Watching

E 5-2
DATA

At Ms. Wilson's machine shop, all workers are expected to make between 50 and 65 metal parts each day. Ms. Wilson has graphs made each week to see how many parts were made by the workers. Match each graph to the situations described.

Week A:

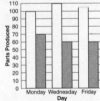

Week B:

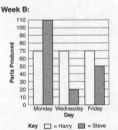

1. After which week would Ms. Wilson likely question Steve about his inconsistent work?

   Week B

2. After which week would Ms. Wilson likely praise Harry for his outstanding work?

   Week A

Week C:

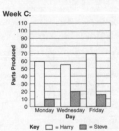

3. After which week would Ms. Wilson likely attempt to motivate Steve to do better work?

   Week C

Use with Lesson 5-2. **61**

Name_____

Bar Graphs

PS 5-2

Pet Sales A pet store keeps track of its sales each month by the type of animal that is sold. The list shows the number of amphibians and reptiles that were sold in April and May.

Amphibian and Reptile Sales

	April Sales	May Sales
Frog	17	6
Lizard	5	5
Salamander	7	10
Snake	3	18
Turtle	13	2

1. Complete the graph.

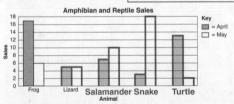

2. How many frogs were sold in April? In May?

   17 frogs in April; 6 frogs in May

3. Which two animals sold better in May than in April?

   Salamanders and snakes

4. During which month were the greatest number of animals sold?   **April**

5. **Writing in Math** Rank the animals for the two-month period in order from the least number sold to the greatest number sold. Write the total number sold for each animal. Explain how you determined the ranking.

   Lizard: 10, turtle: 15, salamander: 17, snake: 21, and frog: 23; Sample answer: I added the totals for each animal and put them in order.

Use with Lesson 5-2. **61**

© Pearson Education, Inc. 5

Name_____

Line Graphs

P 5-3

1. Make a line graph of the data. Use a scale from 550 to 600 and an interval of 5 for the number of species.

Endangered U.S. Plants

Year	Number of Species
1997	553
1998	567
1999	581
2000	592
2001	595

Endangered U.S. Plants

2. What is the trend in the data in the graph to the right?

The number of endangered species is increasing.

Endangered U.S. Birds

3. How many more species of birds were endangered in 2000 than in 1980?

20 more species

Test Prep

4. Which is the trend if the line on a graph is rising from left to right?

   A. Staying the same   (B) Increasing

   C. Decreasing   D. Doubling

5. **Writing in Math** The numbers in a data file are 71, 56, 62, 77, and 38. What scale would you use to graph the data? Explain your choice.

   ## Sample answer: Scale of 10; The scale will make the graph easy to read.

Name_____

Line Graphs

R 5-3

A line graph is often used to show a **trend** in data. By looking at the graph, you can tell if the data is increasing or decreasing.

The trend on this graph shows that there is a steady increase in the amount of weight Dave lifted over time.

Dave's Weightlifting

How to make a line graph

Step 1
Decide on a scale and its intervals. Draw the graph. Label the axes.

	Ron's Earnings				
Time	0 hr	1 hr	2 hr	3 hr	4 hr
Earnings	$0	$4.50	$9.00	$13.50	$18.00

Step 2
Graph the data by plotting the points.

Step 3
Connect the points for each set of data.

Step 4
Title your graph.

Ron's Earnings

1. Make a line graph of the data. Use a scale from 0–450 and an interval of 50 for people donating blood.

Data File

Blood Drive

Week	Number of Donors
1	73
2	162
3	257
4	399

Sample answers:

Blood Drive

Name_____

What Would You Do?

E 5-3
DECISION MAKING

Answer each question based on the data in the line graphs.

Sample answers are given.

1. Dan and his friend obtained some data on the average weights of bluegill caught during 4 months in the previous year. When should Dan and his friend go fishing next year? Why do you think so?

May, because there are larger fish

Average Weight of Bluegills Caught

2. Connie is thinking of investing some money in the A-3 company. Based on the data, do you think this would be a good investment? Why or why not?

No, because the company has been losing money

A-3 Annual Earnings

3. Greg takes people on guided tours of a nearby wooded area so that they can see bald eagles in the wild. Based on last year's data, when would be the best time for Greg to take people out? Why?

There is no best time because the number changes.

Bald Eagles Sighted

Name_____

Line Graphs

PS 5-3

Growth A good indication of children's health and nutrition is the rate at which they grow. The graph shows the growth rate of one average healthy child from birth to age 5.

Rate of Growth

1. How tall was the child at age 5?

About 48 in.

2. Between which ages did the child grow the most?

Between ages 2 and 3

3. Between which ages did the child grow the least?

Between ages 3 and 4

4. How many inches did the child grow from birth to age 5?

About 28 in.

5. Describe the trend shown by the graph. Explain.

Rising; Sample answer: The child's height is increasing.

6. **Writing in Math** Look at the line graph and explain how the line showing the greatest increase in height is different from the line showing the least increase in height.

Sample answer: The line showing the greatest increase, between ages 2 and 3, is steeper and longer than the line showing the least increase, between ages 3 and 4.

Name_____

Stem-and-Leaf Plots

P 5-4

The data file below shows the ages of people in a movie theater.

Ages of People at the Movie Theater
25, 16, 42, 34, 65, 54, 10, 18, 45, 34,
23, 33, 51, 36, 21, 19, 18, 34, 15, 50

Ages of People at the Movie Theater

1	0 5 6 8 8 9
2	1 3 5
3	3 4 4 4 6
4	2 5
5	0 1 4
6	5

Key: 1 | 0 = 10

1. Make a stem-and-leaf plot of the data. Title the plot "Ages of People at the Movie Theater."

2. What is the range of the data? How do you know?

55; You subtract the lowest age from the oldest age.

3. How many people over 20 years old watched the movie?

14 people

4. How many people under 20 years old watched the movie?

6 people

5. What age was most frequent at this movie theater?

34 years old

Test Prep

6. Which age group had the most people at the movie?

(A) People under twenty B. People in their twenties

C. People in their thirties D. People in their forties

7. **Writing in Math** Is Bill's explanation correct? If not, tell why.

No; Bill needed to say list the numbers in order from least to greatest.

Bill's Explanation

How do you make a stem-and-leaf plot?

First, you list all the first digits on the left in the plot.

Then you list all the second digits on the right in the plot.

Use with Lesson 5-4. **63**

Name_____

Stem-and-Leaf Plots

R 5-4

To make a stem-and-leaf plot, first write the data in order from least to greatest:

Stems	Leaves
1	2

12, 14, 23, 27, 32, 36, 38, 38, 39, and 41

Begin with the lowest value, 12. Place the tens digit in 12, or 1, under the Stems heading. Then place the ones digit, or 2, under the Leaves heading.

Use the same method to fill in the remaining values in order. Leaves for each stem have the same tens digit.

Stems	Leaves
1	2 4
2	3 7
3	2 6 8 8 9
4	1

Use the following data to complete Exercises 1–4.

13, 63, 53, 59, 33, 18, 67, 58, 55, 33, 43, 22, 69, 61, 33

1. Make a stem-and-leaf plot of the data.

Stems	Leaves
1	3 8
2	2
3	3 3 3
4	3
5	3 5 8 9
6	1 3 7 9

2. What is the range of the data?

56

3. How many numbers are in the fifties?

4 numbers

4. **Writing in Math** How does this stem-and-leaf plot make it easy to tell which values occurred most frequently?

It helps you quickly identify how the values are distributed.

Use with Lesson 5-4. **63**

Name_____

The Smith Family Reunion

E 5-4
DATA

The Smiths had a family reunion. The ages of the people at the reunion were as follows: 4, 8, 26, 32, 73, 65, 45, 39, 48, 19, 18, 21, 12, 40, 56, 84, 15, 23, 34, 54, and 14. Use the data to complete the exercises below.

1. Use the numeric data to create a stem and leaf plot.

Stem	Leaves
0	4 8
1	2 4 5 8 9
2	1 3 6
3	2 4 9
4	0 5 8
5	4 6
6	5
7	3
8	4

2. What is the range of this data set?

80 years

3. How many of the Smiths were under 21 years of age? **7**

4. Based on the data, which of the following activities would have been the best one to organize at the reunion: running races, jump rope contest, or pie eating contest? Why?

Pie eating. The other two events are more suitable for younger people, and most of the people at the reunion are in their 20s or older.

Use with Lesson 5-4. **63**

Name_____

Stem-and-Leaf Plots

PS 5-4

Points Shelly likes to keep track of how many points she scores in each basketball game. The data shows her scores for the games she has played so far this season.

Scores

32	16	22	24
26	36	42	48
18	28	34	36
40	40	16	18
22	20		

1. Complete the stem-and-leaf plot of the data.

Points Scored per Game

Stem	Leaf
1	6 6 8 8
2	0 2 2 4 6 8
3	2 4 6 6
4	0 0 2 8

2. In how many games did Shelly score 20 or more points?

14 games

3. In how many games did Shelly score fewer than 40 points?

14 games

4. In how many games did Shelly score at least 40 but less than 49 points?

4 games

5. **Writing in Math** Explain why there are two zeros in the leaf following the stem of 4.

Sample answer: Shelly scored 40 points in two different games. Each game must be counted separately, even if the points are the same.

Use with Lesson 5-4. **63**

© Pearson Education, Inc. 5

Name_____

PROBLEM-SOLVING STRATEGY   P 5-5
Make a Graph

Zoos in the United States have different budgets. The table shows budgets for five U.S. zoos in 2001. The budgets are in millions of dollars.

Budgets of U.S. Zoos in 2001	
Zoo **Budget**	
Albuquerque Biological Park	$9
Cleveland Metroparks Zoo	$12
Oregon Zoo	$15
Phoenix Zoo	$16
San Diego Zoo	$56

1. Make a bar graph using the data to the right.

Budgets of U.S. Zoos (2001)

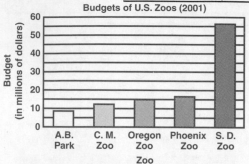

2. Which zoo had the largest budget? The smallest budget?

San Diego Zoo;

Albuquerque Biological Park

3. What was the greatest difference between zoo budgets?

There was a $47 million difference

between the San Diego Zoo and the

Albuquerque Biological Park.

64   Use with Lesson 5-5.

Name_____

PROBLEM-SOLVING STRATEGY   R 5-5
Make a Graph

Book Reading Two classrooms had a contest to see how many extra books the students could read during a two-month period. Which class won the contest?

Mrs. Blane's Class

Books	9	10	11	12	13	14	15	16
Students	2	3	0	2	3	4	4	5

Mr. Parker's Class

Books	9	10	11	12	13	14	15	16
Students	3	6	5	4	0	2	0	2

Read and Understand

Step 1: What do you know?

You know how many students read each number of books.

Step 2: What are you trying to find?

Find which class won the contest.

Plan and Solve

Step 3: What strategy will you use?   **Strategy: Make a graph**

Mrs. Blane's Class   Mr. Parker's Class

Answer: Mrs. Blane's class was more successful. More Xs are at the right end of the plot.

Look Back and Check

Is your answer reasonable?

Yes, the numbers in the table show the same trend.

1. What type of graph could you make with the above data?

Double bar graph

64   Use with Lesson 5-5.

Name_____

Evaluate the Work

E 5-5
REASONING

Country	2001 Population (rounded to nearest million)
Pakistan	145,000,000
Brazil	174,000,000
USA	278,000,000
Italy	58,000,000
Mexico	102,000,000

Mrs. Anders asked her students to make a bar graph of the information in the data file. Harold's graph is shown below.

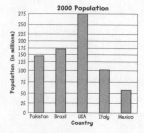

1. Describe three things that are wrong with Harold's graph.

Sample answer:

Error 1: The bars for Italy and Mexico are

reversed. Error 2: The graph is mislabeled.

Error 3: There are not enough lines for

USA.

64   Use with Lesson 5-5.

Name_____

PROBLEM-SOLVING STRATEGY   PS 5-5
Make a Graph

Golf Highland High School and Midway High School compete in a golf league. Each game consists of 9 holes. The game winner is the individual student with the lowest score, but the team winner is the team that has the greater number of lower scores. Which school has the greater number of lower scores, Highland or Midway?

Highland High School

Student	1	2	3	4	5	6	7	8
Score	43	51	47	48	41	56	58	47

Midway High School

Student	1	2	3	4	5	6	7	8
Score	41	45	42	59	41	51	42	43

Read and Understand

1. What are you trying to find?

The team that had the greater number of lower scores

Plan and Solve

2. Complete the stem-and-leaf plots to solve the problem.

Highland	
Stem	Leaf
4	1 3 7 7 8
5	1 6 8

Midway	
Stem	Leaf
4	1 1 2 2 3 5
5	1 9

3. Write the answer in a complete sentence.

Midway High School had more lower scores than Highland did.

Look Back and Check

4. Is your answer reasonable?

Sample answer: Yes, Midway had the lower total.

64   Use with Lesson 5-5.

Name_____

Mean, Median, and Mode

P 5-6

1. Find the mean of this data set: 225 342 288 552 263 — **334**

2. Find the median of this data set: 476 234 355 765 470 — **470**

3. Find the mode of this data set:
   16 7 8 5 16 7 8 4 7 8 16 7 — **7**

4. Find the range of this data set:
   64 76 46 88 88 43 99 50 55 — **56**

5. **Reasoning** Would the mode change if a 76 was added to the data in Exercise 4?

   Yes, there would be two modes— 76 and 88.

The table gives the math test scores for Mrs. Jung's fifth-grade class.

76	54	92	88	76	88
75	93	92	68	88	76
76	88	80	70	88	72

Test Scores

6. Find the mean of the data. — **80**

7. Find the mode of the data. — **88**

8. Find the median of the data. — **78**

9. What is the range of the data set? — **39**

Test Prep

10. Find the mean of this data set: 247, 366, 785, 998.

    A. 599   **B.** 598   **C.** 589   **D.** 579

11. **Writing in Math** Will a set of data always have a mode? Explain your answer.

    No, sometimes there is no number that appears more than any other.

Use with Lesson 5-6. **65**

Name_____

Mean, Median, and Mode

R 5-6

How to find the mean, median, and mode of:
2, 3, 8, 5, 6, 3, 1

Mean

The mean is the average. To find the mean, add all the data and divide by the number of data.

2 + 3 + 8 + 5 + 6 + 3 + 1 = 28

28 ÷ 7 = 4

The mean is 4.

Median

The median is the middle number. To find the median, arrange the data in order from least to greatest.

1, 2, 3, 3, 5, 6, 8

↑
middle number in data

The median is 3.

Mode

The mode is the data value that occurs most often.

1, 2, 3, 3, 5, 6, 8

The number 3 occurs most often.

The mode is 3.

1. Find the mean of this data set: 241, 563, 829, 755. — **597**

2. Find the median of this data set: 12, 18, 25, 32, 67. — **25**

3. Find the mode of this data set: 123, 354, 654, 123, 452, 185. — **123**

4. **Writing in Math** Explain how you would find the mean of this data set: 4, 3, 5.

   Add up the numbers in the set, then divide by 3.

The chart to the right shows the number of silver medals won by American athletes in recent Summer Olympic games.

Year	Medals
2000	24
1996	32
1992	38
1988	31
1984	61
1976	35
1972	31

5. What is the mean of this data set? — **36**

6. What is the median of this data set? — **32**

7. What is the mode of this data set? — **31**

Use with Lesson 5-6. **65**

Name_____

Tom's Bowling Team

E 5-6
NUMBER SENSE

Tom has a bowling team that bowls every Tuesday evening. Last week's scores are shown below. Use the data to complete the exercises below.

	Ralph	Mary	Tom	June
Game 1	202	187	108	212
Game 2	210	141	109	224
Game 3	214	116	121	218

1. Which player on Tom's team had the best average for all 3 games? Round to the nearest pin.

   June had the best average, 218.

2. Which player on Tom's team had the greatest range in his or her scores? What is the value of that range?

   Mary had the greatest range in her scores, 71 pins.

3. What is the mean of all the scores? Round to the nearest pin.

   The mean of the scores is 172.

4. What is the median of all the scores?

   The median of the scores is 194.5.

5. Which bowler or bowlers improved during the evening?

   Ralph and Tom

6. Does the data set have a mode? How can you tell?

   No, because there is no number that appears more than once in the data set.

Use with Lesson 5-6. **65**

Name_____

Mean, Median, and Mode

PS 5-6

Overtime Bruce works overtime almost every day. Last week he worked 4 hr overtime on Monday, 2 hr on Tuesday, 2 hr on Wednesday, 6 hr on Thursday, and 1 hr on Friday.

1. How many hours overtime did Bruce work the most often? What is this number called?

   2 hr; mode

2. How many hours overtime did Bruce average last week? What is this number called?

   3 hr; mean

3. What is the median number of hours Bruce worked last week?

   2 hr

Cousins There are 11 first cousins in the Warner family. They love to get together for parties and picnics.

Warner Family
Grandparents

Parents — Alan - 12, Ben - 17, Carol - 3

Parents — Jordan - 5, Jacob - 5, Michael - 13

Parents — Diane - 7, Lucy - 2, Tim - 9, Victor - 10

Parents — Nikita - 5

4. What is the name and age of the cousin whose age is the median?

   Diane, age 7

5. What is the average age of the cousins? Are there any cousins that age?

   Age 8; No

6. What age is the most frequent of the cousins? Which cousins are that age?

   Age 5; Jacob, Jordan, and Nikita

7. **Writing in Math** Larry said that the median in a set of data is not important. Give one situation where you could use the median.

   Sample answer: The median can be used when you are trying to divide a group into the top half and bottom half of a set of scores.

Use with Lesson 5-6. **65**

© Pearson Education, Inc. 5

Name_____

Circle Graphs
P 5-7

Three thousand fifth graders were asked which foreign continent they would most like to visit. The results are shown in the circle graph.

South America 420
Asia 180
Antarctica 180
Africa 270
Europe 1,200
Australia 750

1. Which continent was most popular?

   Europe

2. How many students were most interested in Africa?

   270 students

3. **Estimation** About how many more students wanted to go to Europe than to Australia?

   About 450 more students

4. Bill surveyed the 100 students in fifth grade. Complete the graph to the right by labeling the missing categories. More students liked baseball than soccer.

   Favorite Sports

   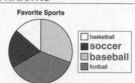

   ☐ basketball
   ■ soccer
   ☐ baseball
   ☐ football

Test Prep

5. 40 people were asked to name their favorite meal. 5 said breakfast, 10 said lunch, 5 said snack, and 20 said dinner. Which meal selection will section 2 represent?

   A. Breakfast   B. Lunch
   C. Snack   (D.) Dinner

6. **Writing in Math** Explain how you would know which sections of the graph would represent the other meal situations.

   Sample answer:

   Section 4 is twice as big as section 1 or 3, so section 1 is breakfast, section 3 is snack, and section 4 is lunch.

© Pearson Education, Inc. 5

Name_____

Circle Graphs
R 5-7

How to read a circle graph

A random group of 100 adults were asked about their favorite source for news. The graph shows how they responded. It shows that more than 50% first get their news from newspapers. The Internet is the second favorite source. Magazines are the least favorite source.

Favorite News Source

☐ Newspaper
■ Internet
☐ TV News
■ Magazine

How to make a circle graph

Suppose that for the previous example you were given the following data for 100 adults who were randomly surveyed.

   Newspaper: 63; Internet: 21; TV News: 10; Magazine: 6

To make a circle graph, you first draw a circle. Then you calculate how much 63% of the circle is. It is more than half but less than 3/4 of the circle. This section is labeled "newspapers." Then do the same for the other responses.

A group of 100 randomly selected people who attended a sports show were recorded for their ages and gender.

☐ Adult Males
■ Adult Females
☐ Boys
■ Girls

Data File	
Adult Males	63
Adult Females	22
Boys	11
Girls	4

Sports Show Attendance

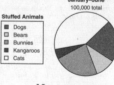

1. Use the information in the data file to complete the circle graph above. Be sure to label the graph.

2. Which group of people had the greatest attendance?

   Adult males

3. Which group of people had the least attendance?

   Girls

4. About how many more adult males were there than girls?

   There were about 60 more adult males than girls.

© Pearson Education, Inc. 5

Name_____

Ken's Money
E 5-7
VISUAL THINKING

Ken's allowance from his parents is $40 per month. He also earns about $100 per month doing odd jobs around the neighborhood, such as cleaning windows, mowing lawns, raking leaves, and shoveling snow. The graphs below show what Ken spent his money on during the months of August, September, and October of last year.

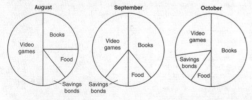

August / September / October

1. Which item or items has Ken spent less on in each successive month?

   Video games

2. Which item or items has Ken spent more on in each successive month?

   Books

3. Which item or items has Ken spent about the same on in each successive month?

   Food and savings bonds

4. Complete the graph to show what you think Ken would likely spend his money on during the month of November.

   Sample answer:

   November
   Video games
   Savings bonds
   Books
   Food

© Pearson Education, Inc. 5

Name_____

Circle Graphs
PS 5-7

The circle graph shows the sales of the first 100,000 stuffed animals sold by the Giant Stuffed Animal Company during the first 6 months of the year.

Stuffed Animals
■ Dogs
■ Bears
☐ Bunnies
■ Kangaroos
☐ Cats

January–June
100,000 total

1. Which stuffed animal had the greatest number of sales?

   Cats

2. Which had the least number of sales?

   Kangaroos

3. Which two stuffed animals' sales were the closest?

   Dogs and bunnies

4. During the second 6 months of the year, the Olympics were held in Australia and sales of kangaroos soared. Draw a circle graph showing over one half of all sales as kangaroos and the rest evenly distributed between dogs, bears, bunnies, and cats.

   Sample answer:
   July–December
   100,000 total

   Stuffed Animals
   ■ Dogs
   ☐ Bears
   ☐ Bunnies
   ☐ Kangaroos
   ☐ Cats

   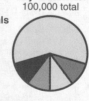

5. **Writing in Math** Compare the number of cats sold during the first 6 months of the year with kangaroos sold during the second 6 months of the year. Which was greater? Explain.

   Kangaroos; Sample answer: The section of cats on the graph for the first 6 months is less than half, and the section of kangaroos on the graph for the second 6 months is greater than half.

© Pearson Education, Inc. 5

Practice

Name_____

Choosing an Appropriate Graph   P 5-8

Tell what type of graph would be most appropriate to represent the data listed.

1. Flower sales over a week **A line graph because**
it shows changes over time

2. Where the total amount of income for one month is spent
A circle graph because a whole is
divided into parts

3. Describe the trend in attendance at the pool for the week of June 3.

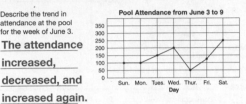

Pool Attendance from June 3 to 9

The attendance
increased,
decreased, and
increased again.

4. Predict what may have been the cause for the decline on Thursday.
Sample answer: Rain

Test Prep

5. Use the graph above. What day did the pool's attendance peak?

A. Thursday   **B.** Saturday   C. Wednesday   D. Sunday

6. **Writing in Math** When should you use a double bar graph or double line graph?

You should use the double bar or double
line graph when you need to compare or
watch the trends of two different items.

Use with Lesson 5-8. **67**

Reteaching

Name_____

Choosing the Appropriate Graph   R 5-8

Barbara did a survey in her fifth-grade class about the students' favorite type of sandwich. Barbara made two graphs with the data.

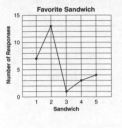

Favorite Sandwich

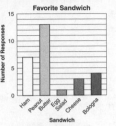

Favorite Sandwich

The line graph suggests that data exists between sandwiches. This graph is not appropriate for the data.

The bar represents the number of responses counted for each sandwich. This is an appropriate graph for the data.

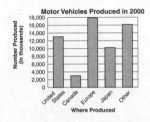

Motor Vehicles Produced in 2000

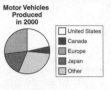

Motor Vehicles Produced in 2000

Legend:
- United States
- Canada
- Europe
- Japan
- Other

1. Which graph is the easiest to use to answer the question "Which place produced the most cars?" Explain your reasoning.

The bar graph, because it shows
Europe produced the most cars.

Use with Lesson 5-8. **67**

Enrichment

Name_____

MacNamara's Bake Sale   E 5-8
REASONABLENESS

Every year, Mr. MacNamara has a bake sale to finance the cost of new instruments for his brass band. He has created several graphs to help him understand the results of the sale. Based on the information provided, decide if Mr. MacNamara has chosen the most appropriate graph. Explain why he did or did not. If he did not, tell which graph Mr. MacNamara might have chosen to better display the data.

1.

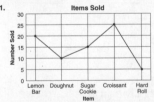

Items Sold

Sample answer: No; The graph does not
show a meaningful trend; bar graph

2.

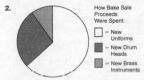

How Bake Sale Proceeds Were Spent:
- = New Uniforms
- = New Drum Heads
- = New Brass Instruments

Sample answer: Yes; He can compare
parts of the group to the whole.

Use with Lesson 5-8. **67**

Problem Solving

Name_____

Choosing the Appropriate Graph   PS 5-8

Dinner Time Sidney took a survey of his neighbors and his teachers. He asked the survey question, "What time do you normally eat your evening meal?" He graphed the results using a line graph, circle graph, and a line plot.

Legend:
- Before 5:00 PM
- 5:00 PM
- 5:30 PM
- 6:00 PM
- 6:30 PM
- 7:00 PM or later

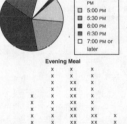

When People Eat Dinner

Evening Meal

1. At what time do most of the people surveyed eat their evening meal?
6:00 P.M.

2. How does each graph show the same result for Exercise 1?
Sample answer:
Line graph: highest point; circle graph:
largest area; line plot: most Xs

3. Which graph is the least appropriate to use for this survey? Why?
Sample answer:
The line graph because it shows change over
time and this problem asks for specific times.

4. **Writing in Math** Which time could be considered the outlier in this survey? Which graph shows you this the best? Why?
Sample answer: 5:00 P.M. The line plot shows this
the best because the Xs are spread out and it is
easy to see.

Use with Lesson 5-8. **67**

Name _____

Writing to Compare

Analyze the graphs below. Then answer the questions.

1. Which store had the greater sales in 2002?   **Store B**

2. In which year did the two stores have the same sales?   **1998**

3. Is there a common trend between the two jeans stores? If so, explain.

   Yes, both have increased their sales since the year 2000.

4. Which graph shows a slow increase over time?   **Store B**

5. If the stores continue the trends that are represented in the graph, which store do you think will have higher sales in 5 years? Explain your answer.

   Sample answer: Store A; The graph shows steeper increases in the past 2 years.

6. Which store has a greater range in sales? What is the range?   **Store B; 2,000**

68 Use with Lesson 5-9.

© Pearson Education, Inc. 5

Name _____

Writing to Compare

The total points scored in the first five games for the Carlton Knights and Baxter Barons are shown in the line graphs.

The number of points scored by both teams has been increasing for each game.

The scoring for the Knights has gone up faster because the line is steeper.

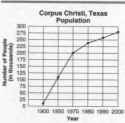 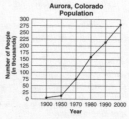

1. Which graph shows a faster increase in population between 1900 and 1950?

   Corpus Christi graph

68 Use with Lesson 5-9.

© Pearson Education, Inc. 5

Name _____

Test Scores

Mr. Davis made a bar graph of all of his students' math quiz scores each week. He looks over the graphs to make sure that all of his students are progressing. Use the graph below to answer the questions that follow.

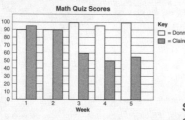

1. Describe the trend in Donna's quiz scores for the 5 weeks shown.

   Sample answer:
   Donna's scores are consistently high.

2. Describe the trend in Claire's quiz scores for the 5 weeks shown.

   Sample answer:
   Claire's scores go down each week.

3. In what ways are the girls' scores similar?

   Both girls' scores started high. They both scored 90 or above the first two weeks.

4. In what ways are the girls' scores different?   **Sample answer:**
   Donna's scores remained consistent, while Claire's scores went down.

68 Use with Lesson 5-9.

© Pearson Education, Inc. 5

Name _____

Writing to Compare

Phone Sales
A telephone company has shown the sales of two types of phones with line graphs. Compare the sales trends.

 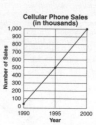

Read and Understand

1. What type of graphs are used and why?

   Sample answer: Line graphs are used because they show change over time.

Plan and Solve

2. Compare the sales trends.   **Sample answer:**
   Both graphs show an increase in sales between 1990 and 1995. The home phone sales graph shows a decrease between 1995 and 2000, while the cellular phone sales graph shows an increase.

Look Back and Check

3. Explain why your answer makes sense.

   Sample answer: It makes sense because the comparison matches the graphs.

68 Use with Lesson 5-9.

© Pearson Education, Inc. 5

Practice

Name_____

Predicting Outcomes   P 5-10

The nature club is planning a field trip. They have decided to write their destination choices on slips of paper and have their instructor select the destination by drawing a slip of paper out of a bag. The slips of paper shown below are the destination choices in the bag.

1. Is it equally likely that the instructor will draw the nature museum or the forest preserve? Explain. **No; There is only 1 nature museum choice and there are 2 forest preserve choices.**

2. Which destination is the instructor least likely to draw? **Nature museum**

3. Which destination is the instructor most likely to draw? **Beach**

Test Prep

4. Use data from Exercises 1–3. What is the chance of the instructor drawing the nature museum?

   A. 3 out of 7   B. 2 out of 7
   (C.) 1 out of 7   D. Impossible event

5. **Writing in Math** Explain the difference between an outcome and a favorable outcome.
   An outcome is any event that can occur. A favorable outcome is the particular result you want.

Use with Lesson 5-10. **69**

Reteaching

Name_____

Predicting Outcomes   R 5-10

You can use an experiment to predict outcomes.

Spinner A	**Event:** Spinning an even number **Favorable outcomes:** 2, 4 2 out of 4 possible outcomes are favorable, so in 2 out of 4 spins, you can expect an even number.	**Event:** Spinning an odd number **Favorable outcomes:** 3, 5 2 out of 4 possible outcomes are favorable, so in 2 out of 4 spins, you can expect an odd number.	Spinning an even number and spinning an odd number are **equally likely** events.
Spinner B	**Event:** Spinning an even number **Favorable outcomes:** 6 1 out of 4 possible outcomes are favorable, so in 1 out of 4 spins, you can expect an even number.	**Event:** Spinning an odd number **Favorable outcomes:** 5, 5, 7 3 out of 4 possible outcomes are favorable, so in 3 out of 4 spins, you can expect an odd number.	Spinning an even number is **less likely** than spinning an odd number. Spinning an odd number is **more likely** than spinning an even number.

Think about tossing a standard number cube.

1. What are the possible outcome numbers? Are the numbers equally likely? Explain.
   The possible outcome numbers are 1, 2, 3, 4, 5, and 6. They are equally likely because there is one of each on the 6 faces of the number cube.

2. In 6 tosses, how many times would you expect to toss the number 6?
   1 time

Use with Lesson 5-10. **69**

Enrichment

Name_____

Prime Patterns   E 5-10 PATTERNS

1. The number box includes all of the prime numbers between 1 and 100. It also includes five numbers that are not prime. Cross out the numbers that are not prime numbers. Remember: A prime number is a number that is divisible only by itself and 1.

Number Box					
2	3	5	7	11	13
17	19	23	29	31	✕
37	41	43	47	✕	53
✕	59	61	67	71	73
79	✕	83	✕	89	97

First Prime Number Pattern

You can make any even number greater than 2 using two prime numbers. For example, 22 = 5 + 17.

Write each even number as the sum of two prime numbers.

For 2–9, sample answers have been given.

2. 30 = **13** + **17**

3. 56 = **19** + **37**

4. 18 = **5** + **13**

5. 44 = **15** + **29**

Second Prime Number Pattern

You can make any odd number greater than 5 using three prime numbers. For example, 9 = 3 + 3 + 3.

Write each odd number as the sum of three prime numbers.

6. 45 = **5** + **11** + **29**

7. 65 = **5** + **13** + **47**

8. 113 = **7** + **47** + **59**

9. 81 = **11** + **29** + **41**

Use with Lesson 5-10. **69**

Problem Solving

Name_____

Predicting Outcomes   PS 5-10

Gifts Every year the adults in the Anderson family draw names and they each buy a present for that one person. There are 10 adults in the family who participate in this drawing. There are 6 males and 4 females.

1. When drawing a name at random, how many possible outcomes are there?
   10 outcomes Sample answer:

2. Is it equally likely that a male name or a female name will be drawn?
   No, a male name is more likely.

3. Without looking, a woman draws a name out of a basket. What are her chances of drawing her own name?
   1 out of 10

4. What are her chances of drawing a name other than her own?
   9 out of 10

5. What are her chances of drawing the name of a male?
   6 out of 10

6. What are her chances of drawing the name of a female other than herself?
   3 out of 10

7. **Writing in Math** Rich says that because he is one of the men, he knows that he will draw another man's name. Does he have a better chance to draw a man's name than if a woman drew a name? Explain.
   Sample answer: No, he is not more likely to get a male name than anyone else. A male name is more likely to be drawn, but each person drawing has the same chance as every other person.

Use with Lesson 5-10. **69**

Listing Outcomes
P 5-11

The coach is trying to decide in what order Jane, Pete, and Lou will run a relay race.

1. Complete the tree diagram below to show the sample space.

1st	2nd	3rd

Jane < Pete — **Lou**
        Lou — **Pete**

Pete < Jane — Lou
           Lou — **Jane**

Lou < **Jane** — **Pete**
       Pete — **Jane**

2. How many possible outcomes are there in the sample space?   6

3. After the first runner is chosen, how many choices are there for the second runner?   2

Test Prep

4. Tom, Bill, John, and Ed are running for school president. The person in second place automatically becomes vice-president. How many possible outcomes are there in the sample space?

   A. 6   B. 9   C. 10   (D.) 12

5. **Writing in Math** Why are Tom, Bill, John, and Ed equally likely to win school president? Explain.

   There are 4 of them, so they each have a 1 out of 4 chance of winning.

Listing Outcomes
R 5-11

Almond, Keisha, and Mona are running for student council president. Barry, Andy, and Maurice are running for vice-president. Each student has an equal chance of being elected.

You can use a tree diagram to find all the possible outcomes. All of the possible outcomes is called the sample space.

President	Vice-President	Outcome
Almond	Barry	Almond, Barry
	Andy	Almond, Andy
	Maurice	Almond, Maurice
Keisha	Barry	Keisha, Barry
	Andy	Keisha, Andy
	Maurice	Keisha, Maurice
Mona	Barry	Mona, Barry
	Andy	Mona, Andy
	Maurice	Mona, Maurice

There are 9 possible outcomes in the sample space.

1. Complete the tree diagram to show the possible outcomes when Spinner A and Spinner B are spun.

Color	Color	Outcome

Black < **Red** — Black, Red
        Blue — **Black Blue**
        Green — **Black** Green

White < Red — **White Red**
        Blue — **White** Blue
        Green — **White Green**

Spinner A
Spinner B

2. How many times does the outcome black/green occur in the tree diagram?

   1 time

The Track Meet
E 5-11
DATA

The track meet has two groups of racers in the 100 m dash. The winner of each of the races will go on to the championship race. Shown are the contestants in each of the races.

Race 1	Race 3
Chris Collins	Karl Smith
Ted Smith	Bill Walters
Peter Jones	Mike Orly

1. Make a tree diagram to show the possibilities of who will make it to the final race.

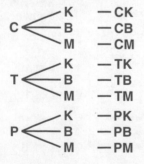

C < K — CK
    B — CB
    M — CM

T < K — TK
    B — TB
    M — TM

P < K — PK
    B — PB
    M — PM

2. What are the chances that one of the Smith boys will be in the final race?

   5 out of 9

3. What are the chances that Mike Orly will be in the final race?

   3 out of 9

Listing Outcomes
PS 5-11

A coin is tossed 4 times. The coin is equally likely to come up heads or tails.

1. Make a tree diagram to show the sample space.

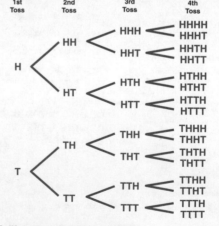

1st Toss	2nd Toss	3rd Toss	4th Toss

H < HH < HHH < HHHH / HHHT
         HHT < HHTH / HHTT
    HT < HTH < HTHH / HTHT
         HTT < HTTH / HTTT

T < TH < THH < THHH / THHT
         THT < THTH / THTT
    TT < TTH < TTHH / TTHT
         TTT < TTTH / TTTT

2. What are your chances of tossing 2 tails?

   6 out of 16

3. **Writing in Math** Melissa says her chances of tossing 3 heads are the same as her chances of tossing 1 tail. Is Melissa correct? Explain.

   Sample answer: Yes, she is correct. Whenever there are 3 heads, there must be 1 tail.

Practice

Name_____

Expressing Probability as a Fraction   P 5-12

Tom put 4 yellow marbles, 2 blue marbles, 6 red marbles,
and 5 black marbles in a bag.

1. Find the P(yellow). $\frac{4}{17}$

2. Find the P(blue). $\frac{2}{17}$

3. Find the P(red). $\frac{6}{17}$

4. Find the P(black). $\frac{5}{17}$

A bag contains 12 slips of paper of the same size. Each slip has
one number on it, 1–12.

5. Find the P(even number). $\frac{6}{12}$ or $\frac{1}{2}$

6. Find the P(a number less than 6). $\frac{5}{12}$

7. Find the P(an odd number). $\frac{6}{12}$ or $\frac{1}{2}$

8. Find the P(a number greater than 8). $\frac{4}{12}$ or $\frac{1}{3}$

9. Describe an impossible event.

You will pull out a number greater than 12.

Test Prep

10. A cube has 6 sides and is numbered 1 through 6. If the cube
is tossed, what is the probability that a 3 will be tossed?

    (A) $\frac{1}{6}$ B. $\frac{2}{6}$ C. $\frac{3}{6}$ D. $\frac{6}{6}$

11. Explain the probability of tossing a prime number when you
toss the cube with numbers 1 through 6.

    **Prime numbers would be 2, 3, and 5,
    so the probability would be $\frac{3}{6}$ or $\frac{1}{2}$.**

Use with Lesson 5-12. **71**

Reteaching

Name_____

Expressing Probability as a Fraction   R 5-12

The probability of an event is a number that describes the
chance that an event will occur. Probability can be expressed as
a fraction.

$$\text{Probability of an event} = \frac{\text{number of favorable outcomes}}{\text{number of possible outcomes}}$$

If Felice spins the spinner, what is the
probability of landing on Orange?

There are 6 possible outcomes (colors)
and 2 favorable outcomes (Orange).

$$\text{Probability (landing on Orange)} = \frac{\text{number of Orange}}{\text{number of colors}} = \frac{2}{6}$$

The probability of landing on Orange is $\frac{2}{6}$ or $\frac{1}{3}$.

The probability of landing on Orange can be written
as $P(\text{Orange}) = \frac{1}{3}$.

1. Find P(object that does not use
   electricity) $\frac{2}{6}$

2. Find P(object that uses electricity) $\frac{4}{6}$

3. Find P(object used for writing) $\frac{1}{6}$

Use with Lesson 5-12. **71**

Enrichment

Name_____

Make Your Own Games   E 5-12
REASONING

Design two games. One game must be fair and the other must
be unfair. Answer the questions below to describe your game.

Fair Game

1. What materials are used in the
   game? Number cubes,
   spinners, or marbles? Explain.

   1–8   Check students' answers.

2. What are the rules of the game?
   How many people play? How do
   players score points? What do
   players do on their turn?

3. How do you win the game?

4. What is the title of the game?

Unfair Game

5. What materials are used in the
   game? Number cubes, spinners,
   or marbles? Explain.

6. What are the rules of the game?
   How many people play? How do
   players score points? What do
   players do on their turn?

7. How do you win the game?

8. What is the title of the game?

Use with Lesson 5-12. **71**

Problem Solving

Name_____

Expressing Probability
as a Fraction   PS 5-12

Lucky Ones At a wedding shower, the bride-to-be has placed
a mark on the bottom of 3 paper plates. There are 27 guests,
and each has a paper plate. The guests who have a mark on
their plate get to choose a door prize.

1. Find P(having a marked plate) $\frac{3}{27}$, or $\frac{1}{9}$

2. Find P(not having a marked plate) $\frac{24}{27}$

Marbles In a bag, there are 15 blue marbles, 6 red marbles,
and 3 white marbles. Sammy draws 1 marble out of the bag.

3. Find P(drawing a red marble) $\frac{6}{24}$, or $\frac{1}{4}$

4. Find P(drawing a blue marble) $\frac{15}{24}$, or $\frac{5}{8}$

5. Find P(drawing a white marble) $\frac{3}{24}$, or $\frac{1}{8}$

6. Find P(not drawing a red marble) $\frac{18}{24}$, or $\frac{3}{4}$

7. **Writing in Math** How are the answers for Exercises 3 and
   6 related? Explain.

   **Sample answer: They are the opposite
   of each other. They add up to 1. All of
   the possible outcomes are covered by
   one of the two possibilities.**

Use with Lesson 5-12. **71**

Name_____

School Uniforms

School uniforms are becoming more popular at grade schools in the United States. A Kids USA Survey asked about 1,600 girls and 1,300 boys what their favorite colors were.

Favorite Uniform Colors for Girls (per 100 surveyed)

Color	Number of Girls
Blue	24
White	8
Red	7
Green	12
Yellow	3
Black	30
Other	16

1. Which color got the most votes? **Black**

   The least? **Yellow**

2. Which two colors were the closest in votes?

   White and red

3. Complete the bar graph for the data.

Favorite Uniform Color (per 100 surveyed)

4. Write the number of boys numbers for each color in increasing order.

   3, 7, 7, 13, 17, 22, 31

Favorite Uniform Colors for Boys (per 100 surveyed)

Color	Number of Boys
Blue	22
White	7
Red	7
Green	13
Yellow	3
Black	31
Other	17

5. What is the median? **13**

6. What is the mode? **7**

Name_____

Sports Data

Susan and Louise are the top scorers on their basketball teams. The graph to the right shows how many points each of them scored in their first three games of the season.

How many total points did Susan score in the first three games?

$20 + 25 + 15 = 60$

So, Susan scored 60 points total.

How many more points did Louise score than Susan in Game 3? 15 points

Points Scored in Basketball Games

The line graph at the right shows how many games the Strikers won from 1999 to 2003. Use it for questions 1–3.

1. During which season did the Strikers win 26 games?

   2000

2. How many fewer games did the Strikers win between the 2000 and 2001 seasons?

   The Strikers won 12 fewer games.

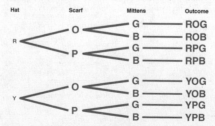

Games Won by the Strikers

3. Describe the trend that is shown in the graph.

   The data shows that the number of Striker victories has been decreasing each year.

Name_____

Circle the letter of the figure that is different from the others in the row.

1.

   a.   b.   c.   d.

2.

   a.   b.   c.   d.

3.

   a.   b.   c.   d.

4.

   a.   b.   c.   d.

Name_____

Winter Show

The cast members in the winter show wore black shirts and pants, but each was to wear a red or yellow hat, an orange or purple scarf, and green or blue mittens. How many different combinations are there?

Read and Understand

1. What are you trying to find?

   How many different combinations there are

Plan and Solve

2. Complete the tree diagram to find the number of combinations.

Hat	Scarf	Mittens	Outcome
R	O	G	ROG
		B	ROB
	P	G	RPG
		B	RPB
Y	O	G	YOG
		B	YOB
	P	G	YPG
		B	YPB

3. Solve the problem and write the answer in a complete sentence.

   There are 8 different combinations.

Look Back and Check

4. Explain why your answer makes sense.

   Sample answer: The tree diagram correctly shows all combinations.

© Pearson Education, Inc. 5

Name_____

Geometric Ideas

Sample answers given for 1–7.

P 6-1

Use the diagram at the right. Name the following.

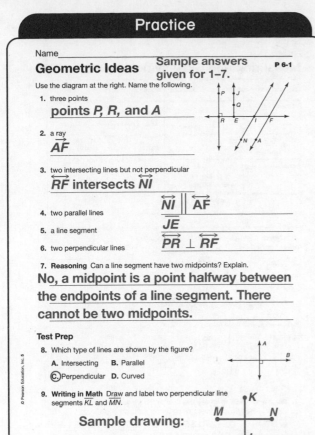

1. three points

points *P*, *R*, and *A*

2. a ray

$\overrightarrow{AF}$

3. two intersecting lines but not perpendicular

$\overleftrightarrow{RF}$ intersects $\overleftrightarrow{NI}$

4. two parallel lines

$\overleftrightarrow{NI} \parallel \overleftrightarrow{AF}$

5. a line segment

$\overline{JE}$

6. two perpendicular lines

$\overleftrightarrow{PR} \perp \overleftrightarrow{RF}$

7. **Reasoning** Can a line segment have two midpoints? Explain.

No, a midpoint is a point halfway between the endpoints of a line segment. There cannot be two midpoints.

Test Prep

8. Which type of lines are shown by the figure?

   A. Intersecting   B. Parallel
   C. Perpendicular   D. Curved

9. **Writing in Math** Draw and label two perpendicular line segments *KL* and *MN*.

Sample drawing:

Name_____

Geometric Ideas

R 6-1

Lines, line segments, and rays are basic geometric ideas. They are sometimes described by the relationship they have to other lines, line segments, and rays.

Draw	Write	Say	Description
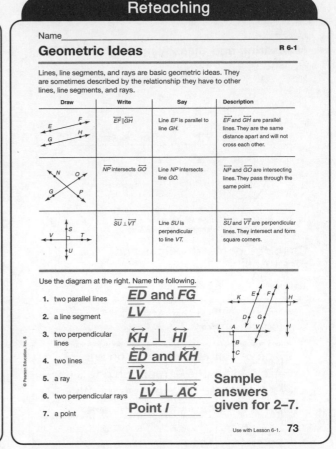	$\overleftrightarrow{EF} \parallel \overleftrightarrow{GH}$	Line *EF* is parallel to line *GH*.	$\overleftrightarrow{EF}$ and $\overleftrightarrow{GH}$ are parallel lines. They are the same distance apart and will not cross each other.
	$\overleftrightarrow{NP}$ intersects $\overleftrightarrow{GO}$	Line *NP* intersects line *GO*.	$\overleftrightarrow{NP}$ and $\overleftrightarrow{GO}$ are intersecting lines. They pass through the same point.
	$\overleftrightarrow{SU} \perp \overleftrightarrow{VT}$	Line *SU* is perpendicular to line *VT*.	$\overleftrightarrow{SU}$ and $\overleftrightarrow{VT}$ are perpendicular lines. They intersect and form square corners.

Use the diagram at the right. Name the following.

1. two parallel lines

$\overleftrightarrow{ED}$ and $\overleftrightarrow{FG}$

2. a line segment

$\overline{LV}$

3. two perpendicular lines

$\overleftrightarrow{KH} \perp \overleftrightarrow{HI}$

4. two lines

$\overleftrightarrow{ED}$ and $\overleftrightarrow{KH}$

5. a ray

$\overrightarrow{LV}$

6. two perpendicular rays

$\overrightarrow{LV} \perp \overrightarrow{AC}$

7. a point

Point *I*

Sample answers given for 2–7.

Name_____

The Streets Have No Names!

E 6-1
VISUAL THINKING

Label the map below by reading the clues that follow.

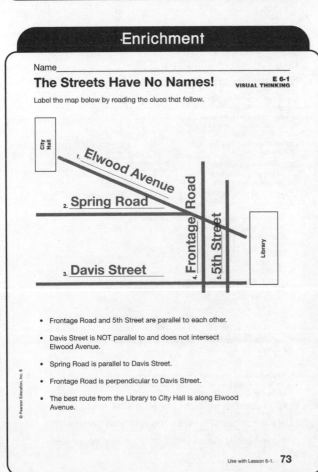

- Frontage Road and 5th Street are parallel to each other.
- Davis Street is NOT parallel to and does not intersect Elwood Avenue.
- Spring Road is parallel to Davis Street.
- Frontage Road is perpendicular to Davis Street.
- The best route from the Library to City Hall is along Elwood Avenue.

Name_____

Geometric Ideas

PS 6-1

Spider Webs The intricate web of a spider is a good example of several geometric concepts. Most spiders begin a web by spinning 3 strands in the shape of a Y. The spider continues to add new strands and then connects them in a circular pattern until it can easily step from one strand onto another.

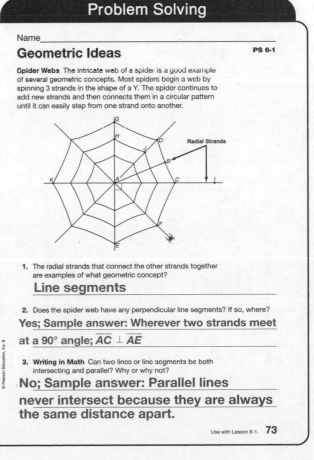

1. The radial strands that connect the other strands together are examples of what geometric concept?

Line segments

2. Does the spider web have any perpendicular line segments? If so, where?

Yes; Sample answer: Wherever two strands meet at a 90° angle; $\overline{AC} \perp \overline{AE}$

3. **Writing in Math** Can two lines or line segments be both intersecting and parallel? Why or why not?

No; Sample answer: Parallel lines never intersect because they are always the same distance apart.

© Pearson Education, Inc. 5

Name_____

Measuring and Classifying Angles

P 6-2

Classify each angle as *acute, right, obtuse,* or *straight.* Then measure each angle. (Hint: Draw longer sides if necessary.)

1. **Right angle; 90°**

2. **Acute angle; 30°**

Draw an angle with each measure.

3. 120°

4. 180°

5. Draw an acute angle. Label it with the letters
   A, B, and *C.* What is the measure of the angle? _____

Check students' drawings and measures.

Test Prep

6. Which kind of angle is shown in the figure below?
   A. Acute   (B) Obtuse
   C. Right   D. Straight

7. **Writing in Math** Explain how to use a protractor to measure an angle.
   Place center of protractor on angle's vertex. Place the 0° mark on one side of angle. Read measure where other side of angle crosses protractor.

74 Use with Lesson 6-2.

Name_____

Measuring and Classifying Angles

R 6-2

The chart below can help you to describe and identify an angle.

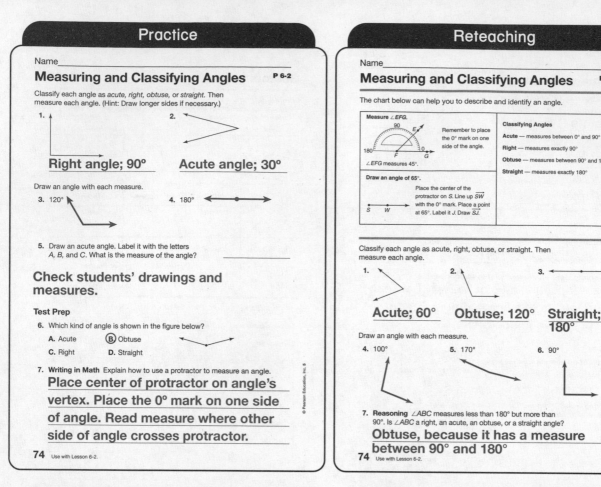

Measure ∠EFG.

Remember to place the 0° mark on one side of the angle.

∠EFG measures 45°.

Draw an angle of 65°.

Place the center of the protractor on S. Line up $\overrightarrow{SW}$ with the 0° mark. Place a point at 65°. Label it J. Draw $\overline{SJ}$.

Classifying Angles

Acute — measures between 0° and 90°

Right — measures exactly 90°

Obtuse — measures between 90° and 180°

Straight — measures exactly 180°

Classify each angle as acute, right, obtuse, or straight. Then measure each angle.

1. **Acute; 60°**

2. **Obtuse; 120°**

3. **Straight; 180°**

Draw an angle with each measure.

4. 100°

5. 170°

6. 90°

7. **Reasoning** ∠ABC measures less than 180° but more than 90°. Is ∠ABC a right, an acute, an obtuse, or a straight angle?
   Obtuse, because it has a measure between 90° and 180°

74 Use with Lesson 6-2.

Name_____

Designing Designs

E 6-2
VISUAL THINKING

1. In the space below, draw a design that is made up of the following.

   • 4 acute angles
   • 4 right angles
   • 4 obtuse angles
   • 4 straight angles

Sample answer:

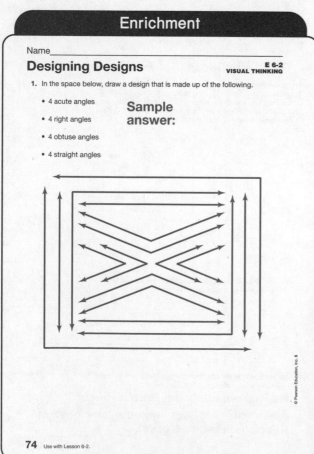

74 Use with Lesson 6-2.

Name_____

Measuring and Classifying Angles

PS 6-2

Roofs Roof designs for houses depend on the weather conditions of an area. A house that is built in an area with heavy snowfall and other extreme weather conditions should have a steep roof.

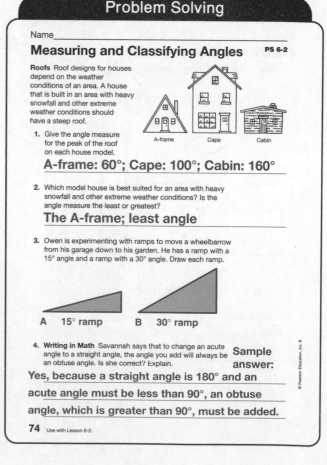

A-frame   Cape   Cabin

1. Give the angle measure for the peak of the roof on each house model.
   A-frame: 60°; Cape: 100°; Cabin: 160°

2. Which model house is best suited for an area with heavy snowfall and other extreme weather conditions? Is the angle measure the least or greatest?
   The A-frame; least angle

3. Owen is experimenting with ramps to move a wheelbarrow from his garage down to his garden. He has a ramp with a 15° angle and a ramp with a 30° angle. Draw each ramp.

   A 15° ramp   B 30° ramp

4. **Writing in Math** Savannah says that to change an acute angle to a straight angle, the angle you add will always be an obtuse angle. Is she correct? Explain.

   Sample answer:
   Yes, because a straight angle is 180° and an acute angle must be less than 90°, an obtuse angle, which is greater than 90°, must be added.

74 Use with Lesson 6-2.

Name_____

Segments and Angles Related to Circles

P 6-3

Identify each figure in circle D.

1. ∠NDI   **Central angle**
2. $\overline{LE}$ **Chord**
3. $\overline{DI}$ **Radius**
4. $\overline{AN}$ **Diameter**
5. point D   **Center of circle**
6. $\overline{DA}$ **Radius**

7. **Reasoning** Is the radius of a circle half of the diameter? Explain.
   Yes; $\overline{ND}$ and $\overline{DA}$ make up $\overline{NA}$.

8. Construct a circle that has a radius with an equal length to the given line segment.

Test Prep

9. A line segment that connects two points on a circle passing through the center is called a
   A. Radius   **B.** Diameter   C. Chord   D. Central angle

10. **Writing in Math** Brenda thinks that a chord can be many different lengths on a given circle. Is she right? Explain your thinking.
    Brenda is right. A chord can be any length connecting two points on a circle.

Use with Lesson 6-3. **75**

Name_____

Segments and Angles Related to Circles

R 6-3

All the points on a **circle** are the same distance from the center. The center of circle C is at point C.

A **radius** goes from the center to any point on the circle. $\overline{RS}$ is a radius of circle R. (plural: radii)

A **chord** has both endpoints on a circle. $\overline{HD}$ is a chord of circle O.

A **diameter** passes through the center of a circle. $\overline{DR}$ is a diameter of circle M. A diameter of a circle is also the longest chord of that circle. A circle's diameter is twice as long as its radius.

A **central angle** is an angle whose vertex is the center. ∠ACB is a central angle.

Use the terms at the top of this page to identify each figure in circle F.

1. point F   **Center**
2. ∠GFS   **Central angle**
3. $\overline{RS}$ **Diameter**
4. $\overline{UV}$ **Chord**
5. $\overline{GI}$ **Radius**

6. **Reasoning** If a circle has a radius of 12 in., what is the circle's diameter?   **24 in.**

Use with Lesson 6-3. **75**

Name_____

Chord Patterns

E 6-3
VISUAL THINKING

A *chord* is a segment whose end points are on a circle.

The same number of chords can be drawn differently to make different numbers of regions.

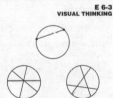

6 regions   7 regions

1. Draw chords in the circles below to help you complete the table.

Number of chords to be drawn	One	Two	Three	Four
Circle				
Greatest number of regions possible	2	4	7	11

What is the difference between the greatest number of regions for

2. one chord and two chords?   **2**
3. two chords and three chords?   **3**
4. three chords and four chords?   **4**

5. How does the number of regions increase when another chord is added to the circle?
   The number of regions increases by the next counting number after the previous increase.

Use with Lesson 6-3. **75**

Name_____

Segments and Angles Related to Circles

PS 6-3

Hubcaps Decorative hubcaps add an element of design to any vehicle. Use the hubcap at the right to identify the parts of a circle.

1. What is one line segment that is a chord?
   AC, AD, or CD

2. The radius of the hubcap is 7.5 in. What is its diameter?
   15 in.

3. Part of the design of the hubcap is the circle divided into three equal angles. What is the angle measure of ∠ABD?   **120°**

4. A flowerpot has a diameter of 8 in. What is its radius?   **4 in.**

5. If a second flowerpot has a radius that is 2 in. greater, what is its diameter?   **12 in.**

6. **Writing in Math** If a circle is divided into 5 sections by 5 radii, and each of the central angles formed are of equal measure, what is the measure of each central angle? Explain how you know.
   Sample answer: The central angles will be 72°. In a circle, the central angles always add up to 360°, so if there are 5 angles that are all equal, I divide 360 by 5 to find the answer.

Use with Lesson 6-3. **75**

© Pearson Education, Inc. 5

Name_____

Polygons

P 6-4

Name each polygon. Then tell if it appears to be a regular polygon.

1.

Octagon;
regular

2.

Quadrilateral;
not regular

3. Name the polygon. Name the vertices.

Quadrilateral;
B, E, H, T

Test Prep

4. Which polygon has eight sides?

A. Quadrilateral   B. Pentagon   C. Hexagon   **D.** Octagon

5. **Writing in Math** Draw two regular polygons and two that are irregular. Use geometric terms to describe one characteristic of each type.

Sample answer: The regular polygons
have congruent sides and the irregular
polygons have different angle measures.

76 Use with Lesson 6–4.

Name_____

Polygons

R 6-4

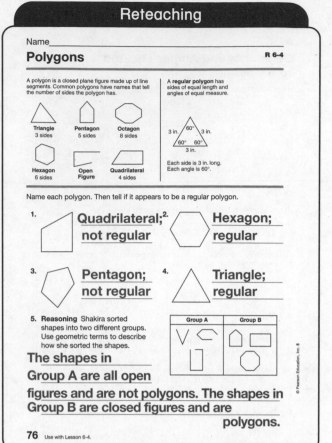

A polygon is a closed plane figure made up of line segments. Common polygons have names that tell the number of sides the polygon has.

A **regular polygon** has sides of equal length and angles of equal measure.

Triangle — 3 sides
Pentagon — 5 sides
Octagon — 8 sides
Hexagon — 6 sides
Open Figure
Quadrilateral — 4 sides

Each side is 3 in. long.
Each angle is 60°.

Name each polygon. Then tell if it appears to be a regular polygon.

1. **Quadrilateral;**
   not regular

2. **Hexagon;**
   regular

3. **Pentagon;**
   not regular

4. **Triangle;**
   regular

5. **Reasoning** Shakira sorted shapes into two different groups. Use geometric terms to describe how she sorted the shapes.

Group A	Group B

The shapes in
Group A are all open
figures and are not polygons. The shapes in
Group B are closed figures and are
polygons.

76 Use with Lesson 6–4.

Name_____

Can You Match This?

E 6-4
PATTERNS

Study the polygon on the left. Then circle the letter of the polygon on the right that has the same name.

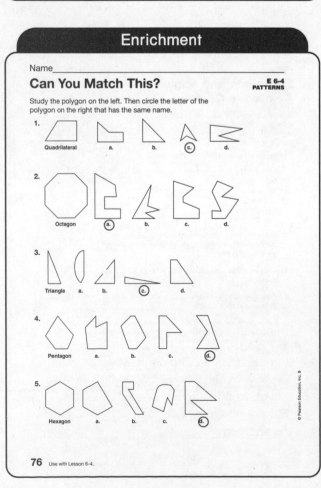

1. Quadrilateral   a.   b.   (c.)   d.

2. Octagon   (a.)   b.   c.   d.

3. Triangle   a.   b.   (c.)   d.

4. Pentagon   a.   b.   c.   (d.)

5. Hexagon   a.   b.   c.   (d.)

76 Use with Lesson 6–4.

Name_____

Polygons

PS 6-4

Building Blocks A child's building-block set has blocks of all shapes and sizes, but they are all the same thickness. Below are the faces of a few of the blocks.

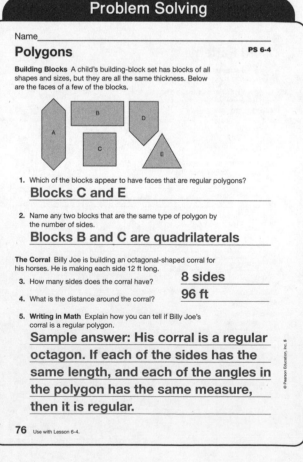

1. Which of the blocks appear to have faces that are regular polygons?

   Blocks C and E

2. Name any two blocks that are the same type of polygon by the number of sides.

   Blocks B and C are quadrilaterals

The Corral Billy Joe is building an octagonal-shaped corral for his horses. He is making each side 12 ft long.

3. How many sides does the corral have?   **8 sides**

4. What is the distance around the corral?   **96 ft**

5. **Writing in Math** Explain how you can tell if Billy Joe's corral is a regular polygon.

   Sample answer: His corral is a regular
   octagon. If each of the sides has the
   same length, and each of the angles in
   the polygon has the same measure,
   then it is regular.

76 Use with Lesson 6–4.

Classifying Triangles

Name_____

Classify each triangle by its sides and then by its angles.

1.

Scalene triangle; right triangle

2.

Equilateral triangle; acute triangle

The measures of two angles of a triangle are given. Find the measure of the third angle.

3. 47°, 62°, **71°**

4. 29°, 90°, **61°**

5. 75°, 75°, **30°**

6. 54°, 36°, **90°**

7. Judy bought a new tent for a camping trip. Look at the side of the tent with the opening to classify the triangle by its sides and its angles.

Isosceles triangle; acute triangle

Test Prep

8. Which describes a scalene triangle?

A. 4 equal sides   B. 3 equal sides   C. 2 equal sides   **D.** 0 equal sides

9. **Writing in Math** The lengths of two sides of a triangle are 15 in. each. The third side measures 10 in. What type of triangle is this? Explain your answer using geometric terms.

It is an isosceles triangle because two of the sides are the same length.

Classifying Triangles

Name_____

You can classify triangles by the lengths of their sides and the sizes of their angles.

acute all angles less than 90°

equilateral all sides the same length

This triangle is both equilateral and acute.

Not all acute triangles are equilateral.

right one right angle

isosceles two sides the same length

This triangle is both isosceles and right.

Not all right triangles are isosceles.

obtuse one obtuse angle

scalene no sides the same length

This triangle is both scalene and obtuse.

Not all obtuse triangles are scalene.

Remember that the sum of the measures of the angles of a triangle is 180°.

Classify each triangle by its sides and then by its angles.

1.   **Isosceles; obtuse**

2. **Equilateral; acute**

3. **Scalene; right**

The measures of two angles of a triangle are given. Find the measure of the third angle.

4. 40°, 100°, **40°**

5. 14°, 98°, **68°**

6. 38°, 38°, **104°**

Can You Draw Me?

Name_____

Is it possible to draw the triangles described? Answer by writing *possible* or *impossible*.

1. An equilateral triangle with sides measuring 8 cm, 9 cm, and 10 cm

Impossible

2. A scalene triangle with sides measuring 7 in., 7 in., and 8 in.

Impossible

3. An acute triangle with angles measuring 60°, 62°, and 58°

Possible

4. An obtuse triangle with angles measuring 45°, 89°, and 46°

Impossible

5. An isosceles triangle with sides measuring 16 ft, 20 ft, and 22 ft.

Impossible

6. A right triangle with angles measuring 35°, 78°, and 67°

Impossible

7. An isosceles, right triangle with angles measuring 45°, 90°, and 45°, and with sides measuring 5 cm, 6 cm, and 5 cm

Impossible

8. An obtuse, right triangle

Impossible

9. An obtuse, scalene triangle

Possible

Classifying Triangles

Name_____

A patchwork design for quilts is made up of triangles of different shapes, sizes, and colors.

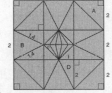

1. Classify triangle A by its sides and angles.

Isosceles triangle, right angle

2. Classify triangle B by its sides and angles.

Isosceles triangle, acute angle

3. Classify triangle C by its sides and angles.

Scalene triangle, obtuse angle

4. Classify triangle D by its sides and angles.

Scalene triangle, right angle

5. Jacob took three sticks that were each 7 in. long. He formed a triangle with the sticks, with the tips of each stick touching another. What is the measure of each of the angles?

60°

6. **Writing in Math** Mindy says that if a triangle has two angles that are both 42°, the triangle is an acute triangle. Is she right? Explain your answer.

Sample answer:

No, the triangle is obtuse. The sum of the angles must be 180°. If two of the angles total 84°, then the other must be 96°. An obtuse triangle has one angle that is more than 90°.

Name_____

Classifying Quadrilaterals
P 6-6

Classify each quadrilateral. Be as specific as possible.

1.

__Trapezoid__

2.
15 cm
8 cm   8 cm
15 cm

__Rectangle__

3.
8 in.
4 in.   4 in.
8 in.

__Parallelogram__

4.
17 cm
17 cm   17 cm
17 cm

__Rhombus__

The measures of three angles of a quadrilateral are given. Find
the measure of the fourth angle.

5. 90°, 145°, 78°, __47°__

6. 110°, 54°, 100°, __96°__

7. Name the vertices of the square.

__F, G, A, L__

F   G

L   A

Test Prep

8. Three of the angles of a quadrilateral measure 80°, 100°,
and 55°. Which is the measure of the fourth angle?

A. 115°   B. 120°   C. 125°   D. 130°

9. Writing in Math Can a trapezoid have four obtuse angles? Explain.

**Sample answer: The figure would not
be able to close the fourth side if all of
the angles were obtuse.**

78 Use with Lesson 6-6.

© Pearson Education, Inc. 5

Name_____

Classifying Quadrilaterals
R 6-6

Quadrilateral	Definition	Example
Parallelogram	A quadrilateral with both pairs of opposite sides parallel and equal in length	5 in. / 2 in. 2 in. / 5 in.
Rectangle	A parallelogram with four right angles	5 ft / 2 ft 2 ft / 5 ft
Rhombus	A parallelogram with all sides the same length	4 in. / 4 in. 4 in. / 4 in.
Square	A rectangle with all sides the same length	1 ft / 1 ft 1 ft / 1 ft
Trapezoid	A quadrilateral with only one pair of parallel sides	2 in. 3 in. / 6 in.

Remember that the sum of the measures of the
angles of a quadrilateral is 360°.

Classify each quadrilateral. Be as specific as possible.

1.
6 ft
3 ft   3 ft
6 ft

__Rectangle__

2.
4 in.
4 in.   4 in.
4 in.

__Rhombus__

3.
7 ft
3 ft   9 ft
6 ft

__Trapezoid__

The measures of three angles of a quadrilateral are given.
Find the measure of the fourth angle.

4. 65°, 150°, 89°, __56°__

5. 100°, 80°, 100°, __80°__

6. 82°, 78°, 90°, __110°__

78 Use with Lesson 6-6.

© Pearson Education, Inc. 5

Name_____

Use Your Logic
E 6-6
REASONABLENESS

In the exercises below, use your knowledge of quadrilaterals to
determine if the statements presented are true or false. Explain
your answers.

1. A square can be a rhombus, and Figure X is a rhombus, so
Figure X must be a square.

**Sample answer: Not true; Figure X is a
rhombus but not necessarily a square. A
rhombus is a parallelogram with sides of
equal length. The internal angles are not
specified, so it is not necessarily a square.**

2. Figure U is a rhombus, and all rhombuses are parallelograms;
therefore, Figure U must be a parallelogram.

**Sample answer: True; Because all
rhombuses are parallelograms with
sides of equal length, and Figure U is a
rhombus, it must also be a parallelogram.**

3. A quadrilateral is the term for any four-sided polygon, and
Figure C is a trapezoid; therefore, Figure C is a quadrilateral.

**Sample answer: True; Because Figure C
is a trapezoid, and a trapezoid is a four-
sided polygon with only one pair of
parallel lines, and a quadrilateral is any
four-sided polygon, Figure C must also be
a quadrilateral.**

78 Use with Lesson 6-6.

© Pearson Education, Inc. 5

Name_____

Classifying Quadrilaterals
PS 6-6

Shapes As part of the real world, there are many things that
could be identified as quadrilaterals. Their angles and sides
determine what type of quadrilateral they are. For each
quadrilateral shown or described, tell the geometric name.

1. The shape of the necklace is what type
of quadrilateral?

**Rhombus or
parallelogram**

2. The shape of the shaded part of the frame of
the doorway is what type of quadrilateral?

Trapezoid

3. The shape of the baseball diamond is
what type of quadrilateral?

Square

4. Writing in Math The qualities of a square match the
definition of two types of parallelograms. Name both and
explain the characteristics for each definition.

**Sample answer: Rectangle: A square
has 2 pairs of parallel sides and 4 right
angles. Rhombus: A square is a
parallelogram with 4 equal sides.**

78 Use with Lesson 6-6.

© Pearson Education, Inc. 5

Name_____

PROBLEM-SOLVING STRATEGY   P 6-7
Solve a Simpler Problem

Solve the simpler problems. Use the solutions to
help you solve the original problem.

1. Reggie is designing a triangular magazine rack with
5 shelves. The top shelf will hold 1 magazine. The
second shelf will hold 3 magazines, and the third
shelf will hold 5 magazines. This pattern continues
to the bottom shelf. How many magazines will the
magazine rack hold altogether?

Simpler Problem What is the pattern?

Each shelf down holds 2 more
magazines than the shelf above.

How many magazines will the fourth   **7 magazines**
shelf hold?

How many magazines will the bottom   **9 magazines**
shelf hold?

Solution: **The magazine rack will hold 25**
magazines.

2. At the deli, you receive 1 free sub after you buy 8 subs.
How many free subs will you receive from the deli if you
buy 24 subs?

3 subs

3. The chef has 5 different kinds of pasta and 3 different flavors
of sauce. How many different meals is she able to make?

15 different meals

Name_____

PROBLEM-SOLVING STRATEGY   R 6-7
Solve a Simpler Problem

Give Away During a grand opening, a mall provides prizes for
the first 70 customers. The 1st customer receives a coupon
book, the 2nd customer, a travel mug, and the 3rd customer, a
T-shirt. If the prizes continue to be given away in the same
pattern, which prize would the 70th customer receive?

| Read and Understand |

Step 1: What do you know?

There are 3 different prizes given away in a pattern.

Step 2: What are you trying to find?

Which gift the 70th customer will receive

| Plan and Solve |

Step 3: What strategy will you use?

Strategy: Solve a simpler problem

I can divide 69 by 3. I know the
69th customer will receive the
3rd prize. The 70th customer
will receive the coupon book.

| Look Back and Check |

Is your work correct?

Yes, 69 can be divided by 3 evenly to find the 3rd prize. The 70th customer would
be next for the 1st prize.

Solve the simpler problem. Use the solution to help you solve
the original problem.

1. Anna can choose from white or yellow paper. She can
choose from thin or wide paintbrushes. She can choose
from green, purple, or blue paint. How many different
combinations of art supplies are possible?

Simpler problem: Use letters to show
art supplies in an organized list;
There are 12 different combinations.

Name_____

Minimum Wage   E 6-7
                              MENTAL MATH

In 2002, the United States required employers to pay a
minimum wage of $5.15 for an hour of work. Use this figure to
complete the exercises below. In each exercise, solve a simpler
problem to get your solution. Show your work.

1. How much money would a worker earn in a 40 hr week?

Sample answer: 10 × 5.15 = 51.50. 4 ×
51.50 = 206. The worker earns $206.00
in a 40 hr week.

2. Suppose the minimum wage was to increase by $0.50
every 5 years. What would the minimum wage be 50 years
from now?

Sample answer: 50 years divided by 5 is
10, so 10 pay raises will occur in 50 years.
10 × $0.50 = 5, and 5 + $5.15 = $10.15. In
50 years, the minimum wage would be
$10.15.

3. Suppose a factory pays 100 workers $22,000 for each
40 hr week they operate. How much more than minimum
wage does each worker earn per hour?

Sample answer: $\frac{22,000}{100}$ = 220, so each
worker earns $220 per week. $\frac{220}{40}$ = 5.5,
so each worker earns $5.50 per hour.
$5.50 − $5.15 = $0.35, so each worker
earns $0.35 more than minimum wage
per hour.

Name_____

PROBLEM-SOLVING STRATEGY   PS 6-7
Solve a Simpler Problem

School Work Margaret's older brother has given her a problem
that he is sure will stump her. He wants to know the sum of the
angles of a 32-sided regular polygon. Margaret knows that a
triangle has 180°, a quadrilateral has 360° and can be divided
into 2 triangles, and a pentagon can be divided into 3 triangles.
What is the answer to her brother's problem?

| Read and Understand |

1. What are you trying to find?   **Sample answer:**
The sum of the angles of a 32-sided figure

| Plan and Solve |

2. Complete the table.

Sides in a Polygon	3	4	5	6	7	8	. . .	32
Number of Triangles	1	2	3	**4**	**5**	**6**	. . .	**30**
Sum of Angles	180°	360°	540°	720°	900°	1,080°	. . .	5,400°

3. Solve the simpler problem by seeing a pattern and
completing a calculation.

Sample answer: The number of triangles is equal
to the number of sides minus 2. Then multiply by
180° in each triangle.

4. Use the answers to the simpler problem to solve the original problem.

Sample answer: 30 triangles × 180° = 5,400°

| Look Back and Check |

5. Is your work correct? Explain how you checked your answer.

Sample answer: Yes. I checked my
figures using a calculator.

© Pearson Education, Inc. 5

Name_____

PROBLEM-SOLVING SKILL   P 6-8
Writing to Describe

Solve each problem. You may use a brainstorming table to help
plan your description.

1. Use geometric terms to describe three properties of a square.

   A square is a parallelogram. It has
   four equal sides. Every angle in a
   square measures 90°.

2. Use mathematical terms to describe
   the numbers in each set.

   Set C: odd numbers;
   Set D: even numbers

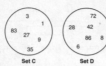

Set C   Set D

3. Mariam created two patterns. Use mathematical terms to
   describe the numbers in each pattern.

   Pattern 1: 12, 16, 20, 24, 28, 32

   Pattern 2: 1, 2, 4, 8, 16, 32, 64

   Pattern 1: increases by 4; Pattern 2:
   doubles

4. Use geometric terms to describe three
   properties of this trapezoid.

   A trapezoid is a
   quadrilateral. It has
   one pair of parallel sides. Two of the
   angles are acute and two are obtuse.

Name_____

PROBLEM-SOLVING SKILL   R 6-8
Writing to Describe

Use geometric terms to describe one characteristic of the lines in each group.

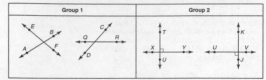

| Group 1 | Group 2 |

You can brainstorm to help you describe the characteristics.

Group 1   Group 2
no right angles   all right angles
not parallel   not parallel
all intersecting   all intersecting
no perpendicular lines   all perpendicular lines

When you write your description, use mathematical terms
correctly and be brief.

   All of the lines in Group 1 are intersecting and not perpendicular.

   All of the lines in Group 2 are intersecting and are perpendicular.

1. Abdul sorted the polygons to the right
   into two groups. Use geometric terms to
   describe a characteristic in each group.

   | Group A | Group B |

   All of the shapes in
   Group A have an
   obtuse angle. All of the shapes in Group B
   have acute angles.

Name_____

Shaping Up   E 6-8
                                                  REASONING

Read each description. Then draw the sets of shapes that are
being described.

1. Group A

   There are 4 shapes in Group A.
   All of the shapes have
   between 3 and 5 sides and are
   not regular. Inside each shape
   there is one acute angle.

   Group A
   Sample answer:

2. Group B

   There are 3 shapes in Group B. All
   of the shapes have between 6 and
   9 sides. There is a regular polygon
   inside of each shape.

   Group B
   Sample answer:

Name_____

PROBLEM-SOLVING SKILL   PS 6-8
Writing to Describe

Birdbath Nancy asked her family
to buy her a birdbath. There were
two similar birdbaths at the store,
so she needs to describe it very
carefully. Use geometric terms to
describe the birdbath that Nancy
wants to buy.

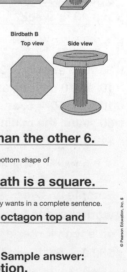

Birdbath A   Nancy likes this one.
Top view   Side view

Birdbath B
Top view   Side view

Read and Understand

1. What are you trying to describe?

   The birdbath using
   geometric terms

Plan and Solve

2. What is a geometric characteristic of
   the top shape of the birdbath that
   Nancy wants?

   The top has 8 sides;
   2 are equal but longer than the other 6.

3. What is a geometric characteristic of the bottom shape of
   the birdbath that Nancy wants?

   The bottom of the birdbath is a square.

4. Write the description of the birdbath Nancy wants in a complete sentence.

   The birdbath has an irregular octagon top and
   stands on a square base.

Look Back and Check

5. Explain how you can check your answer. **Sample answer:**
   I checked my description.

Practice

Do the figures in each pair appear to be similar? If so, are they also congruent?

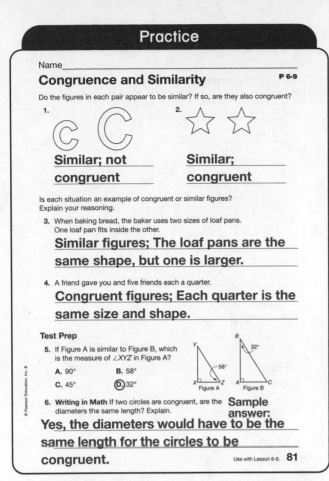

1. **Similar; not congruent**

2. **Similar; congruent**

Is each situation an example of congruent or similar figures? Explain your reasoning.

3. When baking bread, the baker uses two sizes of loaf pans. One loaf pan fits inside the other.

Similar figures; The loaf pans are the same shape, but one is larger.

4. A friend gave you and five friends each a quarter.

Congruent figures; Each quarter is the same size and shape.

Test Prep

5. If Figure A is similar to Figure B, which is the measure of ∠XYZ in Figure A?

   A. 90°   B. 58°

   C. 45°   D. 32°

6. **Writing in Math** If two circles are congruent, are the diameters the same length? Explain.

   Sample answer: Yes, the diameters would have to be the same length for the circles to be congruent.

Reteaching

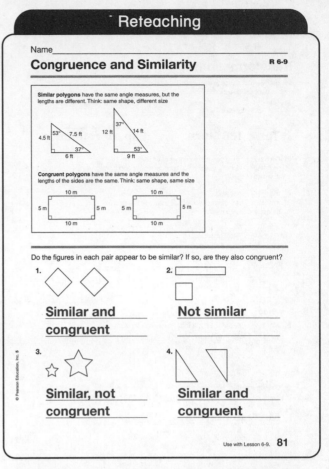

Similar polygons have the same angle measures, but the lengths are different. Think: same shape, different size

Congruent polygons have the same angle measures and the lengths of the sides are the same. Think: same shape, same size

Do the figures in each pair appear to be similar? If so, are they also congruent?

1. **Similar and congruent**

2. **Not similar**

3. **Similar, not congruent**

4. **Similar and congruent**

Enrichment

Complete the sentences below by writing in the letters of the shapes on the blank lines. Each letter may only be used once.

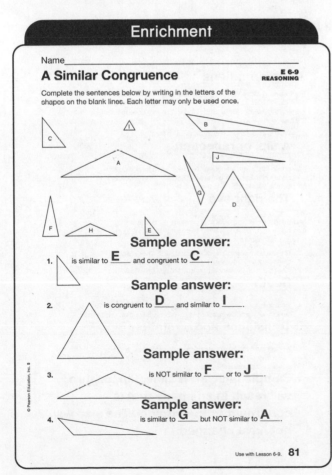

Sample answer:

1. ____ is similar to **E** and congruent to **C**.

Sample answer:

2. ____ is congruent to **D** and similar to **I**.

Sample answer:

3. ____ is NOT similar to **F** or to **J**.

Sample answer:

4. ____ is similar to **G** but NOT similar to **A**.

Problem Solving

Binoculars A pair of binoculars has a magnification of 6 times the actual viewing size.

1. Will the item viewed through the binoculars be congruent to the item viewed with the naked eye?

   No

2. Will it be similar?

   Yes

3. If an object is actually an inch and a half tall, how tall should the image appear to be when you look through the binoculars?

   9 in.

Flags American flags are made in many sizes for ceremonies and everyday display. Two of the most commonly sold sizes are shown.

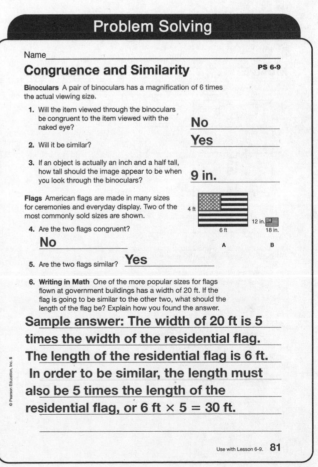

4. Are the two flags congruent?

   No

5. Are the two flags similar? **Yes**

6. **Writing in Math** One of the more popular sizes for flags flown at government buildings has a width of 20 ft. If the flag is going to be similar to the other two, what should the length of the flag be? Explain how you found the answer.

   Sample answer: The width of 20 ft is 5 times the width of the residential flag. The length of the residential flag is 6 ft. In order to be similar, the length must also be 5 times the length of the residential flag, or 6 ft × 5 = 30 ft.

Transformations

Tell whether the figures in each pair are related by a flip, slide, or turn. If a turn, describe it.

1.

Turn; 180° turn

2.

Flip, or reflection

3. On a compass, if you are standing at 0° and you turn to your right to make a 90° turn, what fraction of a turn is that?

$\frac{1}{4}$ **turn**

4. If a figure is flipped over the dashed line and then rotated a $\frac{1}{4}$ turn counterclockwise, which of the figures below shows the result?

Ⓐ   B.   C.   D.

Test Prep

5. Which term describes the mirror image of a figure?

A. Slide   Ⓑ Flip   C. Turn   D. Pattern

6. **Writing in Math** Mark says that the figure above was flipped. Faith says that it made a $\frac{3}{4}$ turn. Steven says that it made a 90° turn. Who is correct?

Mark is correct.

Transformations

The size and shape of a figure do not change when it is slid, flipped, or turned.

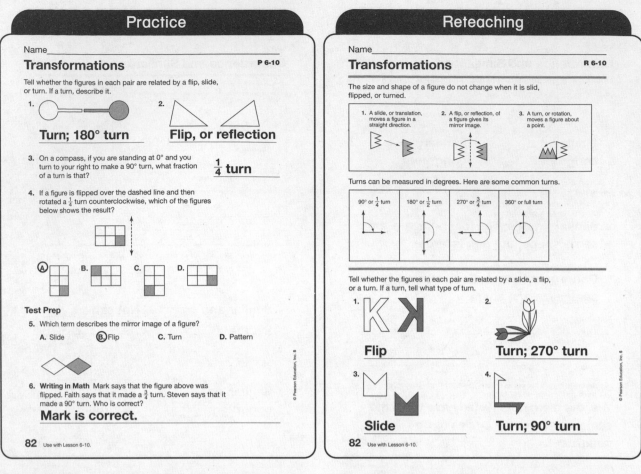

1. A slide, or translation, moves a figure in a straight direction.

2. A flip, or reflection, of a figure gives its mirror image.

3. A turn, or rotation, moves a figure about a point.

Turns can be measured in degrees. Here are some common turns.

90° or $\frac{1}{4}$ turn	180° or $\frac{1}{2}$ turn	270° or $\frac{3}{4}$ turn	360° or full turn

Tell whether the figures in each pair are related by a slide, a flip, or a turn. If a turn, tell what type of turn.

1.

Flip

2.

Turn; 270° turn

3.

Slide

4.

Turn; 90° turn

Move E!

Follow the directions below in order to move the letter E within the grid below.

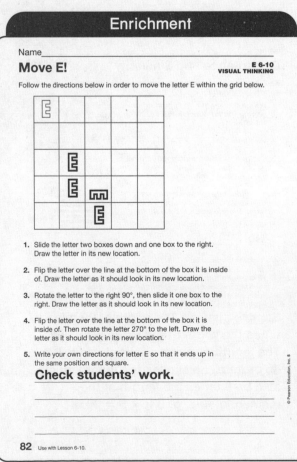

1. Slide the letter two boxes down and one box to the right. Draw the letter in its new location.

2. Flip the letter over the line at the bottom of the box it is inside of. Draw the letter as it should look in its new location.

3. Rotate the letter to the right 90°, then slide it one box to the right. Draw the letter as it should look in its new location.

4. Flip the letter over the line at the bottom of the box it is inside of. Then rotate the letter 270° to the left. Draw the letter as it should look in its new location.

5. Write your own directions for letter E so that it ends up in the same position and square.

Check students' work.

_____

_____

_____

Transformations

Photography Susan is learning photography and has made a mistake. When she developed her film, she printed the image with the film upside down, which caused the print to be made in the back of the negative.

1. What type of transformation is Susan's print?

A flip, or reflection

2. Susan had taken a photo of Jim, who had a freckle under his left eye. Because of Susan's mistake, under which eye did the freckle appear in the photo?

The right eye

Marching In marching drills the command right-face is a 90° turn to the right, left-face is a 90° turn to the left, and about-face is a 180° turn to the right.

3. The drill team enters a stadium facing north. They are given the commands left-face, about-face, and right-face as they march. What direction will they be facing at the end of the drill?

South

4. Since the team has been marching straight ahead as well as turning, what transformations will have occurred to their formation?

Translation and a rotation

5. **Writing in Math** When a transformation of a slide, a flip, or a turn is performed, is the resulting image congruent or similar to the original? Explain.

Sample answer: A slide, flip, or turn will result in an image that is congruent to the original. The size will not have changed.

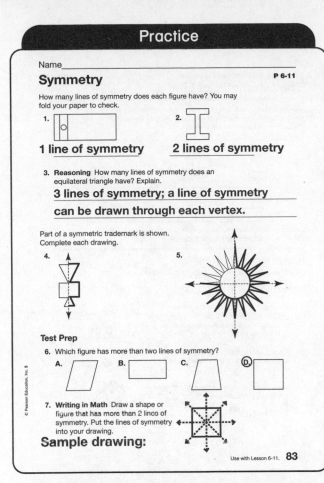

Practice

Name_____

Symmetry

P 6-11

How many lines of symmetry does each figure have? You may fold your paper to check.

1. **1 line of symmetry**

2. **2 lines of symmetry**

3. **Reasoning** How many lines of symmetry does an equilateral triangle have? Explain.

3 lines of symmetry; a line of symmetry can be drawn through each vertex.

Part of a symmetric trademark is shown. Complete each drawing.

4.

5.

Test Prep

6. Which figure has more than two lines of symmetry?

A.   B.   C.   **D.**

7. **Writing in Math** Draw a shape or figure that has more than 2 lines of symmetry. Put the lines of symmetry into your drawing.

Sample drawing:

Use with Lesson 6-11. **83**

Reteaching

Name_____

Symmetry

R 6-11

If a figure is symmetric, it can be split in half so that one side reflects onto the other side. The fold line is called the line of symmetry.

This figure has two lines of symmetry. If you folded along one of the lines, the two sides would fit on top of each other.

This figure has one line of symmetry. There is only one way to fold it exactly in half.

This figure has no lines of symmetry. It cannot be folded in half so that one side reflects onto the other side.

How many lines of symmetry does each figure have? You may trace the figure to check.

1. **0 lines of symmetry**

2. **2 lines of symmetry**

3. **1 line of symmetry**

Part of a symmetric trademark is shown. Complete the drawing.

4.

Use with Lesson 6-11. **83**

Enrichment

Name_____

Reflections

E 6-11
VISUAL THINKING

Write the letter of the figure that would be created by reflecting each shape over the dashed line of symmetry.

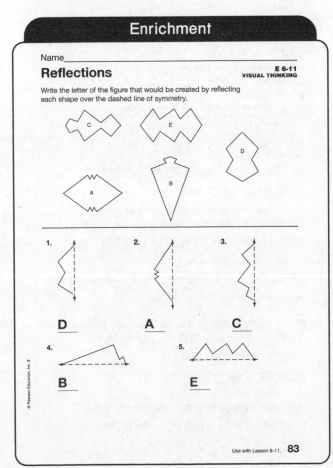

1. **D**   **2.** **A**   **3.** **C**

4. **B**   **5.** **E**

Use with Lesson 6-11. **83**

Problem Solving

Name_____

Symmetry

PS 6-11

1. Complete the drawings using the dotted line as the line of symmetry.

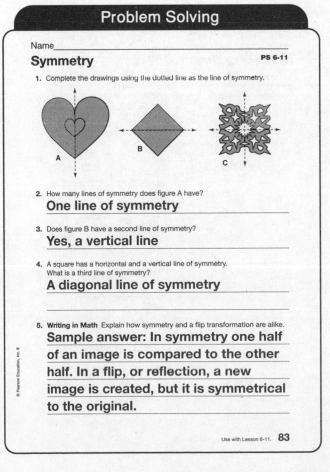

2. How many lines of symmetry does figure A have?

One line of symmetry

3. Does figure B have a second line of symmetry?

Yes, a vertical line

4. A square has a horizontal and a vertical line of symmetry. What is a third line of symmetry?

A diagonal line of symmetry

5. **Writing in Math** Explain how symmetry and a flip transformation are alike.

Sample answer: In symmetry one half of an image is compared to the other half. In a flip, or reflection, a new image is created, but it is symmetrical to the original.

Use with Lesson 6-11. **83**

Name_____

The Shape We Are In

P 6-12

1. Tarah hung an American flag from the front porch of her house. She placed it in a flag stand on one of the posts of the porch. Measure the angle of the flagpole from the post.

The angle measures 40°.

2. Construct a circle. Use the measure of the radius below.

3. Karen and Willie took a walk on the streets near their home. The path of their walk is shown at the right. Classify the triangle formed by the path by its angles and its sides.

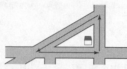

The triangle is scalene and right.

4. Part of a symmetric figure is shown. Complete the drawing.

© Pearson Education, Inc. 5

Name_____

The Geometry of Life

R 6-12

Juanita and her friend Kim decided to meet at the park. Use geometric terms to describe the location of their houses and the park in relation to the line segment.

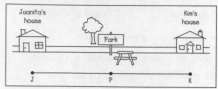

Juanita's house is located at point J on $\overline{JK}$. Kim's house is located at point K on $\overline{JK}$. The park is located at P, the midpoint of $\overline{JK}$.

Use the diagram above for question 1.

1. What is the shape of the chimney at Juanita's house?

Quadrilateral

2. Kenneth's mother ordered a pizza for his graduation party. The pizza has a diameter of 12 in. What is the measurement of the radius of the pizza?

6 in.

3. If it is 3:00 P.M., what is the measure of the angle that can be formed between the hour hand and the minute hand?

90°

4. Angelina saw the sign at the right. What is the name of this polygon?

Pentagon

© Pearson Education, Inc. 5

Name_____

Which Way Does It Go?

E 6-12

Find the pattern in each set of figures. Then draw the next three figures to continue the pattern. Write whether each figure you drew shows a *turn*, *slide*, or *flip* of the last figure in the pattern.

1. turn turn slide

2. turn turn flip

3. slide turn turn

4. turn slide flip

5. turn turn turn

6. turn flip flip

© Pearson Education, Inc. 5

Name_____

Octagon House

PS 6-12

In 1844 Isaiah Wilcox built a landmark house in Rhode Island. In the main room each of the 8 sides was 17 ft long. A regularly shaped home has 90° corners in most rooms for a total of 360°. What is the sum of the interior angles in an octagonal room?

Read and Understand

1. What are you trying to find?

The sum of the interior angles

Plan and Solve

2. Break apart or change the problem(s) into one that is simpler to solve.

Sample answer: I can break an octagon into 6 triangles by making 5 diagonals.

3. Solve the simpler problem(s).

Each triangle's angles must equal 180°.

4. Use the answers to the simpler problem to solve the original problem.

Since there are 6 triangles, 6 × 180° = 1,080°. The sum of the angles in an octagonal room is 1,080°.

Look Back and Check

5. Explain how you can check your answer.

I can check my calculations, and make sure I have not made any errors.

© Pearson Education, Inc. 5

Name_____

Meanings of Fractions

P 7-1

Write the fraction that names the shaded part or point on a number line.

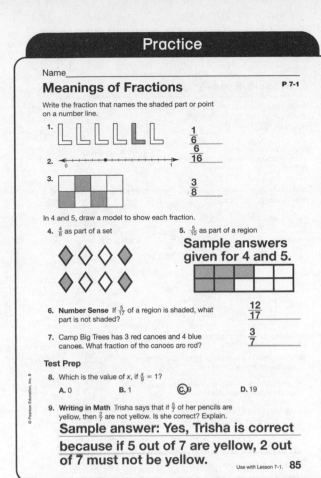

1. L L L L L L $\frac{1}{6}$
$\frac{6}{16}$

2. (number line 0 to 1 with point)

3. (grid with shaded squares) $\frac{3}{8}$

In 4 and 5, draw a model to show each fraction.

4. $\frac{4}{8}$ as part of a set   5. $\frac{5}{10}$ as part of a region

Sample answers given for 4 and 5.

6. **Number Sense** If $\frac{5}{17}$ of a region is shaded, what part is not shaded? $\frac{12}{17}$

7. Camp Big Trees has 3 red canoes and 4 blue canoes. What fraction of the canoes are red? $\frac{3}{7}$

Test Prep

8. Which is the value of x, if $\frac{x}{9} = 1$?

A. 0   B. 1   C. 9   D. 19

9. **Writing in Math** Trisha says that if $\frac{5}{7}$ of her pencils are yellow, then $\frac{2}{7}$ are not yellow. Is she correct? Explain.

Sample answer: Yes, Trisha is correct because if 5 out of 7 are yellow, 2 out of 7 must not be yellow.

Use with Lesson 7-1. 85

© Pearson Education, Inc. 5

Name_____

Meanings of Fractions

R 7-1

What fraction of the set of shapes are squares?

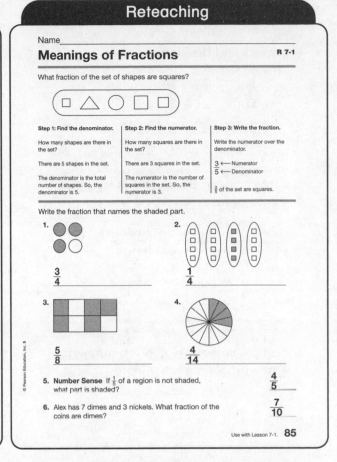

Step 1: Find the denominator.	Step 2: Find the numerator.	Step 3: Write the fraction.
How many shapes are there in the set?	How many squares are there in the set?	Write the numerator over the denominator.
There are 5 shapes in the set.	There are 3 squares in the set.	$\frac{3}{5}$ ← Numerator ← Denominator
The denominator is the total number of shapes. So, the denominator is 5.	The numerator is the number of squares in the set. So, the numerator is 3.	$\frac{3}{5}$ of the set are squares.

Write the fraction that names the shaded part.

1. (circles) $\frac{3}{4}$

2. (ovals with squares) $\frac{1}{4}$

3. (rectangle grid) $\frac{5}{8}$

4. (circle divided) $\frac{4}{14}$

5. **Number Sense** If $\frac{1}{5}$ of a region is not shaded, what part is shaded? $\frac{4}{5}$

6. Alex has 7 dimes and 3 nickels. What fraction of the coins are dimes? $\frac{7}{10}$

Use with Lesson 7-1. 85

© Pearson Education, Inc. 5

Name_____

Dot Designs

E 7-1
VISUAL THINKING

1. Copy each design on the grid below.

A.   B.

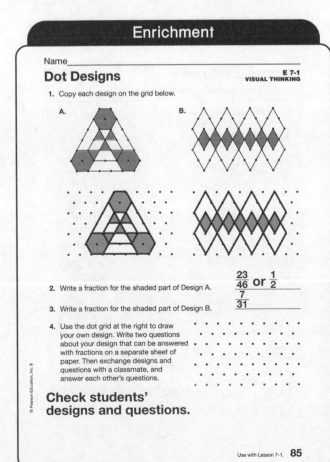

2. Write a fraction for the shaded part of Design A. $\frac{23}{46}$ or $\frac{1}{2}$

3. Write a fraction for the shaded part of Design B. $\frac{7}{31}$

4. Use the dot grid at the right to draw your own design. Write two questions about your design that can be answered with fractions on a separate sheet of paper. Then exchange designs and questions with a classmate, and answer each other's questions.

Check students' designs and questions.

Use with Lesson 7-1. 85

© Pearson Education, Inc. 5

Name_____

Meanings of Fractions

PS 7-1

Names of Days The table shows the days of the week categorized by the number of letters in their names.

Number of Letters in Names of Days

Number of Letters	Names of Days	Number of Days in Week with Given Number of Letters
6	Sunday, Monday, Friday	3
7	Tuesday	1
8	Thursday, Saturday	2
9	Wednesday	1

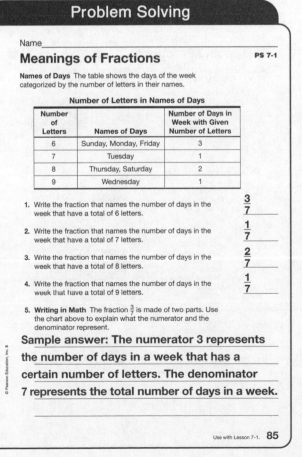

1. Write the fraction that names the number of days in the week that have a total of 6 letters. $\frac{3}{7}$

2. Write the fraction that names the number of days in the week that have a total of 7 letters. $\frac{1}{7}$

3. Write the fraction that names the number of days in the week that have a total of 8 letters. $\frac{2}{7}$

4. Write the fraction that names the number of days in the week that have a total of 9 letters. $\frac{1}{7}$

5. **Writing in Math** The fraction $\frac{3}{7}$ is made of two parts. Use the chart above to explain what the numerator and the denominator represent.

Sample answer: The numerator 3 represents the number of days in a week that has a certain number of letters. The denominator 7 represents the total number of days in a week.

Use with Lesson 7-1. 85

© Pearson Education, Inc. 5

Name_____

Fractions and Division
P 7-2

Give each answer as a fraction.

1. $3 \div 7$ $\dfrac{3}{7}$ 2. $4 \div 9$ $\dfrac{4}{9}$ 3. $1 \div 5$ $\dfrac{1}{5}$

4. $2 \div 11$ $\dfrac{2}{11}$ 5. $3 \div 5$ $\dfrac{3}{5}$ 6. $5 \div 8$ $\dfrac{5}{8}$

At a golf course, there are 18 holes. Of the 18 holes, 3 are par threes, 8 are par fours, and 7 are par fives. What fraction of the holes are

7. par fives? $\dfrac{7}{18}$ 8. par threes? $\dfrac{3}{18}$ 9. par fours? $\dfrac{8}{18}$

10. **Number Sense** Explain how you know that $7 \div 9$ is less than 1.

Sample answer: Because 7 is less than 9, 7 cannot be divided by 9 one time.

11. After school, Chase spends 20 min reading, 30 min practicing the piano, 15 min cleaning his room, and 40 min doing his homework. Chase is busy for 105 min. What fraction of the time does he spend cleaning his room? $\dfrac{15}{105}$

Test Prep

12. Venietta read 4 books in 7 weeks. How many books did she read each week?

A. $\dfrac{6}{7}$ (B.) $\dfrac{4}{7}$ C. $\dfrac{3}{7}$ D. $\dfrac{2}{7}$

13. **Writing in Math** In 5 min, Peter completed 2 math problems. Yvonne says he did $\frac{3}{5}$ of a problem each minute. Is she correct? Explain.

Sample answer: No, Peter completed $\frac{2}{5}$ of a problem each minute.

Name_____

Fractions and Division
R 7-2

Fractions can represent division. You can write a division expression as a fraction. For example:

Write a fraction for $5 \div 7$.

The first number in the division expression is the numerator of the fraction. The second number in the division expression is the denominator of the fraction.

$5 \div 7 \longrightarrow 5$ Numerator
$5 \div 7 \longrightarrow 7$ Denominator

So, $5 \div 7 = \frac{5}{7}$.

Give each answer as a fraction.

1. $3 \div 10$ $\dfrac{3}{10}$ 2. $7 \div 12$ $\dfrac{7}{12}$ 3. $2 \div 3$ $\dfrac{2}{3}$

4. $8 \div 9$ $\dfrac{8}{9}$ 5. $2 \div 5$ $\dfrac{2}{5}$ 6. $1 \div 6$ $\dfrac{1}{6}$

7. $6 \div 10$ $\dfrac{6}{10}$ 8. $9 \div 13$ $\dfrac{9}{13}$ 9. $14 \div 16$ $\dfrac{14}{16}$

Reasoning Each of three congruent circles is divided into three equal parts. Use for 10–12.

10. What part of a whole circle is shown by the white, or unshaded, area of one circle? $\dfrac{1}{3}$

11. What part of a whole circle is shown by the white, or unshaded, area of two circles? $\dfrac{2}{3}$

12. What part of a whole circle is shown by the white, or unshaded, area of three circles? $\dfrac{3}{3}$ or 1

Name_____

Visualizing Fractions
E 7-2
VISUAL THINKING

Read each phrase in the left column. Find the model in the right column that helps you visualize the phrase. Write the letter of that model in the blank.

1. Four students were making collages in art class. There were only three sheets of paper available. How much paper could each art student use for their collage?

C

A.

2. Five campers each tried to cook a pancake, but two of the pancakes flipped into the campfire. How much of a pancake would each camper get?

D

B.

3. Two fifth-grade classes had a treat. Three parents each brought a pan of granola bars. How much of the granola bars could each classroom receive?

A

C.

4. Four hikers sat down for lunch. Unfortunately, one of the hikers sat down on some of the food! The hikers had to share the two sandwiches that were left. How much of a sandwich did each hiker get?

B

D.

Name_____

Fractions and Division
PS 7-2

An analog clock has a face with a set of numbers and an hour and a minute hand.

1. Based on the number of hours, how many equal sections are on the clock?

12 equal sections

2. What part of the whole clock is shown by the shaded section? $\dfrac{5}{12}$

Nurses often spend their time performing different tasks. They also often work in 12 hr shifts.

3. The clock shows how many hours in one 12 hr shift a nurse spent checking on patients. Write a fraction that shows this information. $\dfrac{7}{12}$

4. The clock shows how many hours in one 12 hr shift a nurse spent on paperwork. Write a fraction that shows this information. $\dfrac{3}{12}$ or $\dfrac{1}{4}$

5. **Writing in Math** If a nurse spent 2 hr of one shift and 2 hr of another shift on paperwork, what fraction of one 12-hr period did he or she spend on paperwork? Explain your answer.

$\dfrac{4}{12}$ or $\dfrac{1}{3}$; 2 + 2 = 4, so the nurse spent $\dfrac{4}{12}$ or $\dfrac{1}{3}$ of one shift.

Practice

Name_____

Mixed Numbers

P 7-3

Write an improper fraction and a mixed number for each model.

1.  $\dfrac{7}{3}, 2\dfrac{1}{3}$

2.  $\dfrac{10}{4}, 2\dfrac{2}{4}$

Write each improper fraction as a mixed number.

3. $\dfrac{12}{7}$ $1\dfrac{5}{7}$ 4. $\dfrac{7}{3}$ $2\dfrac{1}{3}$ 5. $\dfrac{5}{2}$ $2\dfrac{1}{2}$

6. $\dfrac{9}{4}$ $2\dfrac{1}{4}$ 7. $\dfrac{29}{13}$ $2\dfrac{3}{13}$ 8. $\dfrac{34}{8}$ $4\dfrac{1}{4}$

Write each mixed number as an improper fraction.

9. $2\dfrac{4}{5}$ $\dfrac{14}{5}$ 10. $8\dfrac{7}{9}$ $\dfrac{79}{9}$ 11. $3\dfrac{6}{7}$ $\dfrac{27}{7}$

12. $7\dfrac{1}{8}$ $\dfrac{57}{8}$ 13. $4\dfrac{3}{7}$ $\dfrac{31}{7}$ 14. $5\dfrac{1}{4}$ $\dfrac{21}{4}$

Test Prep

15. Jasmine has 41 lb of dog food to evenly pour into 5 dishes. How many pounds of dog food should she pour in each dish?

A. $4\dfrac{1}{5}$ lb   **B.** $8\dfrac{1}{5}$ lb   C. 10 lb   D. $11\dfrac{1}{8}$ lb

16. **Writing in Math** Hank needs 3 quarters to play one video game each time. If he has 14 quarters, how many times can he play? Explain.

Sample answer: Hank can play the video game 4 times. He cannot play the game $4\dfrac{2}{3}$ times because the game will not work with only 2 quarters.

Reteaching

Name_____

Mixed Numbers

R 7-3

A mixed number has a whole number and a fraction.

Whole number → $3\dfrac{5}{8}$ ← Fraction

An improper fraction has a numerator greater than or equal to its denominator.

$\dfrac{17}{9}$ ← Numerator is greater than denominator

How to write an improper fraction as a mixed number

$\dfrac{13}{4} = 13 \div 4$

- Divide the numerator by the denominator.
- Write the remainder as a fraction.

$$\begin{array}{r} 3 \\ 4\overline{)13} \\ -12 \\ \hline 1 \end{array}$$

$\dfrac{13}{4} = 3\dfrac{1}{4}$

How to write a mixed number as an improper fraction

$5\dfrac{1}{3}$ = what improper fraction?

- Multiply the denominator by the whole number: $3 \times 5 = 15$.
- Add the numerator: $15 + 1 = 16$.
- Use the same denominator.

$\dfrac{16}{3}$ ← $(3 \times 5) + 1$
← Same denominator from mixed number

$5\dfrac{1}{3} = \dfrac{16}{3}$

Write each improper fraction as a mixed number.

1. $\dfrac{8}{3}$ $2\dfrac{2}{3}$ 2. $\dfrac{10}{7}$ $1\dfrac{3}{7}$ 3. $\dfrac{5}{2}$ $2\dfrac{1}{2}$

4. $\dfrac{7}{4}$ $1\dfrac{3}{4}$ 5. $\dfrac{13}{10}$ $1\dfrac{3}{10}$ 6. $\dfrac{17}{15}$ $1\dfrac{2}{15}$

Write each mixed number as an improper fraction.

7. $1\dfrac{2}{5}$ $\dfrac{7}{5}$ 8. $4\dfrac{6}{7}$ $\dfrac{34}{7}$ 9. $2\dfrac{5}{8}$ $\dfrac{21}{8}$

10. $3\dfrac{1}{2}$ $\dfrac{7}{2}$ 11. $5\dfrac{1}{6}$ $\dfrac{31}{6}$ 12. $3\dfrac{2}{9}$ $\dfrac{29}{9}$

13. **Algebra** If $2\dfrac{n}{4} = \dfrac{9}{4}$, what is the value of n?

$n = 1$

Enrichment

Name_____

Swim Meet

E 7-3
REASONING

1. Use the clues to complete the chart. Write the place each school won in the swim meet. Then write *yes* or *no* in the name columns to find out which school each swimmer is from.

CLUES

- The swimmer from Washington School came in last.
- The swimmer from Jackson School finished ahead of the swimmer from Jefferson School.
- The swimmer from Franklin School finished ahead of the swimmer from Jackson School.
- Callie, who does not attend Franklin School, came in ahead of both Paula and Marisa.
- If Marisa had not lost her goggles, she would have finished ahead of Paula.

School Name	Place	Callie	Paula	Marisa	Rita
Washington	4th	No	No	Yes	No
Jackson	2nd	Yes	No	No	No
Jefferson	3rd	No	Yes	No	No
Franklin	1st	No	No	No	Yes

Use the information from the completed chart to write the names, schools, and places in the sentences below. Write your answers in order starting with first place.

2. **Rita** from **Franklin** School was **1st**

3. **Callie** from **Jackson** School was **2nd**

4. **Paula** from **Jefferson** School was **3rd**

5. **Marisa** from **Washington** School was **4th**

Problem Solving

Name_____

Mixed Numbers

PS 7-3

Mineral water is a very popular drink in the United States and all over the world. Mineral water is often sold in 6-bottle packs.

1. Suppose you have 11 bottles of mineral water. Write the number of 6-bottle packs you have as a mixed number.

$1\dfrac{5}{6}$ packs

2. Suppose you have two 6-bottle packs of mineral water. Write the number of 6-bottle packs you have as an improper fraction.

$\dfrac{12}{6}$ packs

3. Suppose you have 15 bottles of mineral water. Write the number of 6-bottle packs you have as both a mixed number and an improper fraction.

$2\dfrac{3}{6}$ packs; $\dfrac{15}{6}$ packs

Betty bought a photo album to put some pictures in. Each page of the album holds 4 photos.

4. If Betty has 14 photos she wants to put in the album, how many pages can she fill? Write your answer as an improper fraction.

$\dfrac{14}{4}$ pages

5. If Betty has 25 photos she wants to put in the album, how many pages can she fill? Write your answer as a mixed number.

$6\dfrac{1}{4}$ pages

6. **Writing in Math** If Betty filled $6\dfrac{3}{4}$ pages of the album with photos, how many photos did she put in the album? Explain how changing $6\dfrac{3}{4}$ to an improper fraction helps you find the answer.

27 photos; Sample answer: The numerator of the improper fraction is the number of photos.

Name _____

Estimating Fractional Amounts
P 7-4

Estimate the shaded part of each. **Sample answers are given for 1–9.**

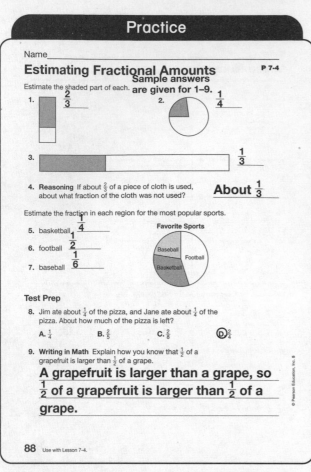

1. $\frac{2}{3}$

2. $\frac{1}{4}$

3. $\frac{1}{3}$

4. **Reasoning** If about $\frac{2}{3}$ of a piece of cloth is used, about what fraction of the cloth was not used?   **About $\frac{1}{3}$**

Estimate the fraction in each region for the most popular sports.

5. basketball $\frac{1}{4}$

6. football $\frac{1}{2}$

7. baseball $\frac{1}{6}$

Favorite Sports

Baseball
Football
Basketball

Test Prep

8. Jim ate about $\frac{1}{4}$ of the pizza, and Jane ate about $\frac{1}{4}$ of the pizza. About how much of the pizza is left?

   A. $\frac{1}{4}$ B. $\frac{2}{5}$ C. $\frac{2}{8}$ D. $\frac{2}{4}$

9. **Writing in Math** Explain how you know that $\frac{1}{2}$ of a grapefruit is larger than $\frac{1}{2}$ of a grape.

   A grapefruit is larger than a grape, so $\frac{1}{2}$ of a grapefruit is larger than $\frac{1}{2}$ of a grape.

Name _____

Estimating Fractional Amounts
R 7-4

Estimate the shaded part of the figure.

Think about benchmark fractions, which include $\frac{1}{4}$, $\frac{1}{3}$, $\frac{1}{2}$, $\frac{2}{3}$, and $\frac{3}{4}$. What benchmark fraction can you use to estimate the shaded region?

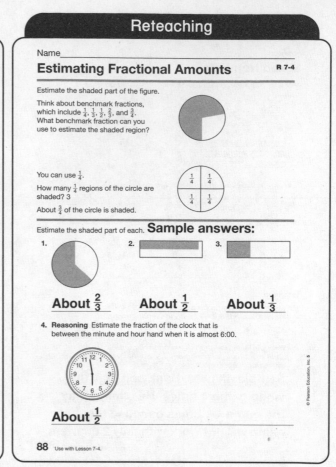

You can use $\frac{1}{4}$.

How many $\frac{1}{4}$ regions of the circle are shaded? 3

About $\frac{3}{4}$ of the circle is shaded.

Estimate the shaded part of each. **Sample answers:**

1. **About $\frac{2}{3}$**

2. **About $\frac{1}{2}$**

3. **About $\frac{1}{3}$**

4. **Reasoning** Estimate the fraction of the clock that is between the minute and hour hand when it is almost 6:00.

   About $\frac{1}{2}$

Name _____

Fractions of Flags
E 7-4
ESTIMATION

Look at the flags below. Under each, estimate the fraction of the flag that is white and the fraction of the flag that is shaded.

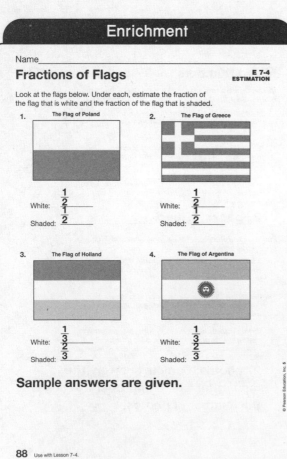

1. **The Flag of Poland**

   White: $\frac{1}{2}$
   Shaded: $\frac{1}{2}$

2. **The Flag of Greece**

   White: $\frac{1}{2}$
   Shaded: $\frac{1}{2}$

3. **The Flag of Holland**

   White: $\frac{1}{3}$
   Shaded: $\frac{2}{3}$

4. **The Flag of Argentina**

   White: $\frac{1}{3}$
   Shaded: $\frac{2}{3}$

Sample answers are given.

Name _____

Estimating Fractional Amounts
PS 7-4

Tall Trees There are four tall trees in Lisa's backyard. The picture shows the heights of the trees.

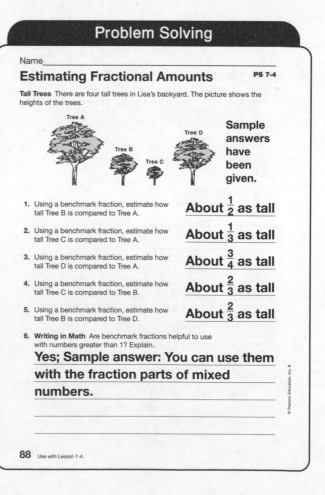

Tree A   Tree B   Tree C   Tree D

Sample answers have been given.

1. Using a benchmark fraction, estimate how tall Tree B is compared to Tree A.   **About $\frac{1}{2}$ as tall**

2. Using a benchmark fraction, estimate how tall Tree C is compared to Tree A.   **About $\frac{1}{3}$ as tall**

3. Using a benchmark fraction, estimate how tall Tree D is compared to Tree A.   **About $\frac{3}{4}$ as tall**

4. Using a benchmark fraction, estimate how tall Tree C is compared to Tree B.   **About $\frac{2}{3}$ as tall**

5. Using a benchmark fraction, estimate how tall Tree B is compared to Tree D.   **About $\frac{2}{3}$ as tall**

6. **Writing in Math** Are benchmark fractions helpful to use with numbers greater than 1? Explain.

   Yes; Sample answer: You can use them with the fraction parts of mixed numbers.

Name_____

Fractions and Mixed Numbers on the Number Line

P 7-5

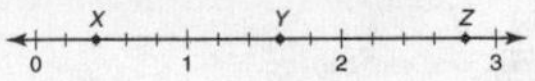

(number line: points X, Y, Z between 0, 1, 2, 3)

What fraction or mixed number represents each point?

1. Point X $\dfrac{2}{5}$ 2. Point Y $1\dfrac{3}{5}$ 3. Point Z $2\dfrac{4}{5}$

Draw a number line to show each set of numbers. Then order the numbers from least to greatest.

4. $\dfrac{2}{3}, \dfrac{5}{6}, \dfrac{1}{6}$

$\dfrac{1}{6}, \dfrac{2}{3}, \dfrac{5}{6}$

(number line with $\frac{1}{6}$, $\frac{2}{3}$, $\frac{5}{6}$ marked between 0 and 1)

Sample drawings for 4 and 5.

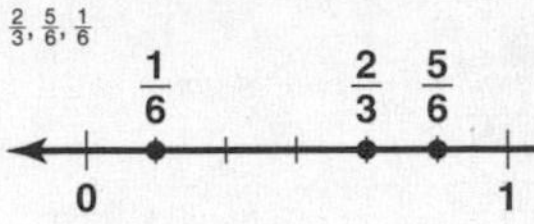

5. $1\dfrac{3}{4}, 1\dfrac{9}{10}, 1\dfrac{1}{2}$

$1\dfrac{1}{2}, 1\dfrac{3}{4}, 1\dfrac{9}{10}$

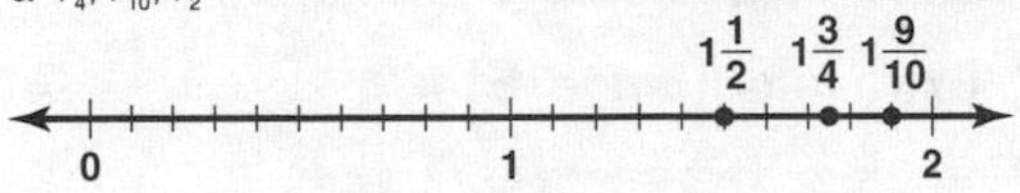

(number line with $1\frac{1}{2}$, $1\frac{3}{4}$, $1\frac{9}{10}$ marked between 0, 1, 2)

Test Prep

6. Which number would be to the right of $7\dfrac{9}{10}$ on a number line?

A. $7\dfrac{10}{12}$ B. $7\dfrac{7}{8}$ C. $7\dfrac{25}{30}$ **D.** $7\dfrac{10}{11}$

7. **Writing in Math** If, on a number line, point R is $3\dfrac{3}{8}$ and point T is $3\dfrac{7}{8}$, where could point S be if it is between points R and T? Explain.

Sample answer: $3\dfrac{1}{2}$; $3\dfrac{1}{2}$ is equivalent to $3\dfrac{4}{8}$, which fits between $3\dfrac{3}{8}$ and $3\dfrac{7}{8}$ on the number line.

© Pearson Education, Inc. 5

Name_____

Fractions and Mixed Numbers on the Number Line

R 7-5

Locate points for $2\dfrac{1}{4}$, $\dfrac{3}{4}$, and $2\dfrac{2}{4}$ on a number line. Then order them from least to greatest.

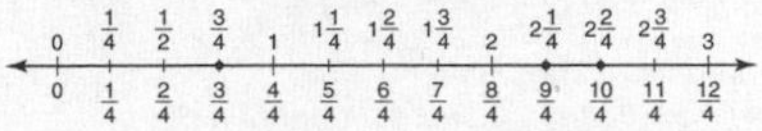

Since $2\dfrac{2}{4}$ is the number farthest to the right, it is the greatest. Since $\dfrac{3}{4}$ is the farthest left, it is the least. Therefore, $\dfrac{3}{4} < 2\dfrac{1}{4} < 2\dfrac{2}{4}$.

Which fraction or mixed number represents each point?

(number line with points A, B, C between 0, 1, 2, 3)

1. Point A $\dfrac{5}{6}$ 2. Point B $1\dfrac{1}{3}$ 3. Point C $2\dfrac{1}{2}$

Draw a number line to show each set of numbers. Then order the numbers from least to greatest.

4. $\dfrac{13}{5}, 2\dfrac{1}{5}, \dfrac{7}{5}$

$\dfrac{7}{5}, 2\dfrac{1}{5}, \dfrac{13}{5}$

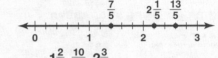

5. $1\dfrac{2}{4}, \dfrac{10}{4}, 2\dfrac{3}{4}$

$1\dfrac{2}{4}, \dfrac{10}{4}, 2\dfrac{3}{4}$

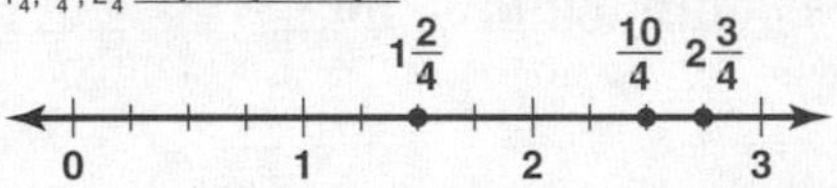

(number line with $1\frac{2}{4}$, $\frac{10}{4}$, $2\frac{3}{4}$ marked between 0, 1, 2, 3)

© Pearson Education, Inc. 5

Name_____

Secret Code

E 7-5
NUMBER SENSE

Place the following points on the number line. Label the points with the letters to find the secret message.

MATH IS FUN FOR EVERYONE

(number line from 0 to 5 with labeled points)

1. A = $\dfrac{1}{4}$ 2. N = $2\dfrac{1}{8}$

3. E = $3\dfrac{7}{8}$ 4. O = $4\dfrac{2}{8}$

5. E = $3\dfrac{5}{8}$ 6. O = $2\dfrac{7}{8}$

7. E = $4\dfrac{1}{2}$ 8. R = $2\dfrac{8}{8}$

9. F = $2\dfrac{3}{4}$ 10. R = $4\dfrac{1}{1}$

11. F = $1\dfrac{7}{8}$ 12. S = $1\dfrac{1}{4}$

13. H = $\dfrac{1}{2}$ 14. T = $\dfrac{3}{8}$

15. I = $1\dfrac{1}{8}$ 16. U = $\dfrac{8}{4}$

17. M = $\dfrac{1}{8}$ 18. V = $3\dfrac{3}{4}$

19. N = $4\dfrac{3}{8}$ 20. Y = $4\dfrac{1}{8}$

© Pearson Education, Inc. 5

Name_____

Fractions and Mixed Numbers on the Number Line

PS 7-5

Free Throws Gail is on the basketball team. Every week after school, she shoots 20 free throws in practice. The chart shows the number of free throws out of 20 she made each day last week.

Day	Free Throws Made/Attempted
Monday	$\dfrac{16}{20}$
Tuesday	$\dfrac{11}{20}$
Wednesday	$\dfrac{9}{20}$
Thursday	$\dfrac{19}{20}$
Friday	$\dfrac{14}{20}$

1. On the number line, show the fractions that represent how many free throws Gail made out of 20.

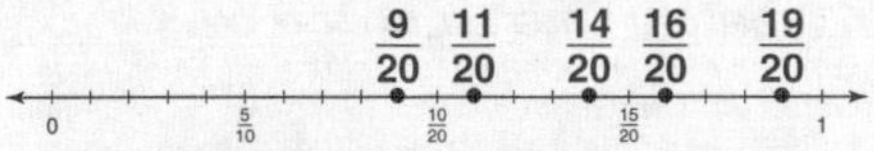

(number line from 0 to 1 with $\frac{9}{20}$, $\frac{11}{20}$, $\frac{14}{20}$, $\frac{16}{20}$, $\frac{19}{20}$ marked)

2. Now write the fractions in order from least to greatest.

$\dfrac{9}{20}, \dfrac{11}{20}, \dfrac{14}{20}, \dfrac{16}{20}, \dfrac{19}{20}$

3. Carly, Morris, and Becky went to a book fair. Carly spent $\dfrac{5}{9}$ of her weekly allowance, Morris spent $1\dfrac{2}{9}$, and Becky spent $\dfrac{25}{9}$. Write the fractions in order on the number line. If each receives the same allowance, who spent the greatest amount?

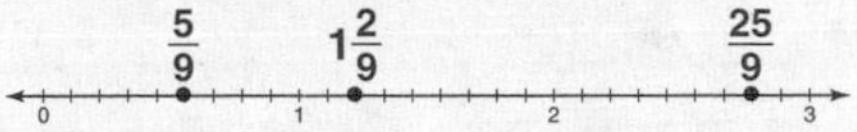

(number line from 0 to 3 with $\frac{5}{9}$, $1\frac{2}{9}$, $\frac{25}{9}$ marked)

Becky

4. **Writing in Math** Explain how you would set up a number line to compare $\dfrac{3}{12}, 2\dfrac{7}{12}, 1\dfrac{1}{12}$, and $\dfrac{11}{12}$.

Sample answer: I would make a number line from zero to 3 that was divided by increments of $\dfrac{1}{12}$.

© Pearson Education, Inc. 5

Name_____

Extra or Missing Information

Decide if each problem has extra or missing information. Solve if you have enough information.

1. Jared and Cody went on a backpacking trip with their class for 3 days. They brought 2 boxes of spaghetti. Each box weighed 16 oz. They also brought 4 cans of sauce. Each can weighed 8 oz. How many ounces did each person carry if each carried the same amount?

Extra information; 32 oz

2. Each backpack weighed 25 lb and each tent weighed 3 lb. If there are 30 backpackers, how much do their backpacks weigh altogether?

Extra information; 750 lb

For 3–5, use the table at the right.

Trail Name	Length
Hiawatha	6 mi
Pontiac	2 mi
Black Hawk	10 mi
Keokuk	7 mi

3. The backpackers hiked the Black Hawk trail on Monday. They planned to hike on Tuesday. What is the total number of trails they hiked on Monday and Tuesday?

Missing information

4. How much longer is twice around the Black Hawk trail than twice around the Hiawatha trail?

No extra or missing information; 8 mi

5. Mariah hiked the Pontiac trail 5 days in 1 week. She did not hike on Wednesday and Friday. How many miles did she hike throughout 1 week?

Extra information; 10 mi

Name_____

Extra or Missing Information

Casseroles Jackie is making casseroles. She has 4 blocks of cheese. Does she have enough cheese to make 6 casseroles?

Read and Understand

Step 1: What do you know? Jackie has 4 blocks of cheese. She wants to make 6 casseroles.

Step 2: What are you trying to find? You want to know if Jackie can make 6 casseroles with 4 blocks of cheese.

Plan and Solve

There is not enough information to solve the problem. To solve the problem, you need to know how much cheese Jackie uses in each casserole.

Decide if each problem has extra or missing information. Solve if you have enough information.

1. Donna bought one pair of shoes for $29.50 and another for half that price. She paid with a $50 bill. How much did the other pair of shoes cost?

Extra information; $14.75

2. Jorge is saving money from mowing lawns. He makes $5.00 for each lawn he mows. Jorge wants to buy a gift for his mother that costs $23.69. Does he have enough money?

Missing information

3. Alexis runs $2\frac{1}{2}$ mi per day. She likes to run through the park near the river. Her friend Tony runs 4 mi per day. How far does Alexis run in 5 days?

Extra information; $12\frac{1}{2}$ mi

Name_____

Leftovers

You have volunteered to bring snacks to the after-school meetings of the math club. Read the description for each week, and decide how you would distribute the snacks. You must always give each person an equal portion. There is more than one way to solve each problem.

Sample answers have been given for 1–4.

1. You have baked 4 batches of granola bars. 9 people have come to the math club meeting. You must have at least $\frac{1}{2}$ of a batch of granola bars left after the meeting for your little sister and her friends. What fraction of a batch of granola bars would you give to each person at the meeting? How much would you have left over?

$\frac{1}{3}$ of a batch; One batch left over

2. You have brought 15 muffins to the meeting. This week there are 10 people at the meeting. You cannot bring any leftovers home on the bus. How many muffins would you give each person? How much would you have left?

$1\frac{1}{2}$ muffins; None left

3. You have made 6 veggie pizzas for the meeting. There are 8 people at the meeting. You give one pizza to the science club. How much pizza would you give to each person at the math club meeting? How much would you have left over?

$\frac{5}{8}$ of a pizza; None left

4. You have brought 6 oranges to the meeting. There are 8 math club members at the meeting. You would like to give a whole orange to the math club advisor. If you have some oranges left over, you can have them for a snack tonight. What portion of an orange would you give to each person at the math club meeting? How much would you have left over?

1 orange to the club advisor; $\frac{1}{2}$ orange to each member; 1 orange left over

---

Name_____

Extra or Missing Information

Rental Car Mr. Bertram rented a car for $225.00 per week. He was given 250 free miles for the week and had to pay $0.10 for each extra mile. When Mr. Bertram returned the car, he paid an additional $23.50 for extra mileage. How much did the rental car cost Mr. Bertram?

Read and Understand

1. How much would Mr. Bertram pay if he drove less than 250 mi?   **$225.00**

2. How much extra did Mr. Bertram pay for driving more than 250 mi?   **$23.50**

3. What are you trying to find?

How much Mr. Bertram paid for the rental car

Plan and Solve

4. Is there enough information to solve the problem?   **Yes**

5. Is there information you do not need to solve the problem? What is it?

Yes; How much Mr. Bertram had to pay for each extra mile

6. Solve the problem. Write your answer in a complete sentence.

Mr. Bertram paid $248.50 for the rental car.

Look Back and Check

7. Is your answer correct?

Yes, the math is correct.

Name_____

Understanding Equivalent Fractions   P 7-7

Write two fractions that name each shaded part.

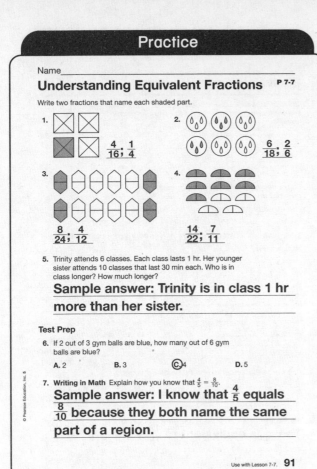

1. $\dfrac{4}{16}$; $\dfrac{1}{4}$

2. $\dfrac{6}{18}$; $\dfrac{2}{6}$

3. $\dfrac{8}{24}$; $\dfrac{4}{12}$

4. $\dfrac{14}{22}$; $\dfrac{7}{11}$

5. Trinity attends 6 classes. Each class lasts 1 hr. Her younger sister attends 10 classes that last 30 min each. Who is in class longer? How much longer?

Sample answer: Trinity is in class 1 hr more than her sister.

Test Prep

6. If 2 out of 3 gym balls are blue, how many out of 6 gym balls are blue?

A. 2   B. 3   (C.) 4   D. 5

7. **Writing in Math** Explain how you know that $\dfrac{4}{5} = \dfrac{8}{10}$.

Sample answer: I know that $\dfrac{4}{5}$ equals $\dfrac{8}{10}$ because they both name the same part of a region.

Name_____

Understanding Equivalent Fractions   R 7-7

Find equivalent fractions for the shaded part of the set shown.

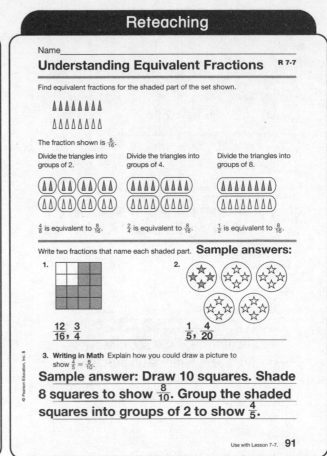

The fraction shown is $\dfrac{8}{16}$.

Divide the triangles into groups of 2.	Divide the triangles into groups of 4.	Divide the triangles into groups of 8.
$\dfrac{4}{8}$ is equivalent to $\dfrac{8}{16}$.	$\dfrac{2}{4}$ is equivalent to $\dfrac{8}{16}$.	$\dfrac{1}{2}$ is equivalent to $\dfrac{8}{16}$.

Write two fractions that name each shaded part. **Sample answers:**

1. $\dfrac{12}{16}$, $\dfrac{3}{4}$

2. $\dfrac{1}{5}$, $\dfrac{4}{20}$

3. **Writing in Math** Explain how you could draw a picture to show $\dfrac{4}{5} = \dfrac{8}{10}$.

Sample answer: Draw 10 squares. Shade 8 squares to show $\dfrac{8}{10}$. Group the shaded squares into groups of 2 to show $\dfrac{4}{5}$.

Name_____

If It's All the Same to You   E 7-7
NUMBER SENSE

Each box is labeled with a fraction. In each box, draw two models to represent the fraction, and write two equivalent fractions. **Sample answers are given.**

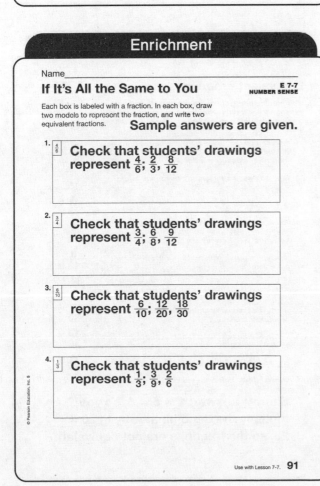

1. $\dfrac{4}{6}$ **Check that students' drawings represent $\dfrac{4}{6}$; $\dfrac{2}{3}$, $\dfrac{8}{12}$**

2. $\dfrac{3}{4}$ **Check that students' drawings represent $\dfrac{3}{4}$; $\dfrac{6}{8}$, $\dfrac{9}{12}$**

3. $\dfrac{6}{10}$ **Check that students' drawings represent $\dfrac{6}{10}$; $\dfrac{12}{20}$, $\dfrac{18}{30}$**

4. $\dfrac{1}{3}$ **Check that students' drawings represent $\dfrac{1}{3}$; $\dfrac{3}{9}$, $\dfrac{2}{6}$**

Name_____

Understanding Equivalent Fractions   PS 7-7

Everglades National Park Everglades National Park in southern Florida is home to thousands of wildlife creatures. The park has changed as people have used water for other purposes. The Florida panther has become an endangered species. In 2002, experts estimated that there are only about 30 Florida panthers living in Florida. They also estimated that only about 10 of the panthers were living in the Everglades.

1. Write a fraction that compares the estimated number of Florida panthers in the Everglades to the total estimated number of Florida panthers in Florida. $\dfrac{10}{30}$

2. What is an equivalent fraction for the fraction you found in Exercise 1?   **Sample answer:** $\dfrac{1}{3}$

3. Find the equivalent fraction for $\dfrac{1}{3}$ that has a denominator of 6. Draw fraction strips to show why they are equivalent. $\dfrac{2}{6}$

Check students' drawings.

4. Suppose 10 new panthers were discovered in Florida, and they were not in the Everglades. What fraction would compare the estimated number of Florida panthers living in the Everglades to the total estimated number of Florida panthers in Florida? Also write an equivalent fraction for your answer. $\dfrac{10}{40}$; **Sample answer:** $\dfrac{1}{4}$

5. **Writing in Math** Is $\dfrac{5}{8}$ an equivalent fraction for $\dfrac{2}{3}$? Explain how you can tell using fraction strips.

No; Sample answer: Using fraction strips you can see that $\dfrac{6}{9}$, not $\dfrac{5}{8}$, is an equivalent fraction for $\dfrac{2}{3}$.

Equivalent Fractions

Name_____

Equivalent Fractions　　　　　　　　P 7-8

Sample answers given for 1–6.
Name two equivalent fractions for each fraction.

1. $\frac{5}{15}$　$\frac{1}{3}, \frac{10}{30}$　　2. $\frac{6}{36}$　$\frac{1}{6}, \frac{3}{18}$　　3. $\frac{2}{12}$　$\frac{1}{6}, \frac{4}{24}$

4. $\frac{4}{28}$　$\frac{2}{14}, \frac{1}{7}$　　5. $\frac{3}{21}$　$\frac{6}{42}, \frac{1}{7}$　　6. $\frac{2}{11}$　$\frac{4}{22}, \frac{6}{33}$

Find the missing number to make the fractions equivalent.

7. $\frac{9}{13} = \frac{18}{x}$　$x = 26$　　　8. $\frac{12}{30} = \frac{n}{90}$　$n = 36$

9. $\frac{q}{54} = \frac{2}{9}$　$q = 12$　　　10. $\frac{14}{h} = \frac{7}{20}$　$h = 40$

11. Renie gave each of six people $\frac{1}{10}$ of a veggie pizza. Renie has $\frac{2}{5}$ of the pizza left. Explain how this is true.

Sample answer: Renie gave away $\frac{6}{10}$, or $\frac{3}{5}$, of the pizza, so $\frac{2}{5}$, or $\frac{4}{10}$, of it is left.

Test Prep

12. Which fraction is equivalent to $\frac{3}{7}$?

A. $\frac{3}{6}$　　　B. $\frac{6}{14}$　　　C. $\frac{3}{17}$　　　D. $\frac{7}{7}$

13. **Writing in Math** Jacqueline has four $5 bills. She bought a shirt for $10. She has spent half of her money. Explain how much money Jacqueline spent. Use equivalent fractions.

Sample answer: Four $5 bills equal $20. After she spent $10, she had $\frac{10}{20}$, or $\frac{1}{2}$, of her money.

92　Use with Lesson 7-8.

© Pearson Education, Inc. 5

Name_____

Equivalent Fractions　　　　　　　　R 7-8

To find an equivalent fraction, multiply or divide the numerator and denominator of a fraction by the same nonzero number. For example:

Name a fraction equivalent to $\frac{3}{5}$.

$$\frac{3 \times 7}{5 \times 7} = \frac{21}{35} \qquad \frac{3}{5} = \frac{21}{35}$$

Both numerator and denominator were multiplied by 7.

Sometimes you must find a missing numerator or a denominator.

Find the missing denominator.　　　Find the missing numerator.

$\frac{3}{7} = \frac{6}{\square}$　　　　　　$\frac{6}{9} = \frac{\square}{3}$

Think: What number times 3 equals 6?　　Think: What number can 9 be divided by to get 3?

Multiply 3 and 7 by 2.　　　　　Divide 6 and 9 by 3.

$\frac{3 \times 2}{7 \times 2} = \overset{\longrightarrow 6}{\longrightarrow 14}$　　　$\frac{6 \div 3}{9 \div 3} = \overset{\longrightarrow 2}{\longrightarrow 3}$

So, $\frac{3}{7} = \frac{6}{14}$.　　　　So, $\frac{6}{9} = \frac{2}{3}$.

Name two equivalent fractions for each fraction.

1. $\frac{1}{3}$　$\frac{2}{6}, \frac{4}{12}$　　2. $\frac{2}{12}$　$\frac{1}{6}, \frac{4}{24}$

3. $\frac{4}{20}$　$\frac{1}{5}, \frac{2}{10}$　　4. $\frac{2}{16}$　$\frac{1}{8}, \frac{4}{32}$

Sample answers given for 1–4.

Find the missing number to make the fractions equivalent.

5. $\frac{4}{7} = \frac{8}{\square}$　14　　6. $\frac{\square}{18} = \frac{4}{6}$　12　　7. $\frac{3}{4} = \frac{\square}{12}$　9　　8. $\frac{15}{\square} = \frac{3}{4}$　20

9. **Number Sense** Are $\frac{3}{4}$ and $\frac{12}{16}$ equivalent fractions? Explain.
Yes; $\frac{3}{4}$ is equivalent to $\frac{12}{16}$ since $\frac{3 \times 4}{4 \times 4} = \frac{12}{16}$.

92　Use with Lesson 7-8.

© Pearson Education, Inc. 5

Name_____

Where Do the Numbers Go?　　　E 7-8
　　　　　　　　　　　　　NUMBER SENSE

Rearrange the numerators to form three equivalent fractions.

1. $\frac{1}{9}, \frac{2}{3}, \frac{3}{6}$　　2. $\frac{2}{15}, \frac{4}{5}, \frac{6}{10}$　　3. $\frac{1}{12}, \frac{3}{8}, \frac{2}{4}$
$\frac{3}{9}, \frac{1}{3}, \frac{2}{6}$　　　$\frac{6}{15}, \frac{2}{5}, \frac{4}{10}$　　$\frac{3}{12}, \frac{2}{8}, \frac{1}{4}$

4. $\frac{15}{6}, \frac{5}{12}, \frac{10}{18}$　　5. $\frac{3}{18}, \frac{9}{3}, \frac{6}{9}$　　6. $\frac{8}{9}, \frac{12}{18}, \frac{4}{27}$
$\frac{5}{6}, \frac{10}{12}, \frac{15}{18}$　　$\frac{6}{14}, \frac{3}{7}, \frac{9}{21}$　　$\frac{4}{9}, \frac{8}{18}, \frac{12}{27}$

Rearrange the denominators to form three equivalent fractions.

7. $\frac{3}{12}, \frac{2}{36}, \frac{1}{24}$　　8. $\frac{7}{9}, \frac{9}{11}, \frac{11}{7}$　　9. $\frac{10}{21}, \frac{15}{7}, \frac{5}{14}$
$\frac{3}{36}, \frac{2}{24}, \frac{1}{12}$　　$\frac{7}{9}, \frac{9}{11}, \frac{11}{11}$　　$\frac{10}{14}, \frac{15}{21}, \frac{5}{7}$

Rearrange the numerators to form four equivalent fractions.

10. $\frac{14}{9}, \frac{7}{27}, \frac{28}{18}, \frac{21}{36}$　　11. $\frac{24}{60}, \frac{8}{45}, \frac{16}{15}, \frac{32}{30}$
$\frac{7}{9}, \frac{21}{27}, \frac{14}{18}, \frac{28}{36}$　　$\frac{32}{60}, \frac{24}{45}, \frac{8}{15}, \frac{16}{30}$

Use the four numbers to build at least two pairs of equivalent fractions.　**Sample answers are given.**

12. 2, 3, 6, 9　　　　13. 3, 4, 15, 20
$\frac{2}{3} = \frac{6}{9}; \frac{6}{2} = \frac{3}{9}$　　$\frac{3}{4} = \frac{15}{20}; \frac{3}{15} = \frac{4}{20}$

14. 4, 5, 8, 10　　　　15. 7, 12, 28, 48
$\frac{4}{5} = \frac{8}{10}; \frac{4}{8} = \frac{5}{10}$　　$\frac{7}{12} = \frac{28}{48}; \frac{7}{28} = \frac{12}{48}$

16. 2, 4, 7, 14　　　　17. 5, 9, 15, 27
$\frac{2}{4} = \frac{7}{14}; \frac{2}{7} = \frac{4}{14}$　　$\frac{5}{9} = \frac{15}{27}; \frac{5}{15} = \frac{9}{27}$

92　Use with Lesson 7-8.

© Pearson Education, Inc. 5

Name_____

Equivalent Fractions　　　　　　　　PS 7-8

Many scientists believe that dinosaurs ruled the Earth millions of years ago. Today, the only evidence we have of these reptiles comes from fossils that are discovered in different parts of the world.

1. A giraffe is about $\frac{1}{3}$ the size of the average *Brachiosaurus* dinosaur. Find the equivalent fraction for $\frac{1}{3}$ with a denominator of 9.　　$\frac{3}{9}$

2. Now find the equivalent fraction for $\frac{1}{3}$ with a numerator of 5.　　$\frac{5}{15}$

3. Is $\frac{10}{30}$ equivalent to $\frac{1}{3}$?　　**Yes**

4. An average adult human's height is about $\frac{1}{4}$ the height of a *Tyrannosaurus rex*. Find the equivalent fraction for $\frac{1}{4}$ with a denominator of 20.　　$\frac{5}{20}$

5. Now find the equivalent fraction for $\frac{1}{4}$ with a numerator of 3.　　$\frac{3}{12}$

6. Is $\frac{5}{25}$ equivalent to $\frac{1}{4}$?　　**No**

7. A *Stegosaurus*'s height was about $\frac{3}{10}$ of its length. Find the equivalent fraction for $\frac{3}{10}$ with a denominator of 30.　　$\frac{9}{30}$

8. Find an equivalent fraction for $\frac{3}{10}$ that has a numerator of 12.　　$\frac{12}{40}$

9. Is $\frac{18}{60}$ equivalent to $\frac{3}{10}$?　　**Yes**

10. **Writing in Math** Explain how you found your answer to Exercise 6.

Sample answer: $1 \times 5 = 5$, so you multiply the denominator by 5; $20 \neq 25$, so the fractions are not equivalent.

92　Use with Lesson 7-8.

© Pearson Education, Inc. 5

Name_____

Greatest Common Factor

P 7-9

Find the GCF of each pair of numbers.

1. 15, 50 **5**   2. 6, 27 **3**   3. 10, 25 **5**

4. 18, 32 **2**   5. 7, 28 **7**   6. 54, 108 **54**

7. 25, 55 **5**   8. 14, 48 **2**   9. 81, 135 **27**

10. **Number Sense** Can the GCF of 16 and 42 be less than 16? Explain.

Yes; Sample answer: The greatest common factor will be less than 16 because 42 is not evenly divisible by 16.

11. A restaurant received a shipment of 42 gal of orange juice and 18 gal of cranberry juice. The juice needs to be equally poured into containers. What is the largest amount of juice that each container can hold of each kind of juice?   **6 gal**

12. At a day camp, there are 56 girls and 42 boys. The campers need to be split into equal groups. Each has either all girls or all boys. What is the greatest number of campers each group can have?   **14 campers**

Test Prep

13. Which is the GCF of 24 and 64?

A. 4   B. 8   C. 14   D. 12

14. **Writing in Math** Do all even numbers have 2 as a factor? Explain.

Sample answer: Yes, because all even numbers are divisible by 2.

© Pearson Education, Inc. 5

Name_____

Greatest Common Factor

R 7-9

The greatest common factor (GCF) of two numbers is the greatest number that is a factor of both.

Find the greatest common factor of 12 and 18.

Step 1: List the factors of 12 and 18. Think of all the numbers that can be divided into 12 and 18 evenly.

12: 1, 2, 3, 4, 6, 12

18: 1, 2, 3, 6, 9, 18

Step 2: Circle the common factors.

12: ①, ②, ③, 4, ⑥, 12

18: ①, ②, ③, ⑥, 9, 18

Step 3: Find the greatest common factor.

The greatest common factor of 12 and 18 is 6.

Find the GCF of each pair of numbers.

1. 9, 27 **9**   2. 25, 40 **5**

3. 7, 36 **1**   4. 40, 48 **8**

5. 16, 28 **4**   6. 24, 42 **6**

7. 21, 35 **7**   8. 30, 70 **10**

9. **Number Sense** Can the GCF of 18 and 36 be greater than 18? Explain.

Sample answer: No, a factor of 18 must be 18 or less.

© Pearson Education, Inc. 5

Name_____

We Have a Lot in Common

E 7-9
DATA

Information about some regions of countries of the world is found in the table. Use the data in the table to answer the questions.

Country Division

Country	Region	Number
United States	States	50
Costa Rica	Provinces	7
Germany	States	16
Canada	Provinces	10
Peru	Departments	25
Brazil	States	26

Find the greatest common factor.

1. The number of states in the United States and the number of provinces in Canada   **10**

2. The number of states in Germany and the number of provinces in Canada   **2**

3. The number of states in Brazil and the number of states in Germany   **2**

4. Name two countries whose number of regions have a greatest common factor of 25.

United States and Peru

5. Name two countries whose number of regions have a greatest common factor of 1.

Sample answer: Germany and Peru

6. Name two countries whose number of regions have a greatest common factor of 5.

Canada and Peru

© Pearson Education, Inc. 5

Name_____

Greatest Common Factor

PS 7-9

Life expectancy is the average number of years a person lives. In 2002, the life expectancy of a male in Japan was about 78 years. The life expectancy for a female was about 84 years.

1. What are the factors of 78? Of 84?

78: 1, 2, 3, 6, 13, 26, 39, 78; 84: 1, 2, 3, 4, 6, 7, 12, 14, 21, 28, 42, 84

2. What are the common factors of 78 and 84?   **1, 2, 3, 6**

3. What is the greatest common factor of 78 and 84?   **6**

In 2002, about 15 out of every 100 Japanese citizens were 14 years or younger. In China, about 25 out of every 100 Chinese citizens were 14 years or younger.

4. What are the factors of 15? Of 25?

15: 1, 3, 5, 15; 25: 1, 5, 25

5. What are the common factors of 15 and 25?   **1, 5**

6. What is the greatest common factor of 15 and 25?   **5**

7. **Writing in Math** Is 10 a factor of 15 or 25? Explain how you know.

No; Sample answer: You cannot multiply 10 by any whole number to get a product of 15 or 25.

© Pearson Education, Inc. 5

Fractions in Simplest Form

P 7-10

Write each fraction in simplest form.

1. $\frac{5}{10}$ $\frac{1}{2}$
2. $\frac{6}{24}$ $\frac{1}{4}$
3. $\frac{9}{27}$ $\frac{1}{3}$
4. $\frac{3}{15}$ $\frac{1}{5}$
5. $\frac{10}{12}$ $\frac{5}{6}$
6. $\frac{9}{15}$ $\frac{3}{5}$
7. $\frac{2}{18}$ $\frac{1}{9}$
8. $\frac{25}{60}$ $\frac{5}{12}$
9. $\frac{12}{72}$ $\frac{1}{6}$
10. $\frac{30}{70}$ $\frac{3}{7}$
11. $\frac{22}{48}$ $\frac{11}{24}$
12. $\frac{16}{56}$ $\frac{2}{7}$
13. $\frac{9}{90}$ $\frac{1}{10}$
14. $\frac{72}{81}$ $\frac{8}{9}$
15. $\frac{7}{28}$ $\frac{1}{4}$

16. **Number Sense** Explain how you can tell $\frac{4}{5}$ is in simplest form.

Sample answer: The numerator and the denominator have no common factors other than 1.

Write in simplest form.

17. What fraction of the problems on the math test will be word problems?
$\frac{1}{7}$

> **Math Test**
> ⇒ 20 Multiple-choice problems
> ⇒ 10 Fill in the blanks
> ⇒ 5 Word problems

18. What fraction of the problems on the math test will be multiple-choice problems?
$\frac{4}{7}$

Test Prep

19. Which is the simplest form of $\frac{10}{82}$?
A. $\frac{1}{8}$ B. $\frac{1}{22}$ C. $\frac{10}{82}$ **D. $\frac{5}{41}$**

20. **Writing in Math** Explain how you can find the simplest form of $\frac{100}{1,000}$.
Sample answer: The GCF of 100 and 1,000 is 100. The simplest form is $\frac{100 \div 100}{1,000 \div 100} = \frac{1}{10}$.

Fractions in Simplest Form

R 7-10

There are two different ways to write a fraction in simplest form.

Write $\frac{20}{24}$ in simplest form.

Divide by Common Factors	Divide by the GCF
• Divide by common factors until the only common factor is 1.	• First find the GCF of 20 and 24.
• You can start by dividing by 2, since both numbers are even.	20: 1, 2, 4, 5, 10, 20
$\frac{20 \div 2}{24 \div 2} = \frac{10}{12}$	24: 1, 2, 3, 4, 6, 8, 12, 24
But both 10 and 12 can be divided by 2.	The GCF of 20 and 24 is 4.
$\frac{10 \div 2}{12 \div 2} = \frac{5}{6}$	• Divide both numerator and denominator by 4.
	$\frac{20 \div 4}{24 \div 4} = \frac{5}{6}$

Write each fraction in simplest form.

1. $\frac{16}{20}$ $\frac{4}{5}$
2. $\frac{8}{16}$ $\frac{1}{2}$
3. $\frac{5}{10}$ $\frac{1}{2}$
4. $\frac{8}{32}$ $\frac{1}{4}$
5. $\frac{18}{42}$ $\frac{7}{3}$ (or $\frac{3}{7}$)
6. $\frac{15}{100}$ $\frac{20}{11}$
7. $\frac{18}{21}$ $\frac{6}{7}$
8. $\frac{24}{40}$ $\frac{3}{5}$
9. $\frac{55}{75}$ $\frac{11}{15}$

10. **Number Sense** Explain how you can tell that $\frac{31}{33}$ is in simplest form.

Sample answer: You can tell because the only common factor of 31 and 33 is 1.

How Simple Can It Be?

E 7-10
MENTAL MATH

In each row, cross out the fractions that are not in simplest form.

1. ✗ $\frac{2}{3}$ ✗ $\frac{21}{22}$ ✗
2. $\frac{5}{7}$ $\frac{5}{9}$ ✗ $\frac{2}{7}$ ✗
3. ✗ ✗ $\frac{1}{89}$ ✗ ✗
4. $\frac{5}{9}$ $\frac{4}{7}$ ✗ ✗ ✗
5. $\frac{99}{100}$ ✗ ✗ $\frac{2}{5}$ $\frac{1}{6}$
6. ✗ $\frac{3}{5}$ ✗ ✗ ✗
7. $\frac{1}{3}$ $\frac{9}{10}$ ✗ ✗ ✗
8. ✗ $\frac{3}{7}$ ✗ ✗ $\frac{1}{9}$
9. $\frac{3}{5}$ $\frac{1}{6}$ ✗ $\frac{3}{22}$ $\frac{2}{29}$
10. ✗ ✗ ✗ ✗ ✗
11. ✗ ✗ $\frac{8}{15}$ $\frac{67}{100}$ ✗
12. $\frac{5}{7}$ $\frac{100}{101}$ ✗ ✗ ✗

13. Write the total number of fractions not crossed out from the rows above as a fraction. Then write in simplest form.
$\frac{24}{60} = \frac{2}{5}$

Fractions in Simplest Form

PS 7-10

Student Survey In 2002, a national survey of students was conducted in the United States. The students responded to many different questions, including the color of their favorite school uniform, as well as questions about the United States.

1. Out of every 100 students, about 16 said they thought the U.S. government was doing enough to protect the environment. What is the greatest common factor of 16 and 100?
4

2. What is $\frac{16}{100}$ in simplest form?
$\frac{4}{25}$

3. Out of every 100 students, about 84 said they thought the U.S. government was not doing enough to protect the environment. What is the greatest common factor of 84 and 100?
4

4. What is $\frac{84}{100}$ in simplest form?
$\frac{21}{25}$

5. Of the students who said they thought the U.S. government was doing enough, about 36 out of every 100 students was a girl. What is $\frac{36}{100}$ in simplest form?
$\frac{9}{25}$

6. Of the students who said they thought the U.S. government was doing enough, about 64 out of every 100 students was a boy. What is $\frac{64}{100}$ in simplest form?
$\frac{16}{25}$

7. **Writing in Math** Explain how you know $\frac{11}{13}$ is in simplest form.

Sample answer: There is no common factor other than 1 for both numbers.

Practice

Name_____

Understanding Comparing Fractions P 7-11

Write >, <, or = for each ◯. You may use fraction strips or drawings to help.

1. $\frac{4}{12}$ ⧁ $\frac{4}{16}$ 2. $\frac{7}{14}$ ⧀ $\frac{3}{5}$

3. $\frac{5}{10}$ ⊜ $\frac{1}{2}$ 4. $\frac{1}{9}$ ⧀ $\frac{1}{6}$

5. $\frac{2}{6}$ ⧁ $\frac{2}{7}$ 6. $\frac{3}{9}$ ⊜ $\frac{1}{3}$

7. $\frac{4}{5}$ ⧁ $\frac{5}{10}$ 8. $\frac{6}{10}$ ⧀ $\frac{7}{8}$

9. **Number Sense** Kelvin says that $\frac{22}{30}$ is greater than $\frac{22}{32}$. Do you agree? Explain.

Sample answer: Yes, Kelvin is right, because when the numerator is the same, the fraction with the lesser denominator is greater.

10. Jane bought $\frac{3}{5}$ lb of apples. Jack bought $\frac{2}{7}$ lb of apples. Who bought more pounds of apples?   **Jane**

11. Lyman and Amalia each painted part of the garage and their dad painted the rest. Lyman painted $\frac{2}{6}$ of the garage. Amalia painted $\frac{2}{8}$ of the garage. Who painted more?   **Lyman**

Test Prep

12. Which of the fractions is less than $\frac{1}{3}$?

(A) $\frac{2}{7}$ B. $\frac{2}{6}$ C. $\frac{2}{3}$ D. $\frac{3}{4}$

13. **Writing in Math** How do you know $\frac{72}{80}$ is greater than $\frac{7}{8}$? Explain.

Sample answer: $\frac{7}{8}$ is equal to $\frac{70}{80}$, which is less than $\frac{72}{80}$.

Use with Lesson 7-11. 95

© Pearson Education, Inc. 5

Reteaching

Name_____

Understanding Comparing Fractions R 7-11

You can use fraction strips to compare fractions.

Compare $\frac{3}{4}$ and $\frac{7}{10}$.

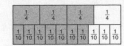

So, $\frac{3}{4} > \frac{7}{10}$.

Write >, <, or = for each ◯.

You may use fraction strips or drawings to help.

1. $\frac{1}{8}$ ⧀ $\frac{3}{10}$ 2. $\frac{3}{4}$ ⧁ $\frac{4}{10}$ 3. $\frac{4}{8}$ ⊜ $\frac{2}{4}$ 4. $\frac{2}{3}$ ⧀ $\frac{3}{4}$

5. **Number Sense** Explain how you can tell $\frac{26}{100}$ is greater than $\frac{1}{4}$.

Sample answer: 25 is $\frac{1}{4}$ of 100. 26 > 25, so $\frac{26}{100} > \frac{1}{4}$.

Dish	Flour Needed
Casserole	$\frac{9}{10}$ c
Breaded beef	$\frac{3}{4}$ c
Enchiladas	$\frac{5}{8}$ c
Waffles	$\frac{1}{2}$ c

6. Which dish needs the most flour?

Casserole

7. Which needs more flour, breaded beef or enchiladas?

Breaded beef

Use with Lesson 7-11. 95

© Pearson Education, Inc. 5

Enrichment

Name_____

Fraction Playground   E 7-11 NUMBER SENSE

To balance a seesaw at the playground, the two people on the seesaw must be the same weight. The same is true for fractions. Two equal fractions will result in a balanced seesaw. When one fraction on a seesaw is greater than the other fraction on the seesaw, the greater fraction will sink and the lesser fraction will rise.

Look at the fractions on the seesaws. For each, circle the fraction or fractions that would result in the seesaw staying in the position shown.

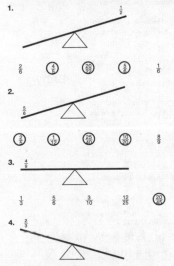

1. $\frac{1}{2}$

$\frac{2}{6}$ ⓸$\frac{4}{4}$ ⓴$\frac{20}{22}$ ⑨$\frac{9}{11}$ $\frac{1}{6}$

2. $\frac{5}{6}$

⑧$\frac{8}{9}$ ⑫$\frac{1}{12}$ ㉕$\frac{25}{40}$ ⑩$\frac{10}{20}$ $\frac{8}{9}$

3. $\frac{4}{9}$

$\frac{1}{3}$ $\frac{5}{6}$ $\frac{3}{10}$ $\frac{12}{25}$ ⓴$\frac{20}{45}$

4. $\frac{2}{3}$

$\frac{2}{3}$ ⑭$\frac{14}{18}$ ⑦$\frac{7}{9}$ $\frac{6}{18}$ $\frac{12}{27}$

Use with Lesson 7-11. 95

© Pearson Education, Inc. 5

Problem Solving

Name_____

Understanding Comparing Fractions PS 7-11

Dog Food Diet is an important part of keeping a dog healthy. One dog food company supplied information for how much dry and canned food to feed a "senior" dog that is 7 years old or older. The amount of each type of dog food depends on the weight of the dog. Use the fraction strips to complete Exercises 1–3. Write >, <, or = for each ____.

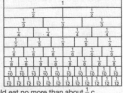

1. One weight class of senior dogs should eat no more than about $\frac{1}{2}$ c of dry food each day. Another weight class of senior dogs should eat no more than about $\frac{7}{8}$ c of dry food each day. Compare the amounts. $\frac{1}{2}$ **<** $\frac{7}{8}$

2. A 10 lb senior dog should eat about $\frac{3}{8}$ c of dry food and about $\frac{1}{3}$ can of canned food each day. Compare the amounts. $\frac{3}{8}$ **>** $\frac{1}{3}$

3. A 20 lb senior dog should eat about $\frac{2}{3}$ c of dry food and about $\frac{4}{6}$ can of canned food each day. Compare the amounts. $\frac{2}{3}$ **=** $\frac{4}{6}$

Reading Over the weekend, Craig, Dottie, and Hale started reading the same book. Craig read $\frac{1}{2}$ of the book, Dottie read $\frac{5}{8}$ of the book, and Hale read $\frac{2}{5}$ of the book.

4. Who read more, Craig or Hale?   **Craig**

5. Who read more, Craig or Dottie?   **Dottie**

6. Who read more, Dottie or Hale?   **Dottie**

7. **Writing in Math** Explain why Craig's having read $\frac{1}{2}$ the book makes it easier to compare who read more.

Sample answer: $\frac{1}{2}$ is a benchmark fraction, so it's easier to compare numbers.

Use with Lesson 7-11. 95

© Pearson Education, Inc. 5

Practice

Name_____

Comparing and Ordering Fractions and Mixed Numbers

P 7-12

Compare. Write >, <, or = for each ◯ .

1. $\frac{6}{7}$ ⊘ $\frac{6}{8}$ 2. $\frac{4}{9}$ ⊘ $\frac{2}{3}$ 3. $1\frac{1}{10}$ ⊘ $1\frac{1}{12}$

4. $2\frac{4}{5}$ ⊘ $2\frac{5}{6}$ 5. $3\frac{6}{9}$ ⊘ $3\frac{2}{3}$ 6. $\frac{2}{5}$ ⊘ $\frac{2}{8}$

Order the numbers from least to greatest.

7. $\frac{4}{5}, \frac{4}{8}, \frac{3}{4}, \frac{4}{5}$ $\frac{4}{8}, \frac{5}{8}, \frac{3}{4}, \frac{4}{5}$

8. $4\frac{1}{4}, 4\frac{1}{8}, 4\frac{10}{11}, 4\frac{2}{15}$ $4\frac{1}{8}, 4\frac{2}{15}, 4\frac{1}{4}, 4\frac{10}{11}$

9. $1\frac{3}{7}, 1\frac{3}{4}, 1\frac{2}{4}, 1\frac{8}{13}$ $1\frac{3}{7}, 1\frac{2}{4}, 1\frac{8}{13}, 1\frac{3}{4}$

10. **Number Sense** How do you know that $5\frac{1}{4}$ is less than $5\frac{4}{10}$?

$5\frac{1}{4}$ is less than $5\frac{4}{10}$ because $\frac{1}{4}$ is less than $\frac{4}{10}$.

11. A mechanic uses four wrenches to fix Mrs. Aaron's car. The wrenches are different sizes: $\frac{5}{16}$ in., $\frac{1}{2}$ in., $\frac{1}{4}$ in., and $\frac{7}{16}$ in. Order the sizes of the wrenches from greatest to least.

$\frac{1}{2}$ in., $\frac{7}{16}$ in., $\frac{5}{16}$ in., $\frac{1}{4}$ in.

Test Prep

12. Which is greater than $6\frac{1}{3}$?

A. $6\frac{1}{6}$ B. $6\frac{1}{5}$ C. $6\frac{1}{4}$ **D.** $6\frac{1}{2}$

13. **Writing in Math** Compare $3\frac{3}{22}$ and $3\frac{2}{33}$. Which is greater? How do you know?

Sample answer: $3\frac{3}{22}$; you can find a common denominator. If you use 66, then $3\frac{3}{22} = 3\frac{9}{66}$ and $3\frac{2}{33} = 3\frac{4}{66}$. So, $3\frac{9}{66} > 3\frac{4}{66}$.

© Pearson Education, Inc. 5

Reteaching

Name_____

Comparing and Ordering Fractions and Mixed Numbers

R 7-12

Compare $\frac{4}{10}$ and $\frac{5}{12}$.

One way to compare fractions is to find a common denominator.

10: 10, 20, 30, 40, 50, ⑥⓪
12: 12, 24, 36, 48, ⑥⓪, 72

Use 60 as the common denominator.

$\frac{4}{10} = \frac{24}{60}$ $\frac{5}{12} = \frac{25}{60}$

Then compare:

$\frac{25}{60} > \frac{24}{60}$, so $\frac{5}{12} > \frac{4}{10}$.

How to order fractions.

Write $\frac{2}{3}, \frac{1}{6}$, and $\frac{1}{3}$ in order from least to greatest.

$\frac{2}{3} > \frac{1}{3}$ because the denominators are the same and 2 > 1.

$\frac{1}{3} > \frac{1}{6}$ because $\frac{1}{3} = \frac{2}{6}$ and $\frac{2}{6} > \frac{1}{6}$.

So $\frac{1}{6} < \frac{1}{3} < \frac{2}{3}$.

Compare. Write >, <, or = for each ◯.

1. $\frac{2}{3}$ ⊘ $\frac{1}{6}$ 2. $\frac{3}{4}$ ⊘ $\frac{1}{2}$ 3. $\frac{6}{8}$ ⊘ $\frac{9}{12}$ 4. $\frac{5}{6}$ ⊘ $\frac{21}{24}$

Order the numbers from least to greatest.

5. $\frac{4}{5}, \frac{3}{5}, \frac{3}{5}$ $\frac{3}{5}, \frac{3}{4}, \frac{4}{5}$ 6. $\frac{6}{12}, \frac{3}{1}, \frac{1}{3}$ $\frac{3}{12}, \frac{1}{3}, \frac{6}{12}$

7. $2\frac{1}{4}, 1\frac{3}{8}, 2\frac{2}{4}$ $1\frac{3}{8}, 2\frac{1}{4}, 2\frac{2}{4}$ 8. $1\frac{5}{6}, 1\frac{3}{6}, 1\frac{5}{12}$ $1\frac{1}{6}, 1\frac{3}{6}, 1\frac{5}{6}$

9. **Number Sense** Explain why $\frac{5}{6} < \frac{13}{15}$.

Sample answer: $\frac{5}{6} = \frac{25}{30}$ and $\frac{13}{15} = \frac{26}{30}$, $\frac{25}{30} < \frac{26}{30}$, so $\frac{5}{6} < \frac{13}{15}$.

© Pearson Education, Inc. 5

Enrichment

Name_____

Middle of the Road

E 7-12
NUMBER SENSE

For each pair of numbers below, find a number with a value in between the two given numbers. Write the number in the blank. Then write a sentence explaining how you found your answer. Your answers must be a fraction or a mixed number. There is more than one possible correct answer.

1. $3\frac{1}{4}, 3\frac{5}{8}$ _____

Sample answer: $3\frac{3}{8}$; I converted $\frac{1}{4}$ to $\frac{2}{8}$ to find this number.

2. $\frac{3}{20}, \frac{1}{2}$ _____

Sample answer: $\frac{1}{4}$; I converted $\frac{1}{2}$ to $\frac{10}{20}$ to find this number.

3. $5\frac{6}{7}, 6\frac{2}{8}$ _____

Sample answer: $6\frac{1}{8}$; I know this number is greater than $5\frac{6}{7}$ and less than $6\frac{2}{8}$.

4. $20\frac{9}{10}, 21$ _____

Sample answer: $20\frac{19}{20}$; I know this number is greater than $20\frac{9}{10}$ and less than 21.

5. $\frac{5}{7}, 1\frac{1}{3}$ _____

Sample answer: $\frac{6}{7}$; I know this number is greater than $\frac{5}{7}$ and less than $1\frac{1}{3}$.

© Pearson Education, Inc. 5

Problem Solving

Name_____

Comparing and Ordering Fractions and Mixed Numbers

PS 7-12

Babies Babies learn to do things at different ages. Medical research and baby product companies often conduct studies to learn more about baby development. Suppose a group studied the development of two babies.

1. Baby 1 learned to walk after $1\frac{1}{4}$ years. Baby 2 learned to walk after $\frac{19}{12}$ years. Which baby walked first?   **Baby 1**

2. Suppose Baby 1 developed teeth after $\frac{1}{2}$ year and Baby 2 developed teeth after $\frac{5}{12}$ years. Which baby developed teeth first?   **Baby 2**

3. Suppose Baby 1 learned to point to the eyes, ears, and nose after $2\frac{1}{3}$ years. Baby 2 learned to do it after $2\frac{5}{12}$ years. Which baby learned first?   **Baby 1**

Rock Collections Edward and Steven collect rocks. Edward's rocks are $1\frac{3}{4}, 2\frac{7}{9}, 2\frac{5}{6}$, and $1\frac{2}{5}$ in. long. Steven's rocks are $2\frac{3}{5}, 1\frac{4}{7}, 2\frac{1}{2}$, and $1\frac{5}{8}$ in. long.

4. Order Edward's collection from least to greatest.

$1\frac{2}{5}, 1\frac{3}{4}, 2\frac{7}{9}, 2\frac{5}{6}$

5. Order Steven's collection from least to greatest.

$1\frac{4}{7}, 1\frac{5}{8}, 2\frac{1}{2}, 2\frac{3}{5}$

6. **Writing in Math** How can you tell that $\frac{4}{7}$ is greater than $\frac{1}{2}$ without finding a common denominator?

Sample answer: It is easy to tell because 4 is more than half of 7.

© Pearson Education, Inc. **5**

Practice

Name_____

Fractions and Decimals   P 7-13

Write each decimal and a fraction in simplest form for the shaded portion of each model.

1.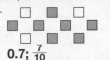

$0.7; \frac{7}{10}$

2.

$0.16; \frac{4}{25}$

Write each decimal as a fraction or mixed number in simplest form.

3. 2.25 $2\frac{1}{4}$ 4. 3.74 $3\frac{37}{50}$

5. 0.08 $\frac{2}{25}$ 6. 0.375 $\frac{3}{8}$

Write each fraction or mixed number as a decimal.

7. $\frac{2}{16}$ **0.125**   8. $10\frac{3}{4}$ **10.75**

9. $7\frac{2}{5}$ **7.4**   10. $\frac{8}{40}$ **0.2**

11. In Ron's school, 12 out of 30 students wear brown shoes. Write the decimal that shows the portion of students who wear brown shoes. **0.4**

Test Prep

12. Which is the decimal equivalent of the mixed number $3\frac{3}{6}$?

A. 3.36   **B.** 3.5   C. 3.56   D. 3.63

13. **Writing in Math** Explain how knowing that $5 ÷ 8 = 0.625$ helps you find the decimal for $4\frac{5}{8}$.

Sample answer: Knowing that $5 ÷ 8 = 0.625$ helps find that $4\frac{5}{8} = 4.625$.

Use with Lesson 7-13. **97**

Reteaching

Name_____

Fractions and Decimals   R 7-13

Fractions can also be named using decimals.

8 out of 10 sections are shaded.

The fraction is $\frac{8}{10}$.

The word name is eight tenths.

The decimal is 0.8.

Write $\frac{2}{5}$ as a decimal.	Write $3\frac{3}{5}$ as a decimal.	Write 0.07 as a fraction.
Sometimes a fraction can be rewritten as an equivalent fraction that has a denominator of 10 or 100. $\frac{2}{5} = \frac{2 \times 2}{5 \times 2} = \frac{4}{10}$ $\frac{4}{10} = 0.4$ So, $\frac{2}{5} = 0.4$.	First write the whole number. 3 Change the fraction to a decimal. $\frac{3}{5} = \frac{3 \times 2}{5 \times 2} = \frac{6}{10} = 0.6$ Write the decimal next to the whole number. 3.6 So, $3\frac{3}{5} = 3.6$.	The word name for 0.07 is seven hundredths. "Seven" is the numerator, and "hundredths" is the denominator. So, $0.07 = \frac{7}{100}$.

Write each fraction or mixed number as a decimal.

1. $\frac{1}{5}$ **0.2**   2. $\frac{6}{25}$ **0.24**   3. $2\frac{3}{4}$ **2.75**   4. $3\frac{9}{10}$ **3.9**

Write each decimal as a fraction or mixed number in simplest form.

5. 1.25 $1\frac{1}{4}$ 6. 3.29 $3\frac{29}{100}$

7. 0.65 $\frac{13}{20}$ 8. 5.6 $5\frac{3}{5}$

9. **Number Sense** Dan says $\frac{3}{5}$ is the same as 3.5. Is he correct? Explain.

Sample answer: No, $\frac{3}{5} = 0.6$, while $3.5 = 3\frac{1}{2}$.

Use with Lesson 7-13. **97**

Enrichment

Name_____

Triple Treat   E 7-13
                                         VISUAL THINKING

Draw a line from the fraction in the triangle to the equivalent decimal in the circle. Then draw a line to connect the decimal to the correct model in the box.

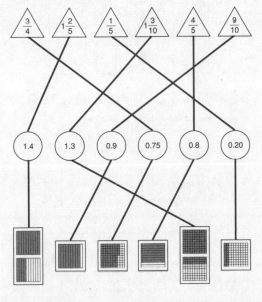

Use with Lesson 7-13. **97**

Problem Solving

Name_____

Fractions and Decimals   PS 7-13

Budgets Every state must carefully track the income it receives and the money it spends. This data is usually found in a state's annual budget. The chart shows the state income for Arkansas in 2000.

	2000 Arkansas Income Report
Income Source	**Fraction or Decimal Amount of Total State Income**
General revenues	$\frac{38}{100}$
Federal funds	0.250
Special revenues	$\frac{80}{1,000}$
Cash funds	0.060
Trust funds	$\frac{18}{100}$
Other	0.050

1. General revenues were $\frac{38}{100}$ of the state's income. Write $\frac{38}{100}$ as a decimal.

0.38

2. Federal funds were 0.250 of the state's income. Write 0.250 as a fraction.

$\frac{25}{100}$ or $\frac{1}{4}$

3. Special revenues were $\frac{80}{1,000}$ of the state's income. Write $\frac{80}{1,000}$ as a decimal. **0.080**

4. Cash funds were 0.060 of the state's income. Write 0.060 as a fraction.

$\frac{60}{1000}$ or $\frac{3}{50}$

5. Trust funds were $\frac{18}{100}$ of the state's income. Write $\frac{18}{100}$ as a decimal. **0.18**

6. Funds from other sources were 0.050 of the state's income. Write 0.050 as a fraction.

$\frac{5}{100}$ or $\frac{1}{20}$

7. **Writing in Math** Explain why you can use division to convert a fraction to a decimal.

Sample answer: A fraction is equal to dividing the numerator by the denominator, so you can use division to convert.

Use with Lesson 7-13. **97**

Name_____

Fractions and Decimals on the Number Line

P 7-14

Show each set of numbers on the same number line. Then order the numbers from least to greatest.

1. $0.75, \frac{8}{10}, 0.2, \frac{2}{5}$ $0.2, \frac{2}{5}, 0.75, \frac{8}{10}$

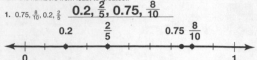

Write a fraction or mixed number in simplest form and a decimal that name each point.

2. Point Q $\frac{3}{10}$; 0.3   3. Point R $\frac{4}{5}$; 0.8   4. Point S $1\frac{2}{5}$; 1.4

5. Uma recorded the distances that volunteers walked in the charity event. Grace walked $1\frac{3}{5}$ mi, Wendell walked 1.3 mi, and Simon walked $1\frac{1}{10}$ mi. Show these amounts on a number line. Who walked the farthest?   **Grace**

Sample drawing:

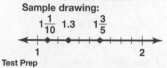

Test Prep

6. Which is a decimal that could go between the mixed numbers $4\frac{3}{5}$ and $4\frac{9}{10}$ on a number line?

A. 4.45   B. 4.5   C. 4.75   D. 4.92

7. **Writing in Math** Explain how you know that 5.5 is to the right of $5\frac{1}{4}$ on the number line.

Sample answer: $5\frac{1}{4} = 5.25; 5.25 < 5.5;$ So, 5.5 must be to the right of $5\frac{1}{4}$.

98   Use with Lesson 7-14.

Name_____

Fractions and Decimals on the Number Line

R 7-14

Show $\frac{2}{5}$, 1.2, and $1\frac{3}{5}$ on the same number line.

Step 1: Write each fraction or mixed number as a decimal.

$\frac{2}{5} = \frac{2 \times 2}{5 \times 2} = \frac{4}{10} = 0.4$

$1.2 = 1.2$

$1\frac{3}{5} = 1\frac{6}{10} = 1.6$

Step 2: Place the numbers on the number line.

The point for $\frac{2}{5}$ or 0.4 is between 0 and 1.

The point for $1\frac{3}{5}$ or 1.6 is between 1 and 2.

The point for 1.2 is between 1 and 2.

Write a fraction or a mixed number in simplest form and a decimal that name point A.

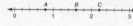

Step 1: Determine how the number line is separated.

The number line is separated into tenths.

Step 2: Write a fraction for point A.

Point A is at $2\frac{3}{10}$.

Step 3: Change $2\frac{3}{10}$ to a decimal.

$2\frac{3}{10} = 2.3$

Show each set of numbers on the same number line. Then order the numbers from least to greatest.

1. 1.2, 1.9, $1\frac{3}{5}$.   **1.2, $1\frac{3}{5}$, 1.9**

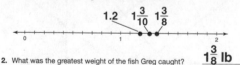

Write a fraction or mixed number in simplest form and a decimal that name each point.

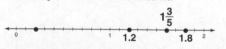

2. Point A $\frac{4}{5}$, 0.8   3. Point B $1\frac{3}{5}$, 1.6   4. Point C $2\frac{1}{5}$, 2.2

98   Use with Lesson 7-14.

Name_____

What's My Line?

E 7-14
REASONING

Plot three points on the number line below. Label the points A, B, and C. Your points can be any combination of fractions, decimals, and mixed numbers. For each point, complete the three sentences that describe the point.

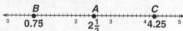

1. **Point A** **Sample answer:**

Point A is located in between $\underline{2}$ and $\underline{3}$. (Insert whole numbers or zeros in the blanks.)

Point A is equivalent to $\underline{2.5}$. (If your point is a decimal, give the fraction equivalent; if your point is a fraction or mixed number, give the decimal equivalent.)

The value of Point A is $\underline{2\frac{1}{2}}$.

2. **Point B** **Sample answer:**

Point B is located in between $\underline{0}$ and $\underline{1}$.

Point B is equivalent to $\underline{\frac{3}{4}}$.

The value of Point B is $\underline{0.75}$.

3. **Point C** **Sample answer:**

Point C is located in between $\underline{4}$ and $\underline{5}$.

Point C is equivalent to $\underline{4\frac{1}{4}}$.

The value of Point C is $\underline{4.25}$.

98   Use with Lesson 7-14.

Name_____

Fractions and Decimals on the Number Line

PS 7-14

Greg, Donna, and Pat went fishing. Each caught three fish. The fish Greg caught weighed $1\frac{3}{10}$ lb, $1\frac{3}{8}$ lb, and 1.2 lb. The fish Donna caught weighed 1.8 lb, $1\frac{3}{5}$ lb, and 1.2 lb. The fish Pat caught weighed $1\frac{4}{8}$ lb, 1.4 lb, and $\frac{2}{3}$ lb.

1. Show the weights of Greg's fish on the number line.

2. What was the greatest weight of the fish Greg caught? $1\frac{3}{8}$ lb

3. Show the weights of Donna's fish on the number line.

4. What was the greatest weight of the fish Donna caught?   1.8 lb

5. Show the weights of Pat's fish on the number line.

6. What was the greatest weight of the fish Pat caught? $1\frac{4}{8}$ lb

7. **Writing in Math** Explain how placing numbers on a number line can help you find which number is greatest or least.

Sample answer: The number on the far right will be the greatest, and the number on the far left will be the least.

98   Use with Lesson 7-14.

© Pearson Education, Inc. 5

Practice

Name_____

PROBLEM-SOLVING STRATEGY   P 7-15

Use Logical Reasoning

Use the chart and logical reasoning to finish solving each problem.

1. Jenna, Mason, and Sean split the household tasks they had to do on Saturday. Their parents gave them a list of jobs: mow the lawn, wash the car, and do the laundry. Sean and Jenna do not want to mow the lawn. Mason helped Jenna fold the laundry when he was done with his job. Who did which task?

	Mow Lawn	Wash Car	Laundry
Jenna	No	No	Yes
Mason	Yes	No	No
Sean	No	Yes	No

Mason mowed the lawn, Jenna did the laundry, and Sean washed the car.

2. Parker, Jaime, and Quincy need to choose a book to read for a school project. There are 3 kinds of books left and each student must choose a different kind of book. Jaime does not like science fiction. There are 4 consonants in the name of the student who chose mystery. Who chose which book?

	Mystery	Western	Science Fiction
Parker	Yes	No	No
Jaime	No	Yes	No
Quincy	No	No	Yes

Parker chose the mystery book, Jaime chose the western book, and Quincy chose the science fiction book.

© Pearson Education, Inc. 5

Use with Lesson 7-15. **99**

Reteaching

Name_____

PROBLEM-SOLVING STRATEGY   R 7-15

Use Logical Reasoning

The Travelers Justin has visited four states. Aubrey has not visited Ohio or Arizona. Greg has not visited Ohio. Savannah has visited only one state. Two people have visited Ohio. Which two people have visited Ohio?

Read and Understand

Step 1: What do you know?

Four people have traveled to four different states.

Step 2: What are you trying to find?

Which two people have visited Ohio.

Plan and Solve

Step 3: What strategy will you use? Strategy: Use logical reasoning

Use the information you are given and reasoning to make conclusions.

	Arizona	New York	Ohio	Georgia
Aubrey	No	Yes	No	Yes
Greg	Yes	Yes	No	Yes
Savannah	No	No	Yes	No
Justin	Yes	Yes	Yes	Yes

You know Justin has visited Ohio. You know Greg and Aubrey have not, so Savannah must be the second person.

	Orange	Green	Red
Sam	No	Yes	No
Joan	Yes	No	No
Becky	No	No	Yes

1. Sam, Joan, and Becky each like either orange, green, or red best. Sam dislikes orange. Becky knows the people who like green and orange best. Complete the chart to find out which person likes each color best.

© Pearson Education, Inc. 5

Use with Lesson 7-15. **99**

Enrichment

Name_____

The Path to Success

E 7-15
NUMBER SENSE

Follow the path. At each fork, choose the path marked by the fraction with the greater value. Where do you end up? Circle the letter at the end of the correct path.

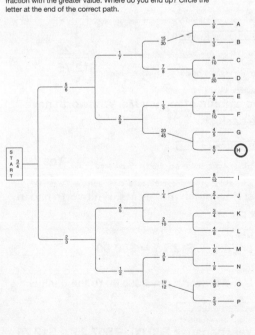

© Pearson Education, Inc. 5

Use with Lesson 7-15. **99**

Problem Solving

Name_____

PROBLEM-SOLVING STRATEGY   PS 7-15

Use Logical Reasoning

Capitals Venezuela, Argentina, Chile, and Colombia are four countries in South America. Their capital cities are Santiago, Bogotá, Caracas, and Buenos Aires, but not necessarily in that order. If you know that Caracas is the capital of Venezuela, that Santiago is not the capital of Argentina, and that Bogotá is the capital of Colombia, then what are the capitals of each country?

Read and Understand

1. What two capitals do you know?

   Caracas and Bogotá

2. What are you trying to find? **Capitals of each country**

Plan and Solve

3. What strategy will you use? **Logical reasoning**

4. Complete the chart to help solve the problem.

	Santiago	Bogotá	Caracas	Buenos Aires
Venezuela	No	No	Yes	No
Argentina	No	No	No	Yes
Chile	Yes	No	No	No
Colombia	No	Yes	No	No

5. Solve the problem. Write your answer in a complete sentence.

   Santiago is the capital of Chile, Bogotá is the capital of Colombia, Caracas is the capital of Venezuela, and Buenos Aires is the capital of Argentina.

Look Back and Check

6. Is your work reasonable? **Yes, the conclusions were the right ones.**

© Pearson Education, Inc. 5

Use with Lesson 7-15. **99**

Use with Chapter 7, Lesson 15 **99**

Practice

PROBLEM-SOLVING APPLICATIONS　　　P 7-16

Helping the Birds

Simone's parents are bird-lovers. There is a birdhouse, some bird feeders, and a birdbath in their backyard. The family likes to watch the birds who come to enjoy the shelter, food, and water.

1. Simone's brother, Randy, says that he saw 12 birds today, and 6 of the birds were blue jays. Write the portion of the birds that were blue jays as a fraction and a decimal.

   $0.5; \frac{1}{2}$

2. Simone and her mother went to the store to buy food for the bird feeders. They bought three different kinds of food. They bought $9\frac{3}{4}$ lb of one kind of food, 9.52 lb of another kind of food, and $9\frac{5}{12}$ lb of a third kind of food. Order the weights of the food from least to greatest.

   $9\frac{5}{12}, 9.52, 9\frac{3}{4}$

3. Simone, Randy, and Kylie needed to clean and prepare the birdhouse, birdbath, and bird feeders for the winter. Randy does not like to clean the birdbath. Simone does the same job every year. Kylie cleaned the birdhouse. Who cleaned what?

	Birdhouse	Birdbath	Bird Feeders
Simone	No	Yes	No
Randy	No	No	Yes
Kylie	Yes	No	No

Simone cleaned the birdbath, Kylie cleaned the birdhouse, and Randy cleaned the bird feeders.

Reteaching

PROBLEM-SOLVING APPLICATIONS　　　R 7-16

Logic, Fractions, and Decimals

The Walkers Jeff walked $1\frac{4}{10}$ mi. Kirsten walked $2\frac{1}{5}$ mi. Sally walked $1\frac{3}{5}$ mi. Which person walked the farthest? Which person walked the least?

Compare the whole number parts first.
Since $2 > 1$, $2\frac{1}{5} > 1\frac{3}{5}$ and $1\frac{4}{10}$. So Kirsten walked farther than Jeff and Sally.

Then compare the fractions.
Since $\frac{6}{10} > \frac{4}{10}$, $1\frac{3}{5} > 1\frac{4}{10}$. So Sally walked farther than Jeff.

Therefore, Kirsten walked the farthest, Sally walked the second farthest, and Jeff walked the least.

Find a common denominator.

5:　5, $\overcircled{10}$, 15
10:　$\overcircled{10}$, 20, 30

$$\frac{3}{5} = \frac{6}{10}$$

Order the numbers from least to greatest.

1. $\frac{3}{4}, 1\frac{1}{4}, \frac{2}{8}$　　**$\frac{2}{8}$, $\frac{3}{4}$, $1\frac{1}{4}$**

2. $3\frac{3}{10}, 3\frac{1}{5}, 3\frac{5}{10}$　　**$3\frac{1}{5}$, $3\frac{3}{10}$, $3\frac{5}{10}$**

Estimate the shaded part of each.

3. [bar]　**$\frac{1}{3}$**　　4. [bar]　**$\frac{1}{4}$**

Use the chart to finish solving the problem.

	Paints	Sculpts	Draws
Nicole	Yes	No	No
Ali	No	No	Yes
Mark	No	Yes	No

5. Nicole, Ali, and Mark are artists. Each either paints, sculpts, or draws. Nicole does not draw. Mark knows the people who paint and draw. What is each person's art?

Nicole paints, Ali draws, and Mark sculpts.

Enrichment

Greatest Common Factor-y　　　E 7-16
NUMBER SENSE

At the Greatest Common Factor-y, pairs of numbers are packaged according to their greatest common factor. The boxes below are being packed at the factory. Write the pairs of numbers from the conveyor belt on the boxes labeled with their greatest common factor.

(15, 20) (18, 6) (6, 9) (12, 16) (21, 28) (64, 24) (14, 35) (21, 18) (20, 24) (60, 18) (25, 35)

GCF: 4
(12, 16)
(20, 24)

GCF: 7
(21, 28)
(14, 35)

GCF: 8
(64, 24)

GCF: 6
(18, 6)
(60, 18)

GCF: 5
(15, 20)
(25, 35)

GCF: 3
(6, 9)
(21, 18)

Problem Solving

PROBLEM-SOLVING APPLICATION　　　PS 7-16

Groceries

Ms. Whitworth bought groceries for $67.25. She received $12.75 in change from the cashier. Ms. Whitworth had $100.00 in her purse. How much money did she give the cashier?

Read and Understand

1. How much did the groceries cost?　　**$67.25**

2. How much change did Ms. Whitworth receive?　　**$12.75**

3. What are you trying to find?

The amount of money Ms. Whitworth gave the cashier

Plan and Solve

4. Is there enough information to solve the problem?　　**Yes**

5. Is there information you do not need to solve the problem? What is it?

Yes; How much money Ms. Whitworth had in her purse

6. Solve the problem.

$67.25 + $12.75 = $80.00

7. Write the answer in a complete sentence.

Ms. Whitworth gave $80.00 to the cashier.

Look Back and Check

8. Is your answer correct?

Yes, because $80.00 − $67.25 = $12.75

Name_____

Adding and Subtracting Fractions with Like Denominators
P 8-1

Add or subtract. Simplify if possible.

1. $\frac{10}{12} + \frac{8}{12} = 1\frac{1}{2}$

2. $\frac{8}{12} - \frac{5}{12} = \frac{1}{3}$

3. $\frac{7}{10} + \frac{2}{10} = \frac{9}{10}$

4. $\frac{2}{3} - \frac{1}{3} = \frac{1}{3}$

5. $\frac{6}{8} + \frac{5}{8} + \frac{3}{8} = 1\frac{3}{4}$

6. $\frac{8}{10} - \frac{3}{10} = \frac{1}{2}$

7. $\frac{1}{4} + \frac{2}{4} + \frac{3}{4} = 1\frac{1}{2}$

8. $\frac{9}{11} - \frac{1}{11} = \frac{8}{11}$

9. $\frac{2}{5} + \frac{2}{5} + \frac{3}{5} = 1\frac{2}{5}$

10. $\frac{7}{8} - \frac{3}{8} = \frac{1}{2}$

11. **Number Sense** What fraction could you add to $\frac{4}{7}$ to get a sum greater than 1?
Sample answer: $\frac{4}{7}$

12. **Reasoning** Write three fractions, using 10 as the denominator, whose sum is 1.
Sample answer: $\frac{4}{10} + \frac{3}{10} + \frac{3}{10} = \frac{10}{10} = 1$

Test Prep

13. Which of the following represents the difference between two equal fractions?

    A. 1   B. $\frac{1}{2}$ C. $\frac{1}{4}$ **(D.) 0**

14. **Writing in Math** In one night, George reads 3 chapters of a book with 27 chapters. After the second night, he has read a total of $\frac{8}{27}$ of the book. Explain how you would determine the number of chapters George read the second night. Solve the problem.
Sample answer: Take the total number of chapters read and subtract the number of chapters read the first night. $\frac{8}{27} - \frac{3}{27} = \frac{5}{27}$

Name_____

Adding and Subtracting Fractions with Like Denominators
R 8-1

When two fractions have the same denominator, their sum or difference also has the same denominator.

Find $\frac{7}{8} - \frac{5}{8}$.

Step 1: Subtract the numerators.
$7 - 5 = 2$

Step 2: Write the difference over the denominator.
$\frac{7}{8} - \frac{5}{8} = \frac{2}{8}$

Step 3: Simplify the difference.
$\frac{2}{8} = \frac{1}{4}$

So, $\frac{7}{8} - \frac{5}{8} = \frac{1}{4}$.

Add or subtract. Simplify, if possible.

1. $\frac{3}{8} + \frac{3}{8} = \frac{3}{4}$

2. $\frac{11}{12} - \frac{5}{12} = \frac{1}{2}$

3. $\frac{9}{10} + \frac{3}{10} = 1\frac{1}{5}$

4. $\frac{7}{9} - \frac{2}{9} = \frac{5}{9}$

5. $\frac{6}{9} + \frac{3}{9} = 1$

6. $\frac{9}{10} - \frac{3}{10} = \frac{3}{5}$

7. $\frac{7}{8} + \frac{1}{8} + \frac{2}{8} = 1\frac{1}{4}$

8. $\frac{17}{18} - \frac{9}{18} = \frac{4}{9}$

9. $\frac{5}{6} + \frac{2}{6} + \frac{1}{6} = 1\frac{1}{3}$

10. $\frac{1}{14} + \frac{1}{14} + \frac{2}{14} = \frac{4}{7}$

11. **Reasoning** Is $\frac{15}{17} + \frac{4}{17}$ greater than or less than 1? Explain.
Greater than; $\frac{15}{17} + \frac{4}{17} = \frac{19}{17}$. $\frac{19}{17}$ **is greater than 1.**

Name_____

Number One
E 8-1
NUMBER SENSE

Complete the following number sentences so that the answer to each is 1.

1. $\frac{12}{15} - \frac{7}{15} + \frac{[10]}{15} = 1$

2. $\frac{2}{3} + \frac{2}{3} - \frac{[1]}{3} = 1$

3. $\frac{25}{20} + \frac{16}{20} + \frac{1}{20} - \frac{[22]}{20} = 1$

4. $\frac{[10]}{17} - \frac{3}{17} + \frac{10}{17} = 1$

5. $\frac{2}{25} - \frac{1}{25} + \frac{[17]}{25} + \frac{7}{25} = 1$

6. $\frac{11}{31} + \frac{[6]}{31} + \frac{14}{31} = 1$

7. $\frac{[19]}{100} + \frac{6}{100} + \frac{75}{100} = 1$

8. $\frac{[14]}{7} - \frac{4}{7} - \frac{3}{7} = 1$

9. $\frac{[18]}{10} - \frac{2}{10} - \frac{4}{10} - \frac{2}{10} = 1$

10. $\frac{11}{12} + \frac{[6]}{12} - \frac{5}{12} = 1$

11. $\frac{18}{20} - \frac{6}{20} + \frac{[8]}{20} = 1$

12. $\frac{5}{23} + \frac{9}{23} + \frac{[9]}{23} = 1$

13. $\frac{17}{35} + \frac{5}{35} + \frac{20}{35} - \frac{[7]}{35} = 1$

14. $\frac{[15]}{29} - \frac{7}{29} + \frac{21}{29} = 1$

15. $\frac{3}{19} - \frac{1}{19} + \frac{7}{19} + \frac{[10]}{19} = 1$

16. $\frac{7}{13} + \frac{[17]}{13} - \frac{11}{13} = 1$

17. $\frac{[18]}{22} + \frac{3}{22} + \frac{1}{22} = 1$

18. $\frac{33}{47} - \frac{8}{47} + \frac{[22]}{47} = 1$

19. $\frac{[106]}{90} - \frac{10}{90} - \frac{4}{90} - \frac{2}{90} = 1$

20. $\frac{4}{5} + \frac{[5]}{5} - \frac{4}{5} = 1$

Name_____

Adding and Subtracting Fractions with Like Denominators
PS 8-1

Gold Gold is a very valuable mineral that is measured in units called troy ounces.

1. Suppose a jeweler uses $\frac{7}{12}$ troy ounces to produce a ring and $\frac{11}{12}$ troy ounces to produce a set of earrings. How many total troy ounces did the jeweler use?
$1\frac{1}{2}$ **troy ounces**

2. In Exercise 1, how many more troy ounces did the jeweler use for the earrings than for the ring?
$\frac{1}{3}$ **more troy ounces**

3. Suppose a jeweler makes a ring that is made of $\frac{7}{8}$ troy ounces of gold. Then the jeweler makes a second ring that has $\frac{3}{8}$ troy ounces of gold. How many total troy ounces did the jeweler use?
$1\frac{1}{4}$ **troy ounces**

4. In Exercise 3, how many more troy ounces did the jeweler use for the first ring than the second ring?
$\frac{1}{2}$ **more troy ounces**

Where Is the Gold? Gold can be found in 40 of the 50 U.S. states. Only 22 states produce gold commercially.

5. Suppose 3 states produce $\frac{7}{16}$ of the gold in the United States each year. Suppose 7 other states produce $\frac{3}{16}$ of the gold. What fraction of the gold produced in the United States each year comes from these 10 states?
$\frac{5}{8}$ **of the gold**

6. **Writing in Math** In Exercise 5, what fraction of the gold is produced by the other states? Explain how you found your answer.
$\frac{3}{8}$ **of the gold; Sample answer: I subtracted** $\frac{5}{8}$ **from 1.**

Name_____

Understanding Adding and Subtracting with Unlike Denominators

P 8-2

Find each sum or difference. Simplify the answer, if possible.
You may use fraction strips or draw pictures to help.

1. $\frac{10}{12} - \frac{1}{4} =$ $\frac{7}{12}$

2. $\frac{9}{10} - \frac{3}{5} =$ $\frac{3}{10}$

3. $\frac{2}{9} + \frac{1}{3} =$ $\frac{5}{9}$

4. $\frac{3}{4} + \frac{4}{5} =$ $1\frac{11}{20}$

5. $\frac{5}{6} + \frac{4}{9} =$ $1\frac{5}{18}$

6. $\frac{7}{8} - \frac{2}{6} =$ $\frac{13}{24}$

7. $\frac{1}{6} + \frac{5}{12} =$ $\frac{7}{12}$

8. $\frac{7}{12} - \frac{1}{4} =$ $\frac{1}{3}$

9. **Number Sense** Which equivalent fraction would you have to use in order to add $\frac{3}{5}$ to $\frac{21}{25}$? $\frac{15}{25}$

Jeremy collected nickels for one week. He is making stacks of his nickels to determine how many he has. The thickness of one nickel is $\frac{1}{4}$ in.

10. How tall is a stack of 4 nickels? **1 in.**

11. What is the combined height of 3 nickels, 2 nickels, and 1 nickel? **$1\frac{1}{2}$ in.**

12. How much taller is a stack of 3 nickels than 1 nickel? **$\frac{1}{2}$ in. taller**

Test Prep

13. Which fraction is greatest?
A. $\frac{5}{6}$ B. $\frac{7}{9}$ C. $\frac{2}{3}$ D. $\frac{9}{12}$

14. **Writing in Math** Explain why you cannot add fractions with unlike denominators. **Sample answer: Fractions with different denominators represent different parts of a whole and cannot be added unless they are equal.**

Name_____

Understanding Adding and Subtracting with Unlike Denominators

R 8-2

You can use fraction strips to add and subtract fractions with unlike denominators.

Find $\frac{1}{2} + \frac{1}{8}$.

Step 1: Use fraction strips to show $\frac{1}{2} + \frac{1}{8}$.

| $\frac{1}{2}$ | $\frac{1}{8}$ |

Step 2: Exchange the $\frac{1}{2}$ strip with $\frac{1}{8}$ strips to find a fraction for $\frac{1}{2}$ with a denominator of 8.

| $\frac{1}{2}$ | $\frac{1}{8}$ |
| $\frac{1}{8}$ | $\frac{1}{8}$ | $\frac{1}{8}$ | $\frac{1}{8}$ | $\frac{1}{8}$ |

Step 3: Count to see how many $\frac{1}{8}$ strips there are. There are 5, or $\frac{5}{8}$.

So, $\frac{1}{2} + \frac{1}{8} = \frac{5}{8}$.

Find each sum or difference. Simplify the answer, if possible.
You may use fraction strips or draw pictures to help.

1. $\frac{1}{2} + \frac{3}{8} =$ $\frac{7}{8}$

2. $\frac{2}{5} - \frac{1}{10} =$ $\frac{3}{10}$

3. $\frac{4}{5} + \frac{1}{10} =$ $\frac{9}{10}$

4. $\frac{3}{4} - \frac{1}{2} =$ $\frac{1}{4}$

5. $\frac{1}{3} + \frac{1}{12} =$ $\frac{5}{12}$

6. $\frac{11}{12} - \frac{5}{6} =$ $\frac{1}{12}$

7. $\frac{1}{6} + \frac{3}{4} =$ $\frac{11}{12}$

8. $\frac{3}{4} - \frac{3}{8} =$ $\frac{3}{8}$

9. **Number Sense** Which equivalent fraction would you use to subtract $\frac{1}{3}$ from $\frac{5}{9}$? $\frac{3}{9}$

10. How much polyester and cotton is there combined? **1 yd combined**

11. How much more silk is there than polyester? **$\frac{3}{8}$ yd more**

Leftover Fabric

Type	Amount
Silk	$\frac{3}{4}$ yd
Polyester	$\frac{3}{8}$ yd
Cotton	$\frac{5}{8}$ yd
Burlap	$\frac{1}{2}$ yd

Name_____

Cook Up Some Fractions

E 8-2
VISUAL THINKING

Add or subtract the amounts shown in the measuring cups. Then draw a line to match each problem to the measuring cup on the right that shows the correct sum or difference.

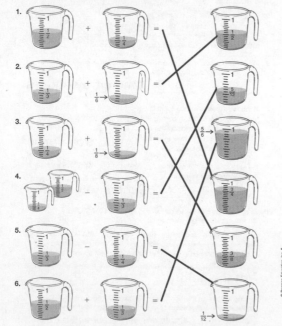

Name_____

Understanding Adding and Subtracting with Unlike Denominators

PS 8-2

Bat Facts Bats are the only mammals in the animal kingdom that can fly. The brown bat reaches an adult wingspan of about 13 to 14 in. The biggest bat in the state of Oregon is the hoary bat, which weighs about 1 oz. For 1–6, you may use fraction strips or draw pictures to help.

1. Suppose a baby brown bat has a wingspan that is $\frac{1}{6}$ of its adult wingspan. Then the bat's wingspan grows another $\frac{1}{4}$ of its adult wingspan. What fraction of its adult wingspan has it reached? **$\frac{5}{12}$ of its adult wingspan**

2. Is it correct to say that the bat in Exercise 1 has reached $\frac{1}{2}$ of its adult wingspan after the second growth period? **No**

3. Suppose one hoary bat weighs $\frac{7}{12}$ oz and a second hoary bat weighs $\frac{3}{4}$ oz. Which bat weighs more? **The $\frac{3}{4}$ oz bat**

4. What do the bats in Exercise 3 weigh altogether? **$1\frac{1}{3}$ oz total**

5. How much lighter is the lighter bat in Exercise 3 than the heavier bat? **$\frac{1}{6}$ oz lighter**

6. What would be the total weight of two bats that weighed $\frac{1}{2}$ and $\frac{1}{3}$ of an ounce? **$\frac{5}{6}$ oz**

7. **Writing in Math** Which fractions would be easier to add, $\frac{1}{6} + \frac{1}{3}$ or $\frac{1}{2} + \frac{1}{2}$? Explain. **Sample answer: $\frac{1}{6} + \frac{1}{3}$, because you only have to convert one fraction to an equivalent fraction.**

Name_____

Least Common Denominator

P 8-3

Find the LCD for each pair of fractions.

1. $\frac{2}{7}$ and $\frac{4}{5}$ **35**   2. $\frac{5}{6}$ and $\frac{4}{9}$ **18**

3. $\frac{7}{9}$ and $\frac{11}{15}$ **45**   4. $\frac{1}{12}$ and $\frac{3}{9}$ **36**

5. $\frac{12}{15}$ and $\frac{8}{10}$ **30**   6. $\frac{5}{8}$ and $\frac{3}{4}$ **8**

7. $\frac{1}{4}$ and $\frac{4}{5}$ **20**   8. $\frac{3}{11}$ and $\frac{7}{8}$ **88**

Two of the shortest fish in the world are the dwarf goby and the dwarf pygmy goby. Both fish are found in Southeast Asia. The table shows the lengths for each of these fish.

Fish	Length (inches)
Male dwarf pygmy goby	$\frac{1}{2}$
Female dwarf pygmy goby	$\frac{3}{4}$
Dwarf goby	$\frac{1}{3}$

9. What would the LCD be for the length of the male and the female dwarf pygmy goby?   **4**

10. What is the combined length of the male and female dwarf pygmy goby?   **$1\frac{1}{4}$ in.**

11. What would the LCD be for the length of all 3 fish?   **12**

12. What is the combined length of the 3 fish?   **$1\frac{7}{12}$ in.**

Test Prep

13. Which is the LCD for $\frac{1}{4}$, $\frac{1}{5}$, and $\frac{1}{6}$?

   A. 20   B. 30   **C. 60**   D. 80

14. **Writing in Math** Explain the difference between the LCM and the LCD.

Sample answer: The LCM is the lowest multiple of two numbers. The LCD is the lowest multiple of two denominators.

Name_____

Least Common Denominator

R 8-3

To find the least common denominator (LCD) of two or more fractions, you need to find the least common multiple (LCM) of the denominators.

How to find the least common multiple:	How to find the least common denominator:
Find the least common multiple of 6 and 9.	Find the least common denominator of $\frac{5}{6}$ and $\frac{3}{4}$.
Step 1: List the multiples of each number.	**Step 1:** List the multiples of each denominator.
Multiples of 6: 6, 12, **18**, 24, 30, **36**, 42, 48, 54	Multiples of 6: 6, **12**, 18, **24**, 30, . . .
Multiples of 9: 9, **18**, 27, **36**, 45, **54**, 63	Multiples of 4: 4, 8, **12**, 16, 20, **24**, . . .
Step 2: Find the multiples the numbers have in common: 18, 36, 54.	**Step 2:** Look for the smallest multiple that 6 and 4 have in common. Both numbers have 12 and 24 in common. 12 is the least number that they have in common.
Step 3: Find the least multiple the numbers have in common: 18.	
So, 18 is the least common multiple of 6 and 9.	So, 12 is the least common denominator of $\frac{5}{6}$ and $\frac{3}{4}$.

Find the LCM of each pair of numbers.

1. 4 and 3   **12**   2. 8 and 12   **24**

3. 5 and 6   **30**   4. 10 and 2   **10**

Find the LCD for each pair of fractions.

5. $\frac{4}{9}$ and $\frac{1}{6}$ **18**   6. $\frac{2}{3}$ and $\frac{3}{4}$ **12**

7. $\frac{5}{6}$ and $\frac{7}{12}$ **12**   8. $\frac{7}{10}$ and $\frac{3}{5}$ **10**

9. $\frac{3}{8}$ and $\frac{5}{12}$ **24**   10. $\frac{3}{7}$ and $\frac{2}{3}$ **21**

11. $\frac{3}{4}$ and $\frac{1}{2}$ **4**   12. $\frac{9}{10}$ and $\frac{1}{3}$ **30**

13. **Mental Math** Can the LCD of $\frac{4}{8}$ and $\frac{13}{17}$ be less than 17? Explain.

Sample answer: No, the LCD has to be at least 17 to be a multiple of 17.

Name_____

Denominator Runners

E 8-3
NUMBER SENSE

Which pair of fractions is the winner? For each runner, find the pair of fractions with a least common denominator that matches the number on his shirt. Write the correct letter on the line above each runner.

A. $\frac{5}{12}$, $\frac{7}{8}$ B. $\frac{1}{3}$, $\frac{4}{5}$ C. $\frac{3}{4}$, $\frac{1}{8}$

D. $\frac{1}{2}$, $\frac{9}{10}$ E. $\frac{6}{12}$, $\frac{1}{4}$

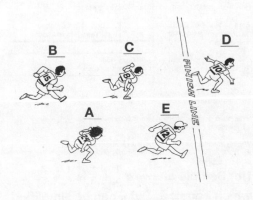

Name_____

Least Common Denominator

PS 8-3

Snack Time Carlos has a snack every day after he gets home from school. On Tuesday his snack was a small bag of carrots. He ate $\frac{1}{3}$ of the bag before doing his homework and $\frac{3}{7}$ of the bag after finishing his homework.

1. What is the LCM of 3 and 7?   **21**

2. What is the LCD of $\frac{1}{3}$ and $\frac{3}{7}$?   **21**

3. How much of the bag of carrots did Carlos eat altogether?   **$\frac{16}{21}$**

Schedule Over the weekend Vicki spends $\frac{2}{5}$ of her free time visiting with family, $\frac{1}{6}$ doing chores, $\frac{1}{9}$ playing with friends, and $\frac{3}{8}$ doing homework.

4. What is the LCD of the fraction of time Vicki spends visiting with family and doing chores?   **18**

5. What is the LCD of the fraction of time Vicki spends playing with friends and doing homework?   **40**

6. What is the LCD of the fraction of time Vicki spends visiting with family and playing with friends?   **45**

7. What is the LCD of the fraction of time Vicki spends doing homework and doing chores?   **24**

8. What is the LCD of the fraction of time Vicki spends doing chores and playing with friends?   **30**

9. What is the LCD of the fraction of time Vicki spends doing homework and visiting with family?   **72**

10. **Writing in Math** Victor said that it is not always necessary to find the LCD to compare the sizes of fractions. Do you agree? Explain.

Sample answer: Yes; Sometimes you can use benchmark fractions.

Name_____

Adding and Subtracting Fractions with Unlike Denominators

P 8-4

Add or subtract. Simplify, if possible.

1. $\begin{array}{r}\frac{3}{8}\\+\frac{4}{5}\\\hline\end{array}$ $1\frac{7}{40}$

2. $\begin{array}{r}\frac{5}{12}\\-\frac{1}{3}\\\hline\end{array}$ $\frac{1}{12}$

3. $\begin{array}{r}\frac{9}{10}\\+\frac{2}{5}\\\hline\end{array}$ $1\frac{3}{10}$

4. $\begin{array}{r}\frac{11}{12}\\-\frac{1}{4}\\\hline\end{array}$ $\frac{2}{3}$

5. $\frac{4}{9}+\frac{1}{3}+\frac{5}{6}=$ $1\frac{11}{18}$

6. $\frac{1}{2}+\frac{7}{8}+\frac{3}{10}=$ $1\frac{27}{40}$

7. $\frac{7}{8}-\frac{2}{3}=$ $\frac{5}{24}$

8. $\frac{7}{10}-\frac{1}{4}=$ $\frac{9}{20}$

9. $\frac{3}{4}+\frac{1}{2}+\frac{1}{12}=$ $1\frac{1}{3}$

10. $\frac{6}{7}-\frac{1}{3}=$ $\frac{11}{21}$

11. **Number Sense** Write three fractions with different denominators that are equal to $\frac{1}{2}$.

Sample answer: $\frac{5}{10}, \frac{4}{8}, \frac{6}{12}$

The vervain hummingbird and the ruby-throated hummingbird lay the world's smallest bird eggs.

Egg Sizes

Bird	Length	Weight
Vervain hummingbird	$\frac{4}{10}$ in.	$\frac{13}{1,000}$ oz
Ruby-throated hummingbird	$\frac{5}{8}$ in.	$\frac{1}{50}$ oz

12. What is the difference in length between the ruby-throated hummingbird egg and the vervain hummingbird egg? $\frac{9}{40}$ in. longer

13. What is the difference in weight between the ruby-throated hummingbird egg and the vervain hummingbird egg? $\frac{7}{1,000}$ oz heavier

Test Prep

14. Which is the sum of $\frac{8}{9} + \frac{4}{15} + \frac{3}{5}$ in simplest form?

(A) $1\frac{34}{45}$ B. $\frac{79}{45}$ C. $\frac{15}{29}$ D. $1\frac{27}{45}$

15. **Writing in Math** Explain why $\frac{21}{14}$ is equal to $1\frac{1}{2}$.

Sample answer: $\frac{21}{14}$ can be simplified to $\frac{3}{2}$ or $1\frac{1}{2}$.

Name_____

Adding and Subtracting Fractions with Unlike Denominators

R 8-4

Moira's bread recipe calls for $\frac{3}{4}$ c of white flour and $\frac{1}{8}$ c of wheat flour. What is the total amount of flour needed for the recipe?

Step 1: Find the LCM of the denominators.

Multiples of 4: 4, 8, 12, 16, 20, ...

Multiples of 8: 8, 16, 24, 32, 40, ...

The LCD is 8.

Step 2: Write equivalent fractions with a denominator of 8.

Step 3: Add the fractions. Write the sum in simplest form.

$\frac{6}{8} + \frac{1}{8} = \frac{7}{8}$

So, the recipe calls for $\frac{7}{8}$ cups of flour.

Add or subtract. Simplify, if possible.

1. $\begin{array}{r}\frac{3}{4}\\-\frac{2}{5}\\\hline\end{array}$ $\frac{7}{20}$

2. $\begin{array}{r}\frac{4}{5}\\+\frac{1}{2}\\\hline\end{array}$ $1\frac{3}{10}$

3. $\begin{array}{r}\frac{7}{10}\\-\frac{1}{5}\\\hline\end{array}$ $\frac{1}{2}$

4. $\begin{array}{r}\frac{8}{9}\\+\frac{5}{6}\\\hline\end{array}$ $1\frac{13}{18}$

5. $\frac{5}{12} - \frac{1}{4} =$ $\frac{1}{6}$

6. $\frac{4}{9} + \frac{3}{4} =$ $1\frac{7}{36}$

7. $\frac{5}{6} - \frac{3}{8} =$ $\frac{11}{24}$

8. $\frac{1}{2} + \frac{1}{6} + \frac{3}{4} =$ $1\frac{5}{12}$

9. $\frac{23}{24} - \frac{7}{8} =$ $\frac{1}{12}$

10. $\frac{2}{3} + \frac{1}{9} + \frac{5}{6} =$ $1\frac{11}{18}$

11. **Reasoning** Is the sum of $\frac{9}{12}$ and $\frac{1}{6}$ greater than or less than 1?

Less than 1

Name_____

Scrambled Subtraction

E 8-4
REASONING

There are one or more mistakes in each of the subtraction problems on this page. For each exercise, circle the mistake, then write a sentence describing the error.

Sample answers are given.

1. $\begin{array}{r}\frac{7}{8} \times \frac{5}{5} = \frac{35}{40}\\-\frac{1}{5} \times \frac{5}{5} = \frac{5}{25}\\\hline\frac{30}{15}\end{array}$

The common denominator was not found correctly.

2. $\begin{array}{r}\frac{3}{4} \times \frac{3}{3} = \frac{9}{12}\\-\frac{1}{6} \times \frac{2}{2} = \frac{2}{12}\\\hline\frac{7}{0}\end{array}$

The denominators should not have been subtracted.

3. $\begin{array}{r}\frac{1}{8} \times \frac{5}{5} = \frac{5}{40}\\-\frac{1}{10} \times \frac{4}{4} = \frac{4}{40}\\\hline\frac{9}{40}\end{array}$

The numerators were added instead of subtracted.

4. $\begin{array}{r}\frac{20}{30} \times \frac{1}{1} = \frac{20}{30}\\-\frac{9}{15} \times \frac{2}{2} = \frac{18}{15}\\\hline\frac{2}{15}\end{array}$

The common denominator was not found correctly.

Name_____

Adding and Subtracting Fractions with Unlike Denominators

PS 8-4

Lunch Jesse, Veronica, Sal, and Juanita went out to lunch for pizza. Jesse ate $\frac{3}{10}$ of a pizza, Veronica ate $\frac{1}{4}$ of a pizza, Sal ate $\frac{3}{8}$ of a pizza, and Juanita ate $\frac{1}{3}$ of a pizza.

1. How much did Jesse and Veronica eat altogether? $\frac{11}{20}$

2. How much did Sal and Veronica eat altogether? $\frac{5}{8}$

3. How much did Jesse, Sal, and Veronica eat altogether? $\frac{37}{40}$

4. How much did Veronica, Juanita, and Jesse eat altogether? $\frac{53}{60}$

Teachers Look at the data for the fraction of Illinois teachers with graduate degrees.

Fraction of Total Public School Teachers in Illinois

	1991	1996	2001
Teachers with Graduate Degrees	$\frac{9}{20}$	$\frac{11}{25}$	$\frac{47}{100}$

5. What is the difference between the fraction of teachers with graduate degrees in 2001 and 1996? $\frac{3}{100}$

6. What is the difference between the number of teachers with graduate degrees in 2001 and 1991? $\frac{1}{50}$

7. **Writing in Math** Louisa says that if you add fractions using the LCD, you will never have to simplify the answer. Is she correct? Explain.

No; Sample answer: $\frac{1}{6} + \frac{1}{3}$ is $\frac{1}{6} + \frac{2}{6}$, which equals $\frac{3}{6}$. But $\frac{3}{6}$ can be simplified to $\frac{1}{2}$.

Name_____

Understanding Adding and Subtracting Mixed Numbers

P 8-5

Find each sum or difference. Simplify the answer, if necessary. You may use fraction strips or draw pictures to help.

1. $4\frac{1}{5} + 2\frac{2}{5} = $ **$6\frac{3}{5}$**   2. $8\frac{3}{7} + 5\frac{1}{7} = $ **$13\frac{4}{7}$**   3. $6\frac{7}{8} - 2\frac{5}{8} = $ **$4\frac{1}{4}$**

4. $5\frac{8}{11} - 5\frac{3}{11} = $ **$\frac{5}{11}$**   5. $7\frac{5}{8} + 6\frac{3}{8} = $ **14**   6. $10 - 3\frac{7}{8} = $ **$6\frac{1}{8}$**

Kevin is making lemonade for his family. The ingredients are shown in the table.

One Batch of Lemonade	
Ingredient	**Amount**
Water	$4\frac{3}{8}$ c
Lemon juice	$\frac{5}{8}$ c
Sugar	$2\frac{1}{4}$ c

7. How many cups of liquid (water and lemon juice) will Kevin use?
5 c

8. How much water should Kevin use if he wants to decrease the amount of water by $\frac{5}{8}$ c?
$3\frac{3}{4}$ c

9. How much lemon juice should Kevin use if he wants to increase the amount used by $\frac{3}{8}$ c?
1 c

10. **Number Sense** Explain why $8\frac{3}{5}$ is the same as $7\frac{8}{5}$.
Sample answer: $\frac{8}{5}$ can be simplified as $1\frac{3}{5}$. Adding $1\frac{3}{5}$ to 7 gives a sum of $8\frac{3}{5}$.

Test Prep

11. In order to subtract $6\frac{7}{16}$ from $7\frac{1}{16}$, what must you do?

A. Rename $6\frac{7}{16}$ **B.** Rename $7\frac{1}{16}$

C. Rename both $6\frac{7}{16}$ and $7\frac{1}{16}$ D. You cannot subtract $6\frac{7}{16}$ from $7\frac{1}{16}$

12. **Writing in Math** Explain what happens when you add $\frac{1}{8}$ to $3\frac{7}{8}$.
Sample answer: The $\frac{1}{8}$ added to $\frac{7}{8}$ makes $\frac{8}{8}$, which is 1. 1 + 3 = 4

Use with Lesson 8-5. **105**

Name_____

Understanding Adding and Subtracting Mixed Numbers

R 8-5

Homework Jerome worked on his English homework for $1\frac{1}{6}$ hr and his science homework for $1\frac{3}{6}$ hr. How much time did Jerome spend on homework?

You can use fraction strips to help you add the mixed numbers.

Step 1: Use fraction strips to show $1\frac{1}{6} + 1\frac{3}{6}$.

Step 2: Combine the $\frac{1}{6}$ strips. Then combine the 1 strips.

Step 3: Count the strips.
$1 + 1 + \frac{1}{6} + \frac{1}{6} + \frac{1}{6} + \frac{1}{6} = 2\frac{4}{6}$
So, $1\frac{1}{6} + 1\frac{3}{6} = 2\frac{4}{6}$.
$2\frac{4}{6}$ in simplest form is $2\frac{2}{3}$.

Jerome will spend $2\frac{2}{3}$ hr on homework.

Find each sum or difference. Simplify the answer, if necessary. You may use fraction strips or draw pictures to help.

1. $1\frac{5}{8}$
$+ 2\frac{2}{8}$
$3\frac{7}{8}$

2. $5\frac{3}{4}$
$- 2\frac{1}{4}$
$3\frac{1}{2}$

3. 6
$+ 3\frac{7}{12}$
$9\frac{7}{12}$

4. $5\frac{6}{7}$
$- 3\frac{2}{7}$
$2\frac{4}{7}$

5. $2\frac{9}{16} + 7\frac{5}{16} = $ **$9\frac{7}{8}$**   6. $5 - 3\frac{1}{2} = $ **$1\frac{1}{2}$**

7. $3\frac{1}{10} + \frac{4}{10} = $ **$3\frac{1}{2}$**   8. $4\frac{9}{16} - \frac{5}{16} = $ **$4\frac{1}{4}$**

9. $4\frac{3}{11} + 12\frac{5}{11} = $ **$16\frac{8}{11}$**   10. $8\frac{4}{9} - 8\frac{1}{9} = $ **$\frac{1}{3}$**

11. **Number Sense** If you want to subtract $\frac{3}{7}$ from 12, how should you rename 12?
$11\frac{7}{7}$

Use with Lesson 8-5. **105**

Name_____

Mountain Math

E 8-5
DATA

The illustration below shows the heights in kilometers of the seven highest mountains in the United States.

Tallest Mountains in the United States

Mt. Vancouver	Mt. Sanford	Mt. Blackburn	Mt. Bona	Mt. Foraker	Mt. St. Elias	Mt. McKinley
$4\frac{9}{10}$ km	5 km	5 km	5 km	$5\frac{3}{10}$ km	$5\frac{5}{10}$ km	$6\frac{2}{10}$ km

1. How much higher is Mt. McKinley than Mt. Vancouver?
$1\frac{3}{10}$ km

2. If a climber has climbed to the peak of Mt. Foraker and Mt. St. Elias, what is the total number of kilometers climbed?
$10\frac{4}{5}$ km

3. If a climber has climbed both Mt. McKinley and Mt. St. Elias, would the combined total be more than 12 km?
No

4. How much higher is Mt. Bona than Mt. Vancouver?
$\frac{1}{10}$ km

5. How much higher is Mt. St. Elias than Mt. Foraker?
$\frac{1}{5}$ km

6. If a climber has climbed to the peak of Mt. Vancouver, Mt. McKinley, and Mt. St. Elias, what is the total number of kilometers climbed?
$16\frac{3}{5}$ km

7. Which three mountains have a combined height of 17 km?
Mt. McKinley, Mt. St. Elias, and Mt. Foraker

Use with Lesson 8-5. **105**

Name_____

Understanding Adding and Subtracting Mixed Numbers

PS 8-5

Growth Spurt Usually, the weight of a human baby doubles within the first four months of life and then triples by the end of the first year. Suppose a baby gains $2\frac{1}{6}$ lb in the first month and $1\frac{5}{6}$ lb in the second month. For 1–3, you may use fraction strips or draw pictures to help.

1. How much weight did the baby gain in the first two months?
4 lb

2. How much more weight did the baby gain in the first month than the second month?
$\frac{1}{3}$ lb more

3. Suppose the baby gains another $1\frac{5}{6}$ lb in the third month. How much weight has the baby gained in the first three months?
$5\frac{5}{6}$ lb

A Swim in the Lake On vacation, the Simon family likes to go swimming in the lake. One day, Rebecca swam for $1\frac{2}{5}$ hr, Paul swam for $1\frac{4}{5}$ hr, Lydia swam for $2\frac{2}{5}$ hr, and Nathan swam for a full 3 hr. For 4–6, you may use fraction strips or draw pictures to help.

4. How long did Rebecca and Lydia swim in total?
$3\frac{4}{5}$ hr

5. How much longer did Lydia swim than Paul?
$\frac{3}{5}$ hr

6. How much longer did Nathan swim than Paul?
$1\frac{1}{5}$ hr

7. **Writing in Math** Did Rebecca and Paul in total swim longer than Nathan did? Explain how you found your answer.
Yes; Sample answer: $1\frac{2}{5} + 1\frac{4}{5}$ equals $3\frac{1}{5}$ hr, which is longer than 3 hr.

Use with Lesson 8-5. **105**

Name

Estimating Sums and Differences of Mixed Numbers

P 8-6

Estimate. First round to the nearest whole number.

1. $\frac{2}{3} + 4\frac{1}{4}$ **5**
2. $7\frac{2}{5} + 8\frac{7}{8}$ **16**
3. $5\frac{6}{7} - 3\frac{1}{3}$ **3**
4. $8\frac{3}{4} - 8\frac{1}{8}$ **1**
5. $1\frac{8}{9} + 1\frac{1}{5} + 1\frac{3}{7}$ **4**
6. $9\frac{1}{8} + 4\frac{3}{4} + 6\frac{2}{5}$ **21**

Distances in miles and time are shown for the Seattle region in Washington.

Travel in Washington

Destinations	Hours	Miles
Seattle → Ellensburg	$1\frac{7}{12}$	104
Ellensburg → Wenatchee	$1\frac{1}{2}$	70
Wenatchee → Everett	$2\frac{3}{4}$	124
Everett → Port Angeles	$1\frac{5}{6}$	84

7. Estimate the driving time between Seattle and Wenatchee.

   About 4 hr

8. Estimate the difference in driving time between the distance from Wenatchee to Everett and the distance from Everett to Port Angeles.

   About 1 hr

9. **Number Sense** The difference between two mixed numbers is about 3. One of the numbers is $4\frac{4}{5}$. What could the other number be?

   Sample answer: $2\frac{1}{4}$

Test Prep

10. Which is a good estimate for the sum of $45\frac{16}{25} + 32\frac{13}{18} + 51\frac{3}{20}$?

    A. 128   B. 129   **C.** 130   D. 131

11. **Writing in Math** Describe a situation in which estimating mixed numbers would not be a good idea.

    Sample answer: A recipe, because accuracy in the measurements is important.

Name

Estimating Sums and Differences of Mixed Numbers

R 8-6

Orange Juice Veronica squeezed $3\frac{7}{8}$ c of orange juice. She drank $2\frac{1}{4}$ c. About how much orange juice was left?

Step 1: Round each mixed number to the nearest whole number.

Round $3\frac{7}{8}$ to 4.

Round $2\frac{1}{4}$ to 2.

Step 2: Subtract.

$4 - 2 = 2$

So, there were about 2 c of orange juice left.

Estimate each sum or difference. Round to the nearest whole number.

1. $5\frac{8}{9} + 2\frac{3}{4}$ **9**
2. $10\frac{1}{8} - 6\frac{5}{6}$ **3**
3. $2\frac{13}{16} - \frac{7}{8}$ **2**
4. $4\frac{6}{7} - 2\frac{1}{5}$ **3**
5. $6 + 2\frac{1}{3} + 4\frac{11}{12}$ **13**
6. $9 - 6\frac{9}{10}$ **2**
7. $5\frac{3}{4} + 2\frac{10}{11} + 3\frac{7}{8}$ **13**
8. $\frac{15}{16} + 3\frac{7}{9} + 2\frac{13}{14}$ **8**

9. **Number Sense** Is the difference between $2\frac{3}{4}$ and $1\frac{1}{8}$ greater than or less than 1? Explain.

   Sample answer: Greater than, because $2\frac{3}{4}$ rounds to 3 and $1\frac{1}{8}$ rounds to 1. $3 - 1 = 2$, which is more than 1.

10. About how much taller is Angela than Austin?

    About 2 in.

Height Chart

Martina	$48\frac{1}{4}$ in.
Zachary	$50\frac{3}{8}$ in.
Angela	$52\frac{1}{16}$ in.
Austin	$49\frac{9}{10}$ in.

Name

It's Great to Estimate!

E 8-6
ESTIMATION

In each box, write two math problems with an estimated answer equal to the number on the box. Your problems can be either addition or subtraction. Each problem must contain two mixed numbers.

Sample answers:

4

$1\frac{2}{3} + 1\frac{2}{3}$

$1\frac{7}{8} + 2\frac{1}{8}$

7

$3\frac{1}{10} + 3\frac{9}{10}$

$4\frac{1}{2} + 2\frac{1}{2}$

6

$1\frac{7}{8} + 4\frac{1}{9}$

$7\frac{1}{3} - 1\frac{1}{3}$

3

$5\frac{9}{10} - 3\frac{1}{8}$

$1\frac{1}{3} + 2\frac{1}{4}$

8

$4\frac{2}{3} + 3\frac{1}{4}$

$9\frac{1}{3} - 1\frac{1}{8}$

2

$1\frac{1}{9} + 1\frac{1}{5}$

$5\frac{1}{4} - 2\frac{5}{6}$

Name

Estimating Sums and Differences of Mixed Numbers

PS 8-6

Three Trees Three trees in Melissa's yard are $8\frac{1}{3}$, $11\frac{4}{7}$, and $13\frac{6}{11}$ ft high. Find estimates for 1–4.

1. About how tall are the two shorter trees combined?

   About 20 ft tall

2. About how tall are the two taller trees combined?

   About 26 ft tall

3. About how tall are the shortest and tallest trees combined?

   About 22 ft tall

4. About how tall are all three trees combined?   **About 34 ft tall**

Lace 'Em Up In a school basketball game, Larry plays $2\frac{1}{8}$ quarters, P. J. plays $2\frac{2}{3}$ quarters, and Maurice plays $3\frac{3}{4}$ quarters. Find estimates for 5–7.

5. About how many more quarters did P. J. play than Larry?

   1 more quarter

6. About how many more quarters did Maurice play than Larry?

   About 2 more quarters

7. About how many more quarters did Maurice play than P. J.?

   About 1 more quarter

8. **Writing in Math** If P. J. had played half more of a quarter, would your answer to Exercise 7 change? Explain.

   No; Sample answer: The number of quarters P. J. played would still round to 3, so the answer would not change.

Name_____

Adding Mixed Numbers

P 8-7

Estimate the sum first. Then add. Simplify, if necessary.

1. $7\frac{2}{3} + 8\frac{5}{6}$ **17; $16\frac{1}{2}$**
2. $4\frac{3}{4} + 2\frac{2}{5}$ **7; $7\frac{3}{20}$**
3. $11\frac{9}{10} + 3\frac{1}{20}$ **15; $14\frac{19}{20}$**
4. $7\frac{6}{7} + 5\frac{2}{7}$ **13; $13\frac{1}{7}$**
5. $5\frac{8}{9} + 3\frac{1}{2}$ **10; $9\frac{7}{18}$**
6. $21\frac{11}{12} + 17\frac{2}{3}$ **40; $39\frac{7}{12}$**

7. **Number Sense** Write two mixed numbers with a sum of 3.

Sample answer: $1\frac{1}{4} + 1\frac{3}{4} = 3$

8. What is the total measure of an average man's brain and heart in kilograms?

$1\frac{7}{10}$ kg

Vital Organ Measures

Average woman's brain	$1\frac{3}{10}$ kg	$2\frac{4}{5}$ lb
Average man's brain	$1\frac{2}{5}$ kg	3 lb
Average human heart	$\frac{3}{10}$ kg	$\frac{7}{10}$ lb

9. What is the total weight of an average woman's brain and heart in pounds?

$3\frac{1}{2}$ lb

10. What is the sum of the measures of an average man's brain and an average woman's brain in kilograms?

$2\frac{7}{10}$ kg

Test Prep

11. Which is a good comparison of the estimated sum and the actual sum of $7\frac{7}{8} + 2\frac{11}{12}$?

A. Estimated < actual
B. Actual > estimated
C. Actual = estimated
D. Estimated > actual

12. **Writing in Math** Can the sum of two mixed numbers be equal to 2? Explain why or why not.

No; Sample answer: It is impossible for two mixed numbers to equal 2 because every mixed number is greater than 1.

Use with Lesson 8-7. **107**

Name_____

Adding Mixed Numbers

R 8-7

Find $4\frac{5}{6} + 2\frac{1}{12}$.

Step 1	Step 2	Step 3
Write equivalent fractions with the LCD.	Add the fractions.	Add the whole numbers. Simplify the sum, if necessary.
$4\frac{5}{6} = 4\frac{10}{12}$ $+ 2\frac{1}{12} = 2\frac{1}{12}$	$4\frac{5}{6} = 4\frac{10}{12}$ $+ 2\frac{1}{12} = 2\frac{1}{12}$ $\frac{11}{12}$	$4\frac{5}{6} = 4\frac{10}{12}$ $+ 2\frac{1}{12} = 2\frac{1}{12}$ $6\frac{11}{12}$

So, $4\frac{5}{6} + 2\frac{1}{12} = 6\frac{11}{12}$.

Estimates will vary.

Estimate the sum first. Then add. Simplify, if necessary.

1. $2\frac{5}{8}$ $+ 3\frac{1}{4}$ **6; $6\frac{1}{12}$**
2. $1\frac{3}{8}$ $+ 6\frac{3}{4}$ **8; $8\frac{1}{8}$**
3. $5\frac{2}{5}$ $+ 4\frac{1}{2}$ **10; $9\frac{9}{10}$**
4. $10\frac{1}{3}$ $+ \frac{7}{9}$ **11; $11\frac{1}{9}$**

5. 6 $+ 3\frac{1}{3}$ **9; $9\frac{1}{3}$**
6. $3\frac{1}{4}$ $+ 6\frac{1}{3}$ **10; $9\frac{11}{12}$**
7. $2\frac{1}{3}$ $+ 4\frac{2}{7}$ **6; $6\frac{10}{21}$**
8. $3\frac{2}{5}$ $+ 9\frac{1}{3}$ **12; $12\frac{7}{15}$**

9. $1\frac{5}{7} + 3\frac{1}{2}$ **6; $5\frac{3}{14}$**
10. $4 + 5\frac{15}{16}$ **10; $9\frac{15}{16}$**
11. $7\frac{3}{10} + 5\frac{2}{5}$ **12; $12\frac{7}{10}$**
12. $9\frac{1}{3} + 3\frac{2}{5}$ **12; $12\frac{11}{15}$**

13. **Mental Math** What is the sum of $2\frac{1}{5}$ and $3\frac{4}{5}$? **6**

Use with Lesson 8-7. **107**

Name_____

A Bike Trip

E 8-7
DECISION MAKING

The Paul Bunyan Trail is in Minnesota. The distances between the towns on the trail are shown below. Read the instructions below to plan bicycle trips on the trail. Your trip may begin at any town listed on the table.

From	To	Miles
Baxter	Merrifield	9
Merrifield	Nisswa	$5\frac{4}{5}$
Nisswa	Pequot Lakes	$6\frac{2}{10}$
Pequot Lakes	Backus	$17\frac{16}{20}$
Backus	Hackensack	$7\frac{3}{5}$
Hackensack	Walker	$16\frac{24}{30}$
Benedict	Laporte	$5\frac{4}{20}$

Sample answers are given.

1. Plan a trip that is more than 20 mi long, but less than 30 mi long. Where will you start? Where will you finish? How many miles will you have traveled?

Start: Nisswa; finish: Backus; 24 mi

2. Plan a trip that is more than 40 mi long, but less than 50 mi long. Where will you start? Where will you finish? How many miles will you have traveled?

Start: Pequot; finish: Walker; $42\frac{1}{5}$ mi

3. Plan a trip that is less than 15 mi long. Where will you start? Where will you finish? How many miles will you have traveled?

Start: Baxter; finish: Nisswa; $14\frac{4}{5}$ mi

4. What is the shortest trip that will allow you to visit one town between the towns in which you start and finish? Where will you start? Where will you finish? How many miles will you have traveled?

Merrifield to Pequot; 12 mi

Use with Lesson 8-7. **107**

Name_____

Adding Mixed Numbers

PS 8-7

Jill's Day On Friday, Jill's mother drove her to school. After school, they drove to the library to check out a book and then to the grocery store to shop. Afterward, they drove home. The distances between each location are shown on the drawing. The arrows show the direction of the route Jill and her mother took.

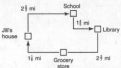

1. Jill and her mother drove from Jill's house to school, then they drove to the library. How far did they drive?

$4\frac{7}{15}$ mi

2. How far was the drive from the school to the grocery store?

$4\frac{8}{35}$ mi

3. How far was the drive from the library to home?

$3\frac{31}{56}$ mi

Meals in Space Because of limited space, astronauts can only eat so much food each day. Suppose a space shuttle astronaut eats about $2\frac{5}{8}$ lb of food each day and that the packaging weighs $1\frac{1}{2}$ lb. Also suppose that an astronaut eats a total of $7\frac{1}{3}$ lb of meat and $5\frac{3}{4}$ lb of vegetables in one week.

4. What is the combined weight of the food an astronaut eats each day and its packaging?

$3\frac{29}{40}$ lb

5. What is the combined weight of the meat and vegetables an astronaut eats each week?

$13\frac{1}{12}$ lb

6. **Writing in Math** Find an estimate for the answer to Exercise 3. Is your exact answer reasonable? Explain.

Sample answer: $1\frac{1}{8}$ rounds down to 1 and $2\frac{3}{7}$ rounds down to 2, and $1 + 2$ equals 3. The answer was reasonable.

Use with Lesson 8-7. **107**

Name_____

Subtracting Mixed Numbers

P 8-8

Estimate the difference first. Then subtract.
Simplify, if necessary.

1. $10\frac{3}{4}$
$-\ 7\frac{1}{4}$

4; $3\frac{1}{2}$

2. $7\frac{3}{7}$
$-\ 2\frac{8}{21}$

5; $5\frac{1}{21}$

3. 3
$-\ 2\frac{2}{3}$

0; $\frac{1}{3}$

4. $17\frac{7}{8}$
$-\ 12\frac{3}{12}$

6; $5\frac{5}{8}$

5. $9\frac{5}{9} - 6\frac{5}{6}$ **3; $2\frac{13}{18}$**

6. $4\frac{3}{4} - 2\frac{2}{3}$ **2; $2\frac{1}{12}$**

7. $6\frac{1}{4} - 3\frac{1}{3}$ **3; $2\frac{11}{12}$**

8. $5\frac{1}{5} - 3\frac{7}{8}$ **1; $1\frac{13}{40}$**

9. $8\frac{2}{7} - 7\frac{1}{3}$ **1; $\frac{20}{21}$**

10. $2\frac{9}{10} - 2\frac{1}{3}$ **1; $\frac{17}{30}$**

The table shows the length and width of several kinds of bird eggs.

Egg Sizes

Bird	Length	Width
Canada goose	$3\frac{2}{5}$ in.	$2\frac{3}{10}$ in.
Robin	$\frac{3}{4}$ in.	$\frac{3}{5}$ in.
Turtledove	$1\frac{1}{5}$ in.	$\frac{9}{10}$ in.
Raven	$1\frac{9}{10}$ in.	$1\frac{3}{10}$ in.

11. How much longer is the Canada goose egg than the raven egg?

$1\frac{1}{2}$ in. longer

12. How much wider is the turtledove egg than the robin egg?

$\frac{3}{10}$ in. wider

Test Prep

13. Which is the difference of $21\frac{5}{16} - 18\frac{3}{16}$?

A. $2\frac{7}{16}$ **B.** $2\frac{9}{16}$ C. $3\frac{7}{16}$ D. $3\frac{9}{16}$

14. Writing in Math Explain why it is necessary to rename $4\frac{1}{4}$ if you subtract $\frac{3}{4}$ from it.

Sample answer: You cannot subtract $\frac{3}{4}$ from $\frac{1}{4}$, so you must borrow 1 whole from the 4 and rename $4\frac{1}{4}$ as $3\frac{5}{4}$.

Name_____

Subtracting Mixed Numbers

R 8-8

Find $4\frac{1}{2} - 1\frac{5}{8}$.

Step 1	Step 2	Step 3
Write equivalent fractions with the LCD.	Rename $4\frac{4}{8}$ to show more eighths.	Subtract the fractions. Then subtract the whole numbers. Simplify the difference.
$4\frac{1}{2} = 4\frac{4}{8}$ $-1\frac{5}{8} = 1\frac{5}{8}$	$4\frac{1}{2} = 4\frac{4}{8} = 3\frac{12}{8}$ $-1\frac{5}{8} = 1\frac{5}{8} = 1\frac{5}{8}$	$4\frac{1}{2} = 4\frac{4}{8} = 3\frac{12}{8}$ $-1\frac{5}{8} = 1\frac{5}{8} = 1\frac{5}{8}$ $2\frac{7}{8}$

So, $4\frac{1}{2} - 1\frac{5}{8} = 2\frac{7}{8}$.

Find $9 - 3\frac{1}{6}$.

Step 1	Step 2
Rename 9 to show sixths.	Subtract the fractions. Then subtract the whole numbers.
$9 = 8\frac{6}{6}$ $-3\frac{1}{6} = 3\frac{1}{6}$	$9 = 8\frac{6}{6}$ $-3\frac{1}{6} = 3\frac{1}{6}$ $5\frac{5}{6}$

So, $9 - 3\frac{1}{6} = 5\frac{5}{6}$.

Estimate the difference first. Then subtract. Simplify, if necessary.

1. $4\frac{3}{5}$
$-\ 2\frac{1}{3}$

3; $2\frac{4}{15}$

2. $5\frac{6}{7}$
$-\ 1\frac{1}{2}$

4; $4\frac{5}{14}$

3. 3
$-\ 1\frac{3}{4}$

1; $1\frac{1}{4}$

4. $6\frac{5}{6}$
$-\ 5\frac{1}{2}$

1; $1\frac{1}{3}$

Estimates will vary.

Name_____

What's Missing?

E 8-8
ALGEBRA

Each of the subtraction problems is missing a number. Find the number from the number bank that will correctly complete the problem, and write it in the blank.

Number Bank

$10\frac{1}{6}$			$2\frac{1}{2}$
$5\frac{1}{3}$	$10\frac{1}{2}$	$9\frac{10}{15}$	$3\frac{1}{4}$
$3\frac{1}{2}$	$2\frac{2}{6}$	$2\frac{3}{20}$	$9\frac{1}{4}$
	$9\frac{3}{5}$	$9\frac{1}{8}$	$5\frac{1}{6}$

1. $6\frac{7}{8} - $ **$3\frac{1}{2}$** $= 3\frac{3}{8}$

2. **$9\frac{10}{15}$** $- 5\frac{1}{3} = 4\frac{3}{5}$

3. $10\frac{2}{8} - 8\frac{1}{10} = $ **$2\frac{3}{20}$**

4. **$9\frac{3}{5}$** $- 6\frac{1}{3} = 3\frac{4}{15}$

5. $7\frac{2}{9} - $ **$5\frac{1}{6}$** $= 2\frac{1}{18}$

6. **$10\frac{1}{2}$** $- 3\frac{1}{3} = 7\frac{1}{6}$

7. $7\frac{5}{8} - $ **$2\frac{2}{6}$** $= 5\frac{1}{2}$

8. $12\frac{1}{2} - 3\frac{1}{4} = $ **$9\frac{1}{4}$**

9. **$5\frac{1}{3}$** $- 4\frac{1}{2} = \frac{5}{6}$

10. $7\frac{3}{4} - $ **$3\frac{1}{4}$** $= 4\frac{1}{2}$

Name_____

Subtracting Mixed Numbers

PS 8-8

Thirsty Corn Corn is one of the main farming products in the state of Iowa. As you might guess, rain is very important to the farming industry in Iowa. Suppose in Sibley, Iowa, there was a total of $1\frac{7}{12}$ in. of rain during the second week of July, $3\frac{1}{12}$ in. during the third week, and $3\frac{5}{8}$ in. during the fourth week.

1. How much more rain fell in Sibley during the third week than the second week?

$1\frac{1}{2}$ more inches

2. How much more rain fell in Sibley during the fourth week than the second week?

$2\frac{1}{24}$ more inches

3. How much more rain fell in Sibley during the fourth week than the third week?

$\frac{13}{24}$ more inches

Soccer Allisa, Kay, and Fran played in a game of soccer on a hot day. During the game, Allisa drank $2\frac{3}{5}$ glasses of water, Kay drank 4 glasses of water, and Fran drank $3\frac{1}{6}$ glasses of water.

4. How much more water did Kay drink than Allisa?

$1\frac{2}{5}$ more glasses

5. How much more water did Kay drink than Fran?

$\frac{5}{6}$ more glasses

6. How much more water did Fran drink than Allisa?

$\frac{17}{30}$ more glasses

7. Writing in Math Explain why you had to rename the number 4 twice to solve the exercises in the Soccer problem.

Sample answer: 4 had to be renamed twice because there were different denominators in each problem.

Practice

PROBLEM-SOLVING STRATEGY   Sample answers   P 8-9
Work Backward   are given.

Solve each problem by working backward. Write the answers in complete sentences.

Barbara is refilling her bird feeders and squirrel feeders in her yard.

1. After filling her bird feeders, Barbara has $3\frac{1}{2}$ c of mixed birdseed left. The two feeders in the front yard took $4\frac{1}{4}$ c each. The two feeders in the backyard each took $2\frac{3}{4}$ c. The two feeders next to the living room window each took $3\frac{1}{4}$ c. How much mixed birdseed did Barbara have before filling the feeders?

Barbara began with $24\frac{1}{2}$ c of birdseed.

2. After Barbara fills each of her 4 squirrel feeders with $2\frac{2}{3}$ c of peanuts, she has $1\frac{3}{4}$ c of peanuts left. How many cups of peanuts did Barbara start with?

Barbara began with $12\frac{5}{12}$ c of peanuts.

Angela is knitting a scarf for her grandmother. Every day she knits a little bit more. The finished scarf will be 36 in. long.

3. Angela's mother starts knitting the scarf to help get her started. Angela knits a $6\frac{1}{2}$ in. section each day. After 5 days, the scarf is done. How many inches did Angela's mother knit?

Angela's mother knitted $3\frac{1}{2}$ in.

4. How many more days would Angela have to knit to make the scarf 48 in. long?

It would take Angela 2 more days.

Clint spends $\frac{1}{2}$ hr practicing trumpet, $\frac{3}{4}$ hr doing tasks around the house, $1\frac{1}{2}$ hr doing homework, and $\frac{1}{4}$ hr cleaning his room. He is finished at 7:30 P.M.

5. When did Clint start?

Clint started at 4:30 P.M.

Reteaching

PROBLEM-SOLVING STRATEGY   R 8-9
Work Backward

Car Wash Jake's neighborhood had a car wash to raise money for improvements to a nearby park. They earned twice as much money on Saturday as they did on Sunday. On Friday they earned $50 less than the amount earned on Saturday. On Thursday the car wash took in $422 which was $38 more than on Friday. What did they earn on Friday, Saturday, and Sunday?

Read and Understand

Step 1: What do you know?

The car wash took in twice as much money on Saturday as on Sunday.

The money raised on Friday was $50 less than the amount earned on Saturday.

Thursday's amount was $422 which was $38 more than was earned on Friday.

Step 2: What are you trying to find?

How much money was earned on Friday, Saturday, and Sunday?

Plan and Solve

Step 3: What strategy will you use?   **Strategy:** Work backward

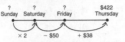 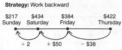

The car wash brought in $384 on Friday, $434 on Saturday, and $217 on Sunday.

Look Back and Check

Step 4: Is your answer reasonable?

Yes, because when I work forward from the initial amount, I get the end result.

Solve the problem by working backward. Write the answer in a complete sentence.

1. Brett has promised he would be back home by 5:30 P.M. It takes him 20 min to skate over to his friend's house. He will stay there for 2 hr. On the way home, he always stops for a snack, so the return trip takes 30 min. If Brett is to keep his promise, by what time must he leave home?

Brett should leave by 2:40 P.M.

Enrichment

Fraction Triangles   E 8-9   NUMBER SENSE

Fill in the circles in the number triangles with fractions or mixed numbers so that the sum of each side equals the number in the middle of the triangle.

1. Sample answers: **2. Sample answers:**

3. Sample answers: **4. Sample answers:**

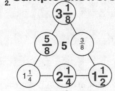

Problem Solving

PROBLEM-SOLVING STRATEGY   PS 8-9
Work Backward

Fuel Mark kept track of the amount of gasoline his car used for 3 days. On the first day, $3\frac{1}{5}$ gal were used. On the second day, $4\frac{1}{4}$ gal were used. On the third day, $2\frac{7}{10}$ gal were used and $1\frac{1}{2}$ gal were left in the tank. How many gallons of gasoline did Mark's car have at the beginning of the 3-day period?

Read and Understand

1. How many gallons of gasoline were used each day?

1st day: $3\frac{1}{5}$ gal; 2nd day: $4\frac{1}{4}$ gal; 3rd day: $2\frac{7}{10}$ gal

2. How many gallons of gasoline were left after 3 days?

$1\frac{1}{2}$ gal

3. What are you trying to find?

The number of gallons of gasoline at beginning of the 3-day period

Plan and Solve

4. What strategy will you use?   **Work backward**

5. Write and solve an equation to solve the problem. Write your answer in a complete sentence.

$n - 3\frac{1}{5} - 4\frac{1}{4} - 2\frac{7}{10} = 1\frac{1}{2}$; $3\frac{1}{5} + 4\frac{1}{4} + 2\frac{7}{10} + 1\frac{1}{2} = n$; $n = 11\frac{13}{20}$; There were $11\frac{13}{20}$ gal of gasoline in Mark's car at the beginning of the 3-day period.

Look Back and Check

6. Is your answer reasonable?

Yes, because $11\frac{13}{20} - 3\frac{1}{5} - 4\frac{1}{4} - 2\frac{7}{10} = 1\frac{1}{2}$.

Practice

Name_____

Multiplying Fractions by Whole Numbers

P 8-10

Find each product.

1. $\frac{1}{4}$ of 96 = **24**
2. $\frac{4}{7}$ of 28 = **16**
3. $\frac{3}{4} \times 72$ = **54**
4. $45 \times \frac{3}{9}$ = **15**
5. $56 \times \frac{7}{8}$ = **49**
6. $42 \times \frac{3}{9}$ = **18**
7. $\frac{1}{2}$ of 118 = **59**
8. $\frac{3}{8}$ of 56 = **21**
9. $\frac{1}{10} \times 400$ = **40**
10. $84 \times \frac{1}{6}$ = **14**
11. $64 \times \frac{5}{16}$ = **20**
12. $40 \times \frac{11}{20}$ = **22**
13. $\frac{5}{8}$ of 48 = **30**
14. $\frac{1}{7}$ of 77 = **11**
15. $\frac{4}{5} \times 90$ = **72**
16. $42 \times \frac{3}{14}$ = **9**
17. $72 \times \frac{5}{8}$ = **45**
18. $18 \times \frac{2}{3}$ = **12**
19. $\frac{5}{6} \times 84$ = **70**
20. $\frac{11}{12} \times 144$ = **132**
21. $\frac{6}{7} \times 42$ = **36**

22. **Patterns** Complete the table by writing the product of each expression in the box below it. Use a pattern to find each product. Explain the pattern.

$\frac{1}{2} \times 32$	$\frac{1}{4} \times 32$	$\frac{1}{8} \times 32$	$\frac{1}{16} \times 32$
16	**8**	**4**	**2**

Sample answer:

The next number is $\frac{1}{2}$ of the one before.

23. **Reasoning** If $\frac{1}{2}$ of 1 is $\frac{1}{2}$, what is $\frac{1}{2}$ of 2, 3, and 4?   **1; 1$\frac{1}{2}$; 2**

Test Prep

24. Which is $\frac{2}{3}$ of 225?

A. 75   B. 113   C. 150   D. 450

25. **Writing in Math** Explain why $\frac{1}{2}$ of 2 equals one whole.

Sample answer: 2 is two 1s, so $\frac{1}{2}$ of 2 is 1.

110   Use with Lesson 8-10.

© Pearson Education, Inc. 5

Reteaching

Name_____

Multiplying Fractions by Whole Numbers

R 8-10

You can use multiplication to find a fraction of a whole number.

Example A

Find $\frac{1}{3}$ of 30. Use mental math.

$\frac{1}{3}$ of 30 gives the same result as dividing 30 by 3.

$30 \div 3 = 10$

So, $\frac{1}{3}$ of 30 = 10.

Example B

Find $8 \times \frac{3}{4}$. Use mental math.

Think: $\frac{3}{4}$ is 3 times as much as $\frac{1}{4}$.

$\frac{1}{4}$ of 8 = 2.

Multiply 2 by 3.

$2 \times 3 = 6$

So, $8 \times \frac{3}{4} = 6$.

Find each product.

1. $20 \times \frac{2}{5}$ = **8**
2. $\frac{1}{6}$ of 18 = **3**
3. $50 \times \frac{3}{10}$ = **15**
4. $\frac{7}{8}$ of 64 = **56**

5. **Reasoning** How could you use the product of $\frac{1}{5} \times 40$ to find the product of $\frac{4}{5} \times 40$?

Multiply the product of $\frac{1}{5} \times 40$ by 4.

The chart shows the maximum speed for different animals.

6. What is $\frac{1}{7}$ the speed of a cheetah?

10 mi per hour

Speeds of Animals

Animal	Speed (in mph)
Cat	30
Cheetah	70
Jackal	35

7. What is $\frac{1}{5}$ the speed of a cat?

6 mi per hour

8. What is $\frac{1}{5}$ the speed of a jackal?

7 mi per hour

110   Use with Lesson 8-10.

© Pearson Education, Inc. 5

Enrichment

Name_____

Xs and Os

E 8-10
NUMBER SENSE

In each row, circle the problem with the greatest product. Cross out the problem with the least product.

1. ~~$\frac{3}{4}$ of 12~~   (⟨$\frac{5}{8}$ of 40⟩) $\frac{2}{10}$ of 100
2. (⟨$\frac{7}{8}$ of 64⟩)   ~~$\frac{5}{20}$ of 100~~ $\frac{4}{5}$ of 50
3. $\frac{2}{3}$ of 60   (⟨$\frac{5}{10}$ of 120⟩)   ~~$\frac{7}{8}$ of 49~~
4. ~~$\frac{1}{4}$ of 100~~   (⟨$\frac{1}{3}$ of 75⟩) $\frac{1}{5}$ of 100
5. (⟨$\frac{2}{8}$ of 40⟩)   ~~$\frac{1}{4}$ of 40~~ $\frac{1}{3}$ of 36
6. (⟨$\frac{1}{6}$ of 66⟩)   ~~$\frac{1}{9}$ of 45~~ $\frac{1}{8}$ of 48
7. (⟨$\frac{8}{10}$ of 50⟩)   ~~$\frac{3}{6}$ of 24~~ $\frac{2}{8}$ of 100
8. ~~$\frac{5}{6}$ of 24~~ $\frac{2}{5}$ of 30   (⟨$\frac{6}{8}$ of 50⟩)
9. ~~$\frac{1}{4}$ of 40~~ $\frac{5}{10}$ of 50   (⟨$\frac{4}{10}$ of 80⟩)
10. $\frac{1}{20}$ of 100   ~~$\frac{2}{4}$ of 14~~   (⟨$\frac{1}{10}$ of 60⟩)
11. ~~$\frac{2}{8}$ of 24~~ $\frac{1}{2}$ of 38   (⟨$\frac{1}{3}$ of 60⟩)
12. (⟨$\frac{3}{8}$ of 64⟩) $\frac{2}{3}$ of 33   ~~$\frac{2}{9}$ of 40~~
13. (⟨$\frac{5}{9} \times 27$⟩)   ~~$\frac{2}{6} \times 24$~~ $\frac{3}{4} \times 16$

110   Use with Lesson 8-10.

© Pearson Education, Inc. 5

Problem Solving

Name_____

Multiplying Fractions by Whole Numbers

PS 8-10

Model Your Money For 1–3, shade the pictures to help you find the answers.

1. Suppose you have 15 $1 bills. You use $\frac{1}{5}$ of the $1 bills to buy a book. How many $1 bills did you use?

3 $1 bills

2. Suppose you have 16 quarters. You use $\frac{3}{8}$ of the quarters to buy 2 cans of juice. How many quarters did you use?

6 quarters

3. Suppose you have nine $5 bills. You use $\frac{1}{3}$ of the $5 bills to buy 2 CDs. How much did you pay for the 2 CDs?

$15

4. **Writing in Math** Explain how you could use mental math to find $\frac{3}{10}$ of 30.

Sample answer: It is easy to find that $\frac{1}{10}$ of 30 is 3, and 3 × 3 equals 9.

110   Use with Lesson 8-10.

© Pearson Education, Inc. 5

Practice

Name_____

Estimating Products of Fractions
P 8-11

Estimate each product. **Sample answers are given.**

1. $\frac{7}{8} \times 57$ **49**   2. $\frac{3}{8} \times 28$ **9**   3. $\frac{8}{9} \times 27$ **27**

4. $24 \times \frac{4}{7}$ **8**   5. $80 \times \frac{4}{7}$ **40**   6. $\frac{5}{7} \times 50$ **35**

7. $\frac{1}{8} \times 46$ **6**   8. $\frac{2}{7} \times 58$ **16**   9. $\frac{4}{9} \times 70$ **32**

10. $18 \times \frac{3}{5}$ **12**   11. $91 \times \frac{1}{10}$ **9**   12. $\frac{3}{4} \times 39$ **30**

13. About how many furlongs is $\frac{2}{3}$ of 1 mi?
About 6 furlongs

Distance Measurements		
40 rods	=	1 furlong
8 furlongs	=	1 mi
3 mi	=	1 league
5,280 ft	=	1 mi

14. About how many rods is $\frac{4}{7}$ of 1 furlong?
About 20 rods

15. About how many miles is $\frac{7}{9}$ of 1 league?
About 2 mi

16. About how many feet is $\frac{23}{48}$ of 1 mi?
About 2,640 ft

17. **Number Sense** Is the product of $\frac{3}{9} \times 100$ greater than or less than 30? Explain.
Greater than; $\frac{3}{9}$ of 100 is a greater fraction than $\frac{3}{10}$ of 100, which is 30.

Test Prep

18. Which is the most reasonable estimate for $55 \times \frac{5}{7}$?
   A. 30   **B. 35**   C. 55   D. 60

19. **Writing in Math** Which is easier, finding $\frac{2}{7}$ of 65 or $\frac{2}{7}$ of 63? Explain your answer.
Sample answer: Finding $\frac{2}{7}$ of 63 is easier because 63 can be divided by 7.

Use with Lesson 8-11. **111**

Reteaching

Name_____

Estimating Products of Fractions
R 8-11

You can use compatible numbers and benchmark fractions to estimate products of fractions.

One Way	Another Way
Find $\frac{2}{3} \times 92$.	Find $\frac{3}{7} \times 40$.
Think: 92 is close to 90.	Change the fraction to the closest benchmark fraction. Remember that benchmarks are numbers like $\frac{1}{2}$ and 1.
$\frac{1}{3} \times 90 = 30$, and $\frac{2}{3} \times 90 = 60$.	**Think:** $\frac{3}{7}$ is close to $\frac{1}{2}$.
So, $\frac{2}{3} \times 92$ is about 60.	$\frac{1}{2} \times 40 = 20$
	So, $\frac{3}{7} \times 40$ is about 20.

Estimate each product. **Sample answers are given.**

1. $\frac{1}{4} \times 17$ **4**   2. $\frac{2}{3} \times 10$ **6**   3. $\frac{1}{5} \times 21$ **4**

4. $\frac{5}{6} \times 37$ **30**   5. $\frac{3}{12} \times 25$ **6**   6. $\frac{4}{5} \times 42$ **32**

7. **Number Sense** Do you think the actual product of $\frac{1}{8} \times 55$ is greater than or less than 7? Explain.
Sample answer: Less, because $\frac{1}{8} \times 56 = 7$.

8. Estimate the amount of orange juice it takes to make 8 pitchers of punch.
Sample answer: About 6 c

Recipe for Pitcher of Tropical Punch	
$\frac{3}{4}$ c	pineapple juice
$\frac{2}{3}$ c	orange juice
$\frac{4}{5}$ c	cranberry juice
$\frac{1}{2}$ c	soda water

9. About how much pineapple juice is needed for 25 pitchers of punch?
Sample answer: About 18 c

Use with Lesson 8-11. **111**

Enrichment

Name_____

You're the Greatest
E 8-11
ESTIMATION

Estimate the product of each expression. Write the expressions in order from least to greatest on the ladder. The expression with the least product should be at the bottom of the ladder, and the expression with the greatest product should be at the top.

$77 \times \frac{3}{4}$

$102 \times \frac{1}{2}$

$115 \times \frac{1}{3}$

$87 \times \frac{1}{3}$

$46 \times \frac{5}{9}$

$22 \times \frac{2}{3}$

Sample estimates are given.

1. $102 \times \frac{1}{2} \approx$ **50**   2. $77 \times \frac{3}{4} \approx$ **60**   3. $115 \times \frac{1}{3} \approx$ **40**

4. $46 \times \frac{5}{9} \approx$ **25**   5. $87 \times \frac{1}{3} \approx$ **30**   6. $22 \times \frac{2}{3} \approx$ **14**

Use with Lesson 8-11. **111**

Problem Solving

Name_____

Estimating Products of Fractions
PS 8-11

Heave It Brett can throw a football farther than any of his friends. His best throw measured 96 ft. For 1–4, estimate each product.

1. Craig can throw a football $\frac{4}{7}$ of the distance Brett can. About how far can Craig throw a football?
About 48 ft

Sample answers given for 1–6.

2. Fred can throw a football $\frac{9}{13}$ of the distance Brett can throw a football. About how far can Fred throw a football?
About 72 ft

3. Sergio can throw a football $\frac{7}{9}$ of the distance Brett can throw a football. About how far can Sergio throw a football?
About 64 ft

Commute In one week, Mr. Jansen drove 48 mi total in 10 trips to and from work.

4. About how many miles did Mr. Jansen drive in 4 trips? Use a benchmark fraction to find your answer.
About 24 mi

5. About how many miles did Mr. Jansen drive in 7 trips? Use compatible numbers to find your answer.
About 35 mi

6. **Writing in Math** Did you use a benchmark fraction or compatible numbers for Exercise 3? Explain.
I used a benchmark fraction because $\frac{7}{9}$ is close to $\frac{6}{8}$, which is $\frac{3}{4}$.

Use with Lesson 8-11. **111**

Name_____

Multiplying Fractions

P 8-12

Write the multiplication problem that each model represents.

1.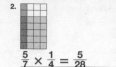

$$\frac{2}{3} \times \frac{1}{6} = \frac{2}{18} = \frac{1}{9}$$

2.

$$\frac{5}{7} \times \frac{1}{4} = \frac{5}{28}$$

Find each product. Simplify, if necessary.

3. $\frac{7}{8} \times \frac{4}{5} =$ $\frac{7}{10}$

4. $\frac{3}{7} \times \frac{2}{3} =$ $\frac{2}{7}$

5. $\frac{1}{6} \times \frac{2}{5} =$ $\frac{1}{15}$

6. $\frac{2}{7} \times \frac{1}{4} =$ $\frac{1}{14}$

7. $\frac{2}{9} \times \frac{1}{2} =$ $\frac{1}{9}$

8. $\frac{3}{4} \times \frac{1}{3} =$ $\frac{1}{4}$

9. $\frac{3}{8} \times \frac{4}{9} =$ $\frac{1}{6}$

10. $\frac{1}{5} \times \frac{5}{6} =$ $\frac{1}{6}$

11. $\frac{2}{3} \times \frac{5}{6} \times \frac{1}{4} =$ $\frac{5}{36}$

12. $\frac{1}{2} \times \frac{1}{3} \times \frac{1}{4} =$ $\frac{1}{24}$

13. **Algebra** If $\frac{4}{5} \times \blacksquare = \frac{2}{5}$, what is $\blacksquare$? $\frac{1}{2}$

14. Ms. Shoemaker's classroom has 35 desks arranged in 5 by 7 rows. How many students does Ms. Shoemaker have in her class if there are $\frac{6}{7} \times \frac{4}{5}$ desks occupied?

24 students

Test Prep

15. Which does the model represent?

  A. $\frac{3}{8} \times \frac{3}{5}$ B. $\frac{5}{8} \times \frac{5}{8}$

  C. $\frac{7}{8} \times \frac{2}{5}$ D. $\frac{4}{8} \times \frac{3}{5}$

16. **Writing in Math** Describe a model that represents $\frac{3}{3} \times \frac{4}{4}$.

Sample answer:

Each fraction represents one whole, so the model would be completely shaded in for both fractions.

Name_____

Multiplying Fractions

R 8-12

	How to multiply two fractions	How to multiply three or more fractions
	Find $\frac{3}{4} \times \frac{2}{5}$.	Find $\frac{1}{4} \times \frac{2}{5} \times \frac{2}{3}$.
Step 1	Multiply the numerators. $\frac{3}{4} \times \frac{2}{5} = \frac{3 \times 2}{} = \frac{6}{}$	Multiply the numerators. $\frac{1}{4} \times \frac{2}{5} \times \frac{2}{3} = \frac{1 \times 2 \times 2}{} = \frac{4}{}$
Step 2	Multiply the denominators. $\frac{3}{4} \times \frac{2}{5} = \frac{3 \times 2}{4 \times 5} = \frac{6}{20}$	Multiply the denominators. $\frac{1}{4} \times \frac{2}{5} \times \frac{2}{3} = \frac{1 \times 2 \times 2}{4 \times 5 \times 3} = \frac{4}{60}$
Step 3	Simplify the product. $\frac{3}{4} \times \frac{2}{5} = \frac{3 \times 2}{4 \times 5} = \frac{6}{20} = \frac{3}{10}$ So, $\frac{3}{4} \times \frac{2}{5} = \frac{3}{10}$.	Simplify the product. $\frac{1}{4} \times \frac{2}{5} \times \frac{2}{3} = \frac{1 \times 2 \times 2}{4 \times 5 \times 3} = \frac{4}{60} = \frac{1}{15}$ So, $\frac{1}{4} \times \frac{2}{5} \times \frac{2}{3} = \frac{1}{15}$.

Find each product. Simplify, if necessary.

1. $\frac{5}{7} \times \frac{1}{2} =$ $\frac{5}{14}$

2. $\frac{4}{5} \times \frac{2}{3} =$ $\frac{8}{15}$

3. $\frac{3}{4} \times \frac{2}{5} =$ $\frac{3}{10}$

4. $\frac{1}{2} \times \frac{3}{8} =$ $\frac{3}{16}$

5. $\frac{1}{5} \times \frac{6}{7} =$ $\frac{6}{35}$

6. $\frac{2}{3} \times \frac{1}{4} =$ $\frac{1}{6}$

7. $\frac{7}{8} \times \frac{1}{2} \times \frac{6}{7} =$ $\frac{7}{24}$

$\frac{7}{8} \times \frac{1}{2} \times \frac{6}{7} =$ $\frac{7}{24}$

8. $\frac{2}{4} \times \frac{4}{5} \times \frac{3}{5} =$ $\frac{6}{25}$

9. **Number Sense** Mark missed $\frac{1}{5}$ of the questions on his test. He corrected $\frac{3}{4}$ of the questions he missed. What fraction of the questions on the test did he correct? $\frac{3}{20}$

Name_____

Half a Batch

E 8-12
NUMBER SENSE

One cold winter day Tim decided to make hot cocoa. When he looked at the recipe, he realized that he only needed to make $\frac{1}{2}$ of a batch of cocoa. Rewrite the recipe so Tim can make $\frac{1}{2}$ of a batch of cocoa.

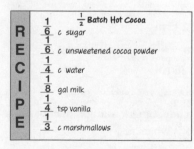

R E C I P E   Hot Cocoa

- $\frac{1}{3}$ c sugar
- $\frac{1}{3}$ c unsweetened cocoa powder
- $\frac{1}{2}$ c water
- $\frac{1}{4}$ gal milk
- $\frac{1}{2}$ tsp vanilla
- $\frac{2}{3}$ c marshmallows

R E C I P E $\frac{1}{2}$ Batch Hot Cocoa

- $\frac{1}{6}$ c sugar
- $\frac{1}{6}$ c unsweetened cocoa powder
- $\frac{1}{4}$ c water
- $\frac{1}{8}$ gal milk
- $\frac{1}{4}$ tsp vanilla
- $\frac{1}{3}$ c marshmallows

Name_____

Multiplying Fractions

PS 8-12

Cantaloupes Michelle went shopping with her dad. They bought 4 cantaloupes, the largest of which weighed $\frac{7}{8}$ lb. For 1–3, simplify your answer, if necessary.

1. If the smallest cantaloupe weighed $\frac{1}{2}$ as much as the largest cantaloupe, how much did it weigh? $\frac{7}{16}$ lb

2. If another of the cantaloupes weighed $\frac{5}{7}$ as much as the largest cantaloupe, how much did it weigh? $\frac{5}{8}$ lb

3. If another of the cantaloupes weighed $\frac{7}{9}$ as much as the largest cantaloupe, how much did it weigh? $\frac{49}{72}$ lb

Nature Trail The nature trail at a park near Justin's home is $\frac{3}{4}$ mi. There are many interesting stops along the way. For 4–5, simplify your answer, if necessary.

4. There is a hill that offers great views $\frac{1}{3}$ of the way from the beginning of the trail. How many miles is the walk to the hill? $\frac{1}{4}$ mi

5. A stream that Justin likes to soak his feet in is $\frac{5}{8}$ of the way from the beginning of the trail. How many miles is the walk to the stream? $\frac{15}{32}$ mi

6. **Writing in Math** Explain how you could use a piece of paper to model the problem $\frac{1}{3} \times \frac{2}{3}$.

Sample answer: Fold a piece of paper vertically in 3 sections and then horizontally in 3 sections. Then shade $\frac{1}{3}$ of the vertical sections red and $\frac{2}{3}$ of the horizontal sections blue. The part that is red and blue is the answer.

© Pearson Education, Inc. 5

Name_____

Multiplying Mixed Numbers

P 8-13

Estimate the product. Then complete the multiplication. **Sample answers are given.**

1. $5\frac{4}{5} \times 7 = \boxed{\frac{29}{5}} \times \frac{7}{1} = \boxed{40\frac{3}{5}}$

2. $3\frac{2}{3} \times 5\frac{1}{7} = \boxed{\frac{11}{3}} \times \boxed{\frac{36}{7}} = \boxed{18\frac{6}{7}}$

Estimate: 42   **Estimate: 20**

Estimate. Then find each product. Simplify.

3. $4\frac{3}{5} \times \frac{2}{3}$ **5; $3\frac{1}{15}$**   4. $6 \times 2\frac{2}{7}$ **12; $13\frac{5}{7}$**

5. $7\frac{4}{5} \times 2\frac{1}{3}$ **16; $18\frac{1}{3}$**   6. $3\frac{3}{4} \times 2\frac{4}{5}$ **12; $10\frac{1}{2}$**

7. $2\frac{1}{5} \times \frac{7}{8}$ **2; $1\frac{37}{40}$**   8. $6\frac{1}{3} \times 1\frac{5}{8}$ **12; $11\frac{11}{18}$**

9. $1\frac{4}{5} \times 1\frac{1}{3} \times 1\frac{3}{5}$ **4; $4\frac{1}{5}$**   10. $\frac{3}{5} \times 2\frac{3}{5} \times 5\frac{1}{5}$ **10; $10\frac{2}{5}$**

11. **Algebra** Write a mixed number for p so that $3\frac{1}{4} \times p$ is more than $3\frac{1}{4}$.   **Sample answer: $1\frac{1}{4}$**

12. A model house is built on a base that measures $9\frac{1}{4}$ in. wide and $8\frac{4}{5}$ in. long. What is the total area of the model house's base?   **$81\frac{2}{5}$ in^2**

Test Prep

13. Which is $1\frac{3}{4}$ of $150\frac{1}{2}$?

A. 263   B. $263\frac{1}{8}$ Ⓒ $263\frac{3}{8}$ D. $264\frac{3}{8}$

14. **Writing in Math** Megan's dog Sparky eats $4\frac{1}{4}$ c of food each day. Explain how Megan can determine how much food to give Sparky if she needs to feed him only $\frac{2}{3}$ as much. Solve the problem.

Sample answer: Megan would multiply $4\frac{1}{4}$ c by $\frac{2}{3}$ to find $2\frac{5}{6}$ c.

Use with Lesson 8-13. **113**

Name_____

Multiplying Mixed Numbers

R 8-13

Estimate $3\frac{3}{4} \times 2\frac{1}{8}$.

$3\frac{3}{4} \times 2\frac{1}{8}$ Round each mixed number to the nearest whole number.

$4 \times 2 = 8$ So, $3\frac{3}{4} \times 2\frac{1}{8}$ is about 8.

	How to multiply a mixed number by a mixed number	How to multiply a mixed number by a fraction	How to multiply a mixed number by a whole number
	Find $1\frac{1}{4} \times 2\frac{1}{2}$.	Find $3\frac{1}{2} \times \frac{1}{3}$.	Find $6 \times 3\frac{1}{3}$.
Step 1	Write the mixed numbers as improper fractions. $1\frac{1}{4} = \frac{5}{4}$ $2\frac{1}{2} = \frac{5}{2}$	Write the mixed number as an improper fraction. $3\frac{1}{2} = \frac{7}{2}$	Write both numbers as improper fractions. $6 = \frac{6}{1}$ $3\frac{1}{3} = \frac{10}{3}$
Step 2	Multiply as you would multiply fractions. $\frac{5}{4} \times \frac{5}{2} = \frac{25}{8}$	Multiply as you would multiply fractions. $\frac{7}{2} \times \frac{1}{3} = \frac{7}{6}$	Multiply as you would multiply fractions. $\frac{6}{1} \times \frac{10}{3} = \frac{60}{3}$
Step 3	Simplify the product. $\frac{25}{8} = 3\frac{1}{8}$ So, $1\frac{1}{4} \times 2\frac{1}{2} = 3\frac{1}{8}$.	Simplify the product. $\frac{7}{6} = 1\frac{1}{6}$ So, $3\frac{1}{2} \times \frac{1}{3} = 1\frac{1}{6}$.	Simplify the product. $\frac{60}{3} = 20$ So, $6 \times 3\frac{1}{3} = 20$.

Estimate. Then find each product. Simplify. **Estimates will vary.**

1. $1\frac{3}{4} \times 2\frac{1}{2} =$ **5; $4\frac{3}{8}$**   2. $1\frac{1}{5} \times 1\frac{2}{3} =$ **2; 2**

3. $2 \times 2\frac{1}{4} =$ **4; $4\frac{1}{2}$**   4. $1\frac{2}{5} \times 2\frac{1}{4} =$ **2; $3\frac{3}{20}$**

5. $2\frac{1}{2} \times 10 =$ **22; 25**   6. $1\frac{2}{3} \times \frac{1}{5} =$ **$\frac{1}{2}$; $\frac{1}{3}$**

7. **Number Sense** Write a multiplication sentence for $4\frac{4}{5} + 4\frac{4}{5} + 4\frac{4}{5}$.

Sample answer: $4\frac{4}{5} \times 3$

Use with Lesson 8-13. **113**

Name_____

Paper Patterns

E 8-13
VISUAL THINKING

The art teacher is measuring paper for various crafts. He must record the length, width, and area (length multiplied by width) for each sheet of paper. Fill in the missing areas for each sheet of paper.

1.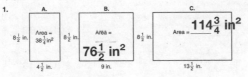

A. $8\frac{1}{2}$ in., Area = $38\frac{1}{4}$ in^2, $4\frac{1}{2}$ in.

B. $8\frac{1}{2}$ in., Area = **$76\frac{1}{2}$ in^2**, 9 in.

C. $8\frac{1}{2}$ in., Area = **$114\frac{3}{4}$ in^2**, $13\frac{1}{2}$ in.

2.

A. $16\frac{1}{4}$ in., $1\frac{1}{4}$ in., Area = **$20\frac{5}{16}$ in^2**

B. $2\frac{1}{2}$ in., Area = **$51\frac{1}{4}$ in^2**, $20\frac{1}{2}$ in.

C. $\frac{3}{4}$ in., Area = **$3\frac{3}{4}$ in^2**, 5 in.

3.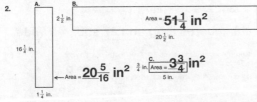

A. $2\frac{1}{2}$ in., $2\frac{1}{2}$ in., Area = **$6\frac{1}{4}$ in^2**

B. $12\frac{1}{2}$ in., Area = **$156\frac{1}{4}$ in^2**, $12\frac{1}{2}$ in.

C. $7\frac{1}{2}$ in., Area = **$56\frac{1}{4}$ in^2**, $7\frac{1}{2}$ in.

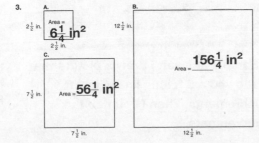

Use with Lesson 8-13. **113**

Name_____

Multiplying Mixed Numbers

PS 8-13

Sandcastles Yvonne, Manny, Raul, and Beatrice were building sandcastles at the beach. They were trying to see who could build the tallest sandcastle. Beatrice's sandcastle was $1\frac{3}{5}$ ft tall.

1. Yvonne's sandcastle was $1\frac{1}{4}$ times as tall as Beatrice's. What is $1\frac{1}{4} \times 1\frac{3}{5}$ ft?   **2 ft**

2. Manny's sandcastle was $1\frac{2}{3}$ times as tall as Beatrice's. What is $1\frac{2}{3} \times 1\frac{3}{5}$ ft?   **$2\frac{2}{3}$ ft**

3. Raul's sandcastle was $2\frac{1}{8}$ times as tall as Beatrice's. What is $2\frac{1}{8} \times 1\frac{3}{5}$ ft?   **$3\frac{2}{5}$ ft**

Land Measures Land areas are often measured in square sections or units. One common land measure is an **acre**. An acre was once defined as the amount of land a pair of oxen could plow in one day. Today, a square acre of land measures about 209 feet on each side.

4. Suppose an area of land is $3\frac{1}{4}$ sections long and $2\frac{7}{8}$ sections wide. What is $3\frac{1}{4} \times 2\frac{7}{8}$?   **$9\frac{11}{32}$**

5. Suppose an area of land is $5\frac{1}{5}$ sections long and $4\frac{5}{6}$ sections wide. What is $5\frac{1}{5} \times 4\frac{5}{6}$?   **$25\frac{2}{15}$**

6. **Writing in Math** The mixed numbers $1\frac{1}{4}$ and $1\frac{2}{5}$ cannot be simplified. Do you need to simplify the answer to $1\frac{1}{4} \times 1\frac{2}{5}$? Explain why or why not.

Yes; Sample answer: When you convert to improper fractions, the problem becomes $\frac{5}{4} \times \frac{7}{5}$, and there is a 5 in a numerator and a denominator.

Use with Lesson 8-13. **113**

Use with Chapter 8, Lesson 13 **113**

Name_____

Understanding Division
with Fractions
P 8-14

Use the pictures to find each quotient.

1. How many $\frac{1}{8}$s are in 1? $1 \div \frac{1}{8} =$ **8**

2. How many $\frac{3}{8}$s are in 3? $3 \div \frac{3}{8} =$ **8**

Find each quotient. You can draw pictures to help you.

3. $9 \div \frac{1}{3} =$ **27**　　　4. $8 \div \frac{2}{5} =$ **20**

5. $4 \div \frac{4}{5} =$ **5**　　　6. $12 \div \frac{4}{7} =$ **21**

7. $18 \div \frac{2}{3} =$ **27**　　　8. $10 \div \frac{1}{8} =$ **80**

9. $6 \div \frac{3}{5} =$ **10**　　　10. $16 \div \frac{4}{9} =$ **36**

11. If a red bead is $\frac{1}{4}$ in. thick, how many can you fit on 2 in. of string?　　**8 red beads**

12. If a blue bead is $\frac{3}{4}$ in. thick, how many can you fit on 3 in. of string?　　**4 blue beads**

13. If you alternate red beads and blue beads, how many red beads and blue beads can you fit on 4 in. of string?

4 red beads and 4 blue beads

Test Prep

14. Which number is the quotient of $36 \div \frac{6}{7}$?

A. 40　　B. 41　　C. 42　　D. 43

15. **Writing in Math** Explain why dividing any fraction by 1 equals the fraction.

Sample answer: When you divide a fraction by 1, you are dividing a fraction into 1 equal part.

Name_____

Understanding Division with Fractions
R 8-14

Find $3 \div \frac{1}{6}$.

Think: How many $\frac{1}{6}$s are in 3?

There are 3 wholes. Each whole is divided into sixths.
By counting, you can see that there are 18 $\frac{1}{6}$s in 3.

Use the picture to find each quotient.

1. How many $\frac{1}{4}$s are in 2?　**8**

2. How many $\frac{2}{4}$s are in 5?　**10**

3. How many $\frac{3}{4}$s are in 6?　**8**

Find each quotient. You can draw pictures to help you.

4. $5 \div \frac{1}{3} =$ **15**

5. $4 \div \frac{1}{5} =$ **20**

6. $1 \div \frac{1}{9} =$ **9**

7. $8 \div \frac{2}{5} =$ **20**

8. $6 \div \frac{3}{8} =$ **16**

9. $9 \div \frac{3}{5} =$ **15**

10. **Number Sense** Brandy has 8 yd of fabric. She is cutting it into $\frac{8}{9}$ yd strips. How many strips can she cut?

9 strips

Name_____

Delightful Division
E 8-14
VISUAL THINKING

You can model division of whole numbers by fractions by using a number line. Look at the example below, and then solve the problems.

$2 \div \frac{2}{5}$

On the number line, use brackets to mark off sections of $\frac{2}{5}$.

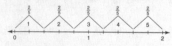

How many $\frac{2}{5}$ sections are in 2? Count the brackets. The answer is 5. So, $2 \div \frac{2}{5} = 5$. It's fun and easy! Give it a try.

1. $5 \div \frac{1}{3} =$ **15**

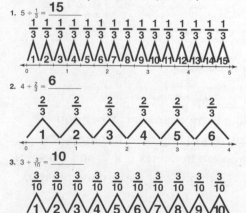

2. $4 \div \frac{2}{3} =$ **6**

3. $3 \div \frac{3}{10} =$ **10**

Name_____

Understanding Division with Fractions
PS 8-14

Quilt Mrs. Bauer's class is making a quilt to donate to a charity. The quilt will be 9 ft wide and 6 ft long. The quilt is being made of squares that are $\frac{1}{4}$ ft long and $\frac{1}{4}$ ft wide.

1. How many squares long will the quilt be? (Hint: The quilt is 6 ft long and each square is $\frac{1}{4}$ ft long.)　　**24 squares**

2. How many squares wide will the quilt be? (Hint: The quilt is 9 ft wide and each square is $\frac{1}{4}$ ft wide.)　　**36 squares**

3. If each square measured $\frac{1}{3}$ ft by $\frac{1}{3}$ ft, how many squares long and wide would the quilt be?

18 squares long and 27 squares wide

Measures A yard is divided into 3 ft. Each foot is divided into 12 in. There are 36 in. in a yard.

4. How many $\frac{1}{3}$ ft segments are there in a yard?　**9**

5. How many $\frac{3}{4}$ in. segments are there in a foot?　**16**

6. How many $\frac{1}{2}$ in. segments are in a yard?　**72**

7. How many $\frac{1}{9}$ ft segments are there in a yard?　**27**

8. **Writing in Math** Explain how you found your answer to Exercise 1.

Sample answer: I drew a picture that showed a 6 ft long line with $\frac{1}{4}$ ft increments. Then I counted the increments.

Name_____

PROBLEM-SOLVING SKILL   P 8-15

Choose an Operation

Draw a picture to show the main idea.
Then choose an operation to solve the problem.

About one-third of all solid waste in the United
States comes from packaging materials.

Material Components of Packaging Waste

Material	Percentage
Paper	$47\frac{7}{10}$%
Glass	$24\frac{1}{2}$%
Plastic	■%
Steel	$6\frac{1}{2}$%
Wood	■%
Aluminum	$2\frac{1}{3}$%

1. The total percentage of packaging waste from plastic and paper is $62\frac{1}{5}$%. What is the percentage of plastic?

$14\frac{1}{2}$%

2. What is the combined total percentage of paper and glass in packaging waste?

$72\frac{1}{5}$%

3. The sum of the percentage from steel, aluminum, and wood is $13\frac{1}{3}$%. What is the percentage from wood?

$4\frac{1}{2}$%

4. If $27\frac{5}{6}$ tons of paper waste were produced in 1 year, how many tons of paper waste would be produced in 5 years?

$139\frac{1}{6}$ tons

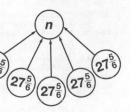

Use with Lesson 8-15. **115**

Name_____

PROBLEM-SOLVING SKILL   R 8-15

Choose an Operation

Bows Hector's store gift wraps customers' purchases at the counter. He is making bows for the packages. The chart shows how much ribbon is needed for each size bow. How much ribbon is needed to make 9 medium bows?

Bow	Ribbon Needed
Small	$\frac{1}{2}$ yd
Medium	$\frac{2}{3}$ yd
Large	$\frac{3}{4}$ yd

Read and Understand

Show the main idea.

$\frac{2}{3}$ of 9

Plan and Solve

Choose an operation. Multiply to find out how much ribbon is needed.

$$\frac{9}{1} \times \frac{2}{3} = \frac{18}{3} = 6$$

It takes 6 yd to make 9 medium bows.

Draw a picture to show the main idea. Then choose an operation to solve the problem. Use the chart above for 1 and 2.

1. How much ribbon is needed to make 16 large bows?

12 yd

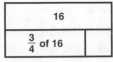

16	
$\frac{3}{4}$ of 16	

2. How much ribbon is needed to make 12 small bows?

6 yd

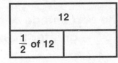

12	
$\frac{1}{2}$ of 12	

Use with Lesson 8-15. **115**

Name_____

Follow the Subtraction Sidewalk

E 8-15
NUMBER SENSE

To follow the subtraction sidewalk, start with the number at the beginning of the sidewalk, and subtract at each square along the sidewalk. Fill in the squares of the sidewalk with fractions or mixed numbers so that the answer at the end is correct. You may not use whole numbers or zero. Each square must contain a number.

1.

Sample answers:

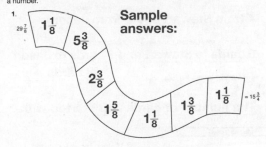

2.

Sample answers:

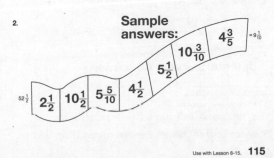

Use with Lesson 8-15. **115**

Name_____

PROBLEM-SOLVING SKILL   PS 8-15

Choose an Operation

Coin Collection Sylvia has a collection of coins from all over the world. She counted her coins and found that she had 35 of them. She also found that $\frac{2}{7}$ of them were from European countries. How many coins were from European countries?

Read and Understand

1. Draw a picture to show the main idea.

Sample picture:

35	
$\frac{2}{7}$ of 35	

2. What are you trying to find?

The number of Sylvia's coins from European countries

Plan and Solve

3. What operation will you use?

Multiplication

4. Write an equation and solve the problem.

$\frac{2}{7} \times \frac{35}{1} = n; n = 10$

5. Write your answer in a complete sentence.

Sylvia has 10 coins from European countries.

Look Back and Check

6. Explain how you can check your answer.

Sample answer: I can estimate to find $\frac{1}{4}$ of 40, which is 10, so my answer is reasonable.

Use with Lesson 8-15. **115**

© Pearson Education, Inc. 5

PROBLEM-SOLVING APPLICATIONS   P 8-16
Natural Facts

Solve. Write your answers in complete sentences.

The skin is considered the heaviest and largest organ of the human body. The table lists some interesting facts about the thickness of the skin.

Skin Facts

Average thickness	$\frac{2}{25}$ in.
Thickest (upper back)	$\frac{1}{5}$ in.
Thinnest (eyelids)	$\frac{1}{50}$ in.

1. How many eyelids have an equal thickness to the skin on the upper back?

10 eyelids have the same thickness.

2. What is the difference in thickness between the average thickness of the skin and the thickness of the skin on the eyelid?

The average thickness is $\frac{3}{50}$ in. greater.

3. How much thicker is the skin on the upper back than the skin of the eyelid?

The skin on the upper back is $\frac{9}{50}$ in. thicker.

The table at the right shows the percentage of some elements in the human body.

The Human Body

Element	Percentage
Carbon	$18\frac{1}{2}$%
Hydrogen	$9\frac{1}{2}$%
Nitrogen	$3\frac{1}{3}$%
Calcium	$1\frac{1}{2}$%
Phosphorous	1%

4. What percentage of the human body do carbon and hydrogen make up?

Hydrogen and carbon make up 28%.

5. How much greater is the percentage of calcium and nitrogen combined than the percentage of phosphorus?

The percentage of nitrogen and calcium is $3\frac{5}{6}$% greater than phosphorus.

© Pearson Education, Inc. 5

PROBLEM-SOLVING APPLICATIONS   R 8-16
Mountain Biking

Anna, Gustavo, and Emily went mountain biking. Each person rode a different trail. Anna rode $7\frac{3}{10}$ mi. Gustavo biked $8\frac{9}{10}$ mi. Emily rode $10\frac{5}{10}$ mi. How many miles combined did the bikers ride?

$$\begin{array}{r} 7\frac{3}{10} \\ 8\frac{9}{10} \\ + 10\frac{5}{10} \\ \hline \frac{17}{10} \end{array} \qquad \begin{array}{r} 7\frac{3}{10} \\ 8\frac{9}{10} \\ + 10\frac{5}{10} \\ \hline 25\frac{17}{10} \end{array} \qquad 25\frac{17}{10} = 26\frac{7}{10}$$

First add the fractions.   Then add the whole numbers.   Simplify the sum, if necessary.

So, they rode a total of $26\frac{7}{10}$ mi.

1. How much farther did Emily bike than Gustavo? How much more than Anna?

$1\frac{3}{5}$ mi; $3\frac{1}{5}$ mi

2. On the second day, Terry joined the group. If you add the distance Terry biked, the group total increases to $35\frac{3}{10}$ mi. How far did Terry bike?

$8\frac{3}{5}$ mi

3. One trail is $\frac{3}{5}$ mi long. Gustavo wants to ride only $\frac{1}{3}$ of the trail, then stop for lunch. How long would the bikers ride?

$\frac{1}{5}$ mi

4. Emily wants to ride the Mountain Trail. The trail is $7\frac{2}{3}$ mi long. If she rides the trail three times, how many miles total will she ride?

23 mi

5. Each of the bikers is carrying a small bag of trail mix. Anna's bag has $\frac{2}{5}$ oz, Gustavo's has $\frac{2}{5}$ oz, and Emily's has $\frac{1}{5}$ oz. How many ounces of trail mix do they have altogether?

$1\frac{7}{10}$ oz

© Pearson Education, Inc. 5

Fraction Riddles   E 8-16
                                              REASONING

Each riddle below describes a fraction. Solve the riddle to find the fraction.

1. I am an improper fraction. I am equal to $9\frac{1}{3}$. My numerator is 56. What fraction am I?

$\dfrac{56}{6}$

2. I am a fraction in simplest form. I am equal to $\frac{80}{100}$. The sum of my numerator and denominator is 9. What fraction am I?

$\dfrac{4}{5}$

3. I am a fraction that is not in simplest form. My numerator is exactly one half of my denominator. My numerator plus my denominator equals 75. What fraction am I?

$\dfrac{25}{50}$

4. I am a fraction with a numerator of one. I am equal to $\frac{30}{90}$. What fraction am I?

$\dfrac{1}{3}$

5. I am an improper fraction. My denominator is 2. I can also be written as $4\frac{1}{2}$. What fraction am I?

$\dfrac{9}{2}$

6. I am a fraction that is not in simplest form. I am equal to $\frac{1}{5}$. The sum of my numerator and denominator is 30. What fraction am I?

$\dfrac{5}{25}$

7. I am an improper fraction. My numerator is 12. I can also be written as 6. What fraction am I?

$\dfrac{12}{2}$

8. I am a fraction in simplest form. My numerator is 2 less than my denominator. The sum of my numerator and my denominator is 8. What fraction am I?

$\dfrac{3}{5}$

© Pearson Education, Inc. 5

PROBLEM-SOLVING APPLICATIONS   PS 8-16
Baseball Cards

Jeff, Stewart, and Jason traded baseball cards. After the trades, Jeff had 48 cards. He had given 6 cards to Stewart in exchange for 4, and he had given 7 cards to Jason in exchange for 9. How many cards did Jeff have before the trades?

Read and Understand

1. How many cards did Jeff receive from Stewart and Jason?

4 from Stewart and 9 from Jason

2. How many cards did Jeff trade away to Stewart and Jason?

6 cards to Stewart and 7 cards to Jason

3. How many cards did Jeff finish with?

48 cards

4. What are you trying to find?

The number of cards Jeff started with

Plan and Solve

5. What strategy will you use?

Work backward

6. Write an equation and solve the problem.

$n - 6 + 4 - 7 + 9 = 48$; $n = 48$

7. Write your answer in a complete sentence.

Jeff started with 48 cards.

Look Back and Check

8. Is your answer reasonable?

Yes, because Jeff gave 2 extra cards to Stewart and received 2 extra cards from Jason.

© Pearson Education, Inc. 5

Practice

Customary Units of Length
P 9-1

Complete.

1. 12 yd = **432** in.
2. 30 ft = **10** yd
3. 75 ft = **900** in.
4. 10 ft 7 in. = **127** in.
5. 6 mi = **31,680** ft
6. 2 mi = **3,520** yd

7. 32 yd 2 ft
   + 4 yd 3 ft
   37 yd 2 ft

8. 6 mi 10 yd
   − 4 mi 9 yd
   2 mi 1 yd

9. 18 ft 4 in.
   + 22 ft 9 in.
   41 ft 1 in.

The Statue of Liberty was a gift to the United States from the people of France. Some of the dimensions of the statue are shown here.

Measurements of the Statue of Liberty

Height from base of statue to the torch	151 ft 1 in.
Length of hand	16 ft 5 in.
Length of index finger	8 ft
Length of nose	4 ft 6 in.
Thickness of right arm	12 ft

10. What is the height, from the base of the statue to the torch, in inches? **1,813 in.**

11. What is the thickness of the statue's right arm in yards? **4 yd**

Test Prep

12. Which is equal to 435 in.?

   A. 37 ft   B. 36 ft   **C.** 12 yd 3 in.   D. 12 ft 3 in.

13. **Writing in Math** Explain how you can find the number of feet in 40 yd.

Sample answer: Because there are 3 ft in 1 yd, I can multiply by 3. 40 × 3 ft = 120 ft

Reteaching

Customary Units of Length
R 9-1

Customary Units of Length

12 inches (in.) = 1 foot (ft)
36 in. = 3 ft = 1 yard (yd)
5,280 ft = 1,760 yd = 1 mile (mi)

How to change between one customary unit of length and another:

A blue whale can measure up to 110 ft long. How long is that in inches?

Remember, 12 in. = 1 ft.

Multiply to find the length in inches.

110 × 12 = 1,320

110 ft is equal to 1,320 in.

So, a blue whale can be up to 1,320 in. long.

How to add and subtract measurements:

3 ft 8 in.
+ 2 ft 9 in.
5 ft 17 in.

17 in. is greater than 1 ft, so you need to rename the answer.

17 in. = 1 ft 5 in.

5 ft + 1 ft + 5 in. = 6 ft 5 in.

So, 3 ft 8 in. + 2 ft 9 in. = 6 ft 5 in.

Complete.

1. 5 ft = **60** in.
2. 3 mi = **15,840** ft
3. 24 ft = **8** yd
4. 108 in. = **9** ft
5. 70 in. = **5** ft **10** in.
6. 13 yd = **39** ft

7. 6 in.
   + 12 ft 2 in.
   12 ft 8 in.

8. 7 yd 8 ft
   − 2 yd 5 ft
   6 yd

9. 5 yd 2 ft
   − 4 ft
   4 yd 1 ft

10. 5 ft 8 in.
    − 1 ft 2 in.
    4 ft 6 in.

11. **Estimation** What unit of length would you use to measure the length of a river?

   Mile

Enrichment

Set the Stage
E 9-1
NUMBER SENSE

1. The school chorus is practicing for their spring concert. There are 8 students that will perform. They will stand in three rows. In row 1, the 2 shortest students will stand. In row 2, the next 3 in height will stand. The last row will have the 3 tallest in the group. Use the information to write where each member of the chorus will stand during the concert.

Chorus Members

Karen: 4 ft, 5 in.
Paulette: 1 yd, 14 in.
Rob: 60 in.
Thomas: 2 ft, 33 in.
Erin: 1 yd, 1 ft, 4 in.
William: 1½ yd
Kate: 58 in.
Nick: 1 yd, 1ft, 3 in.

Row 1: **Nick, Paulette**

Row 2: **Erin, Karen, William**

Row 3: **Thomas, Kate, Rob**

2. Reconstruct the plan if Carmen and Ryan join the chorus. Carmen is 2 ft, 38 in. tall, and Ryan is 1 yd, 1 ft, and 5 in. tall. The set up will follow the same pattern, but there will be 5 students in row 3.

Row 1: **Nick, Paulette**

Row 2: **Erin, Ryan, Karen**

Row 3: **William, Thomas, Kate, Rob, Carmen**

3. Reconstruct the plan from Exercise 2 if Miguel and Louisa join the chorus. Miguel is 49 in. tall, and Louisa is 1 yd, 2 ft, and 4 in. tall. Now, there must be 3 students in row 1, 4 students in row 2, and 5 students in row 3.

Row 1: **Miguel, Nick, Paulette**

Row 2: **Erin, Ryan, Karen, William**

Row 3: **Thomas, Kate, Rob, Carmen, Louisa**

Problem Solving

Customary Units of Length
PS 9-1

The drawing below shows the measurements of a professional basketball court.

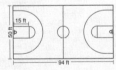

1. How long is a professional basketball court in yards and feet? **31 yd, 1 ft**

2. What is the length of the court in inches? **1,128 in.**

3. How many inches wide is a professional basketball court? **600 in.**

4. What is the width of the court in yards and feet? **16 yd, 2 ft**

5. How many yards is it from the backboard to the free-throw line? **5 yd**

6. How many inches of floor length are there between the backboard of the hoop and the free-throw line? **180 in.**

7. How many inches is the perimeter of the professional basketball court? **3,456 in.**

8. How much greater is the length of the basketball court than the width? Write the answer in inches. **528 in.**

9. **Writing in Math** Explain how to convert 4 yd into inches.

Sample answer: Multiply 4 by 3 to find 12 ft in 4 yd. Then multiply 12 by 12 to find 144 in. in 4 yd.

Practice

Measuring with Fractions of an Inch   P 9-2

Measure each segment to the nearest inch, $\frac{1}{2}$ inch, $\frac{1}{4}$ inch, and $\frac{1}{8}$ inch.

1. _____

   2 in.; $2\frac{1}{2}$ in.; $2\frac{1}{4}$ in.; $2\frac{1}{4}$ in.

2. _____

   2 in.; $1\frac{1}{2}$ in.; $1\frac{1}{2}$ in.; $1\frac{1}{2}$ in.

Use your ruler to draw a line segment of each length.

3. $\frac{3}{4}$ in.   **Check students' drawings.**

4. $2\frac{1}{8}$ in.

5. **Reasoning** Sarah gave the same answer when asked to round $4\frac{7}{8}$ in. to the nearest $\frac{1}{2}$ inch and the nearest inch. Explain why Sarah is correct.

Sample answer: 5 in. is the nearest inch and $\frac{1}{2}$ in. to $4\frac{7}{8}$ in.

6. A real car is 18 times larger than a model car. If the model car is $5\frac{1}{4}$ in. long, how long is the real car?   **$94\frac{1}{2}$ in.**

Test Prep

7. What is the length of the segment? |—————|

   A. $1\frac{7}{8}$ in.   **(B)** $1\frac{3}{4}$ in.   C. $1\frac{1}{2}$ in.   D. 1 in.

8. **Writing in Math** If a line is measured as $1\frac{4}{8}$ in. long, explain how you could simplify the measurement.

Sample answer: I could simplify $1\frac{4}{8}$ to $1\frac{1}{2}$ by dividing the numerator and denominator by 4.

Reteaching

Measuring with Fractions of an Inch   R 9-2

Measure the length of the pen to the nearest inch, nearest $\frac{1}{2}$ inch, nearest $\frac{1}{4}$ inch, and nearest $\frac{1}{8}$ inch.

Step 1: Measure to the nearest inch.	**Step 2:** Measure to the nearest $\frac{1}{2}$ inch.	**Step 3:** Measure to the nearest $\frac{1}{4}$ inch.	**Step 4:** Measure to the nearest $\frac{1}{8}$ inch.
The length is closest to 5 in.	The length of the pen is closest to $4\frac{1}{2}$ in.	The length is closest to $4\frac{3}{4}$ in.	The length is closest to $4\frac{5}{8}$ in.

Measure each object to the nearest inch, $\frac{1}{2}$ inch, $\frac{1}{4}$ inch, and $\frac{1}{8}$ inch.

1.

   5 in., $4\frac{1}{2}$ in., $4\frac{3}{4}$ in., $4\frac{5}{8}$ in.

2.

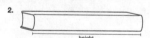

   1 in., 1 in., $1\frac{1}{4}$ in., $1\frac{1}{4}$ in.

Use your ruler to draw a line segment of each length.

3. $\frac{7}{8}$ in.   **Segment should be $\frac{7}{8}$ in. long.**

4. $2\frac{1}{4}$ in.   **Segment should be $2\frac{1}{4}$ in. long.**

5. $3\frac{1}{2}$ in.   **Segment should be $3\frac{1}{2}$ in. long.**

Enrichment

As Close as It Gets   E 9-2
NUMBER SENSE

1. What is the perimeter of this rectangle measured to the nearest inch and the nearest $\frac{1}{2}$ inch? Which is more accurate? Explain.

12 in.; 13 in.; The perimeter to the nearest $\frac{1}{16}$ is $12\frac{5}{8}$ in. So, the perimeter to the nearest $\frac{1}{2}$ inch is more accurate.

2. What is the perimeter of this trapezoid measured to the nearest inch and the nearest $\frac{1}{2}$ inch? Which is more accurate? Explain.

8 in.; 8 in.; The perimeter to the nearest $\frac{1}{16}$ is $7\frac{8}{16}$ in. So, the perimeters are both $\frac{1}{2}$ inch away from this measurement.

3. What similarities did you see when you determined which perimeters were the most accurate?

Sample answer: The perimeters that were measured to the smallest unit of measure were the most accurate.

Problem Solving

Measuring with Fractions of an Inch   PS 9-2

Aneesa is measuring books to see which shelves to put them on. Real books are 4 times taller than the books below. Find the real height of each book.

1.

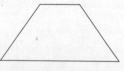
height

   6 in.

2.

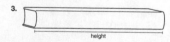
height

   11 in.

3.

height

   13 in.

4.

height

   7 in.

5. **Writing in Math** Explain how you found the height of the book in Exercise 4.

Sample answer:

First, I measured the drawing. Then I multiplied $1\frac{3}{4}$ in. by 4 and got 7 in.

Practice

Name_____

Metric Units of Length

P 9-3

Which unit would be most appropriate for each measurement?
Write mm, cm, m, or km.

1. height of a basketball hoop   **m**

2. distance from Chicago to Miami   **km**

Measure each segment to the nearest centimeter and to the nearest millimeter.

3. ├────────┤   **5 cm, 54 mm**

4. ├──────┤   **4 cm, 39 mm**

Complete each sentence with mm, cm, m, or km.

5. A classroom is about 11 **m** wide.

6. A pencil is about 18 **cm** long.

Some of the events at an upcoming track and field meet are shown at the right.

Track and Field Events
50 m dash
1,500 m dash
400 m dash
100 m dash

7. In which event or events do athletes travel more than a kilometer?

1,500 m dash

8. In which event or events do athletes travel less than a kilometer?

50 m dash, 400 m dash, 100 m dash

Test Prep

9. Which is the correct measurement of the line segment? ├────┤

A. 410 mm   B. 4.1 cm   C. 44 mm   D. 4 km

10. **Writing in Math** List one item in your classroom you would measure using centimeters and one item in the classroom you would measure using meters.

Sample answer: My math book in centimeters; the classroom door in meters

Use with Lesson 9-3. **119**

© Pearson Education, Inc. 5

Reteaching

Name_____

Metric Units of Length

R 9-3

Measurements in the metric system are based on the meter.

Example A

Which metric unit of length would be most appropriate to measure the length of a bumblebee?

A bumblebee is very small, so the millimeter is the most appropriate unit of length.

Example B

Write mm, cm, m, or km to complete the following sentence.

A chair is about 1 _____ tall; and a child's hand is about 8 _____ wide.

A chair is about 1 m tall, and a child's hand is about 8 cm wide.

Example C

What is the length to the nearest centimeter and to the nearest millimeter?

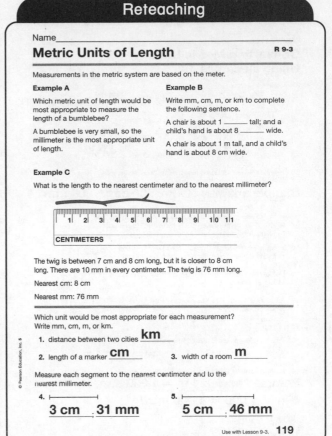

The twig is between 7 cm and 8 cm long, but it is closer to 8 cm long. There are 10 mm in every centimeter. The twig is 76 mm long.

Nearest cm: 8 cm

Nearest mm: 76 mm

Which unit would be most appropriate for each measurement?
Write mm, cm, m, or km.

1. distance between two cities **km**

2. length of a marker **cm**   3. width of a room **m**

Measure each segment to the nearest centimeter and to the nearest millimeter.

4. ├────┤   **3 cm** , **31 mm**

5. ├──────┤   **5 cm** ; **46 mm**

Use with Lesson 9-3. **119**

© Pearson Education, Inc. 5

Enrichment

Name_____

Can You Picture It?

E 9-3
VISUAL THINKING

Draw a picture to solve the following. Then write the answer.

1. There are 7 stools at the Daisy Frozen Yogurt Shop with a total of 24 legs. How many 3-legged and 4-legged stools are there?

Four 3-legged stools and three 4-legged stools

Students' drawings should show four 3-legged stools and three 4-legged stools.

2. A grasshopper can jump 2 stones with each jump. A rabbit can jump 4 stones with each jump. A frog can jump 5 stones with each jump. If all 3 animals start at number 1, what number stone is the first that all three will land on?

Stone 20

Students' drawings should show the grasshopper landing on 2, 4, 6, 8, 10, 12, 14, 16, 18, 20; the rabbit landing on 4, 8, 12, 16, 20; and the frog landing on 5, 10, 15, 20.

Use with Lesson 9-3. **119**

© Pearson Education, Inc. 5

Problem Solving

Name_____

Metric Units of Length

PS 9-3

Reasonable Measurements Choose a measurement from the list. Use each measurement once.

15 cm
1 mm
4 m
100 km

1. length of a car   **4 m**

2. distance between two cities   **100 km**

3. thickness of a fingernail   **1 mm**

4. length of a pencil   **15 cm**

Which Is Longer? Choose the greater length.

5. 3 m or 325 cm   **325 cm**

6. 4,200 mm or 5 m   **5 m**

7. 6 km or 6,345 m   **6,345 m**

8. 716 cm or 8 m   **8 m**

9. 20,000 m or 25 km   **25 km**

10. **Writing in Math** Sandra said she is about 5 m tall. Explain if this is reasonable.

Sample answer: No, this is not reasonable because 5 m is much taller than any real person.

Use with Lesson 9-3. **119**

© Pearson Education, Inc. 5

Name_____

Converting Metric Units Using Decimals

P 9-4

Find each equal measure.

1. 25 m = **2.5** dam
2. 4.5 m = **450** cm
3. 200 hm = **20,000** m
4. 987 mm = **98.7** cm
5. 4.2 km = **4,200** m
6. 0.35 dm = **35** mm
7. 345 cm = **3.45** m
8. 10 m = **10,000** mm

9. **Number Sense** List three measurements with different units equal to 5 m.

Sample answer: 50 dm; 500 cm; 5,000 mm

Mount St. Helens, a volcano in the state of Washington, erupted on May 18, 1980. Before the eruption, Mount St. Helens was 2,950 m high. After the eruption, it was 2,550 m high.

10. What is the difference in height of Mount St. Helens before and after the eruption expressed in meters? **400 m**

11. Before the eruption, how many kilometers high was Mount St. Helens? **2.95 km**

12. After the eruption, how many hectometers high was Mount St. Helens? **25.5 hm**

Test Prep

13. Which measurement is equal to 10 dam?

   A. 100 hm   B. 1 m   C. 0.1 hm   (D) 100 m

14. **Writing in Math** Explain how you would convert 4 m to millimeters.

Sample answer: 1 m = 1,000 mm, so 4 m × 1,000 = 4,000 mm.

Name_____

Converting Metric Units Using Decimals

R 9-4

How to change from one metric unit to another:

In the metric system, every unit is 10 times more or less than the units next to it. This makes it easy to change from one unit to another.

For example:

The Olympic record in the women's high jump is 2.05 m. How many centimeters is that?

Remember, 1 m = 100 cm.

To change meters to centimeters, multiply.

2.05 × 100 = 205

2.05 m = 205 cm

So, the record high jump is 205 cm.

How to change from one metric unit to another when decimals are involved:

To change large units to small units, multiply.

52.07 cm = _____ mm

Remember, 1 cm = 10 mm.

52.07 × 10 = 520.7

So, 52.07 cm = 520.7 mm.

To change small units to large units, divide.

672 mm = _____ cm

Remember, 10 mm = 1 cm.

672 ÷ 10 = 67.2

So, 672 mm = 67.2 cm.

Find each equal measure.

1. 2.4 km = **2,400** m
2. 83 m = **830** dm
3. 0.9 dm = **90** mm
4. 2.4 m = **240** cm
5. 3 m = **300** cm
6. 52 km = **52,000** m
7. 204 cm = **2.04** m
8. 355 mm = **35.5** cm
9. 36 m = **3,600** cm

10. **Number Sense** Is 3.2 m the same as 320 mm? Explain.

No; 3.2 m is equal to 3,200 mm.

Name_____

Climbing High

E 9-4
DATA

Below is a list of some of the highest peaks in the Himalaya Mountains. Complete the table by converting the measurements to kilometers. Then list the peaks from greatest to least height. Number 1 should be the greatest and Number 8 should be the least.

Peak	Height	Height in km
Nanga Parbat	8,126 m	**8.126 km**
Dome Kang	744.2 dam	**7.442 km**
Kambachen	7,902,000 mm	**7.902 km**
Mount Everest	885,000 cm	**8.85 km**
Seg Wang	73,080 dm	**7.308 km**
Peak 38	759,000 cm	**7.59 km**
Abi Gamin	7,355 m	**7.355 km**
Janak Himal	74.51 hm	**7.451 km**

1. **Mount Everest**
2. **Nanga Parbat**
3. **Kambachen**
4. **Peak 38**
5. **Janak Himal**
6. **Dome Kang**
7. **Abi Gamin**
8. **Seg Wang**

Name_____

Converting Metric Units Using Decimals

PS 9-4

Olympic Swimming The chart shows some of the swimming events at the Olympics.

Olympic Swimming Events	
50 m	freestyle
200 m	butterfly
100 m	breaststroke
800 m	freestyle
1,500 m	freestyle

Find the distance of the

1. 50 m freestyle in centimeters. **5,000 cm**
2. 200 m butterfly in dekameters. **20 dam**
3. 100 m breaststroke in decimeters. **1,000 dm**
4. 800 m freestyle in millimeters. **800,000 mm**
5. 1,500 m freestyle in kilometers. **1.5 km**

Which event has a distance of

6. 2 hm? **200 m butterfly**
7. 150,000 cm? **1,500 m freestyle**
8. 10 dam? **100 m breaststroke**
9. 0.8 km? **800 m freestyle**

10. **Writing in Math** Explain how to convert 450 mm to meters.

Sample answer: You divide 450 mm by 1,000 to get 0.45 m.

Name_____

Finding Perimeter   P 9-5

Find the perimeter of each figure.

1. 3 cm 3 cm
   5 cm

2. 7 km 7 km 7 km 7 km

3. 1 m 2 m 3 m 2 m 2 m 1 m

4. 7.5 hm 5 hm 5 hm 7.5 hm

11 cm   **28 km**   **11 m**   **25 hm**

5. **Number Sense** What is the perimeter of a square if one of the sides is 3 mi?

12 mi

The dimensions of a football field are shown at the right.

6. What is the perimeter of the entire football field including the end zones?

1,040 ft

7. What is the perimeter of each end zone?

380 ft

30 ft   300 ft   30 ft
160 ft End zone Playing field End zone 160 ft
30 ft   300 ft   30 ft

Test Prep

8. What is the perimeter of this figure?

   (A.) 18 m   B. 15 m
   C. 12 ft   D. 10 m

   6 m
   6 m   6 m
            3 m
        3 m

9. **Writing in Math** A square has a perimeter of 12 m. How many possible lengths are there for each side? List them and explain your answer.

Sample answer: There is only one possible length for each side (3 m), because all 4 sides of a square are equal in length.

Use with Lesson 9-5. **121**

© Pearson Education, Inc. 5

Name_____

Finding Perimeter   R 9-5

Perimeter is the distance around the outside of a polygon. You can find perimeter in two different ways.

Add the lengths of the sides:

Find the perimeter of the figure.

7 cm
3 cm   5 cm
3 cm   4 cm   3 cm

To find the perimeter, add up the sides.

3 + 3 + 7 + 5 + 3 + 4 = 25

So, the perimeter of the figure is 25 cm.

Use a formula:

Find the perimeter of the rectangle.

11 cm
          3 cm

Perimeter = (2 × length) + (2 × width)
$P = (2 × l) + (2 × w)$
$P = (2 × 11) + (2 × 3)$
$P = 22 + 6 = 28 cm$

So, the perimeter of the rectangle is 28 cm.

Find the perimeter of each figure.

1. 8.9 cm
       4.2 cm

26.2 cm

2. 11 m
   4 m   7 m   3 m
       8 m

33 m

3. 2.5 mm 3 mm
   5 mm   5 mm
       6 mm

21.5 mm

4. 4.7 cm

18.8 cm

5. **Number Sense** The perimeter of a square is 24 in. What is the length of each side?

6 in.

Use with Lesson 9-5. **121**

© Pearson Education, Inc. 5

Name_____

Jewelry Design   E 9-5 ESTIMATION

Pam is making some necklaces and bracelets to sell at a craft show. Use the information to help her decide how many beads will fit on each piece of jewelry. Remember, each piece must have a clasp to hold the item closed. Drawing a picture may also help with your answer.

Bead Sizes	Bracelets	Necklaces	Clasps
1 mm	18 cm	41 cm	2 mm
1.25 mm	21 cm	46 cm	
1.5 mm		50 cm	
1.75 mm			

1. About how many 1.5 mm beads will Pam need to make an 18 cm bracelet with a clasp?

About 118 beads

2. About how many 1.25 mm beads will Pam need to make a 46 cm necklace with a clasp?

About 366 beads

3. About how many 1.75 mm beads will Pam need to make a 21 cm bracelet with a clasp?

About 118 beads

4. About how many 1 mm beads will Pam need to make a 50 cm necklace with a clasp?

About 498 beads

5. About how many 1.25 mm beads will Pam need to make a 41 cm necklace with a clasp?

About 326 beads

Use with Lesson 9-5. **121**

© Pearson Education, Inc. 5

Name_____

Finding Perimeter   PS 9-5

1. The perimeter of a square is 24 ft. What is the length of one side?

6 ft

2. What is the perimeter of a rectangle with a length of 8 in. and a width of 6 in.?

28 in.

3. Find the perimeter of a regular hexagon with a side measuring 15 cm.

90 cm

4. If a regular octagon has a perimeter of 96 ft, what is the length of each side?

12 ft

Find the perimeter of each figure.

5. An equilateral triangle with a side measuring 7 m

21 m

6. A parallelogram with a length of 9 in. and a width of 5 in.

28 in.

7. A regular nonagon with a side measuring 21 ft

189 ft

Find the perimeter of the rectangle with the given dimensions.

8. $l = 12$ mm, $w = 16$ mm

56 mm

9. $l = 41$ cm, $w = 38$ cm

158 cm

10. **Writing in Math** Katie needs to find the dimensions of a rectangle with a perimeter of 18 ft. Explain how she can find the dimensions. List all of the possible whole number lengths and widths.

Sample answer: Katie can find all of the whole number pairs with a sum of 9. The possible dimensions are: 5 ft by 4 ft, 6 ft by 3 ft, 7 ft by 2 ft, and 8 ft by 1 ft.

Use with Lesson 9-5. **121**

© Pearson Education, Inc. 5

Name_____

Finding Circumference

Find each circumference. Use 3.14 for π.

1.
4 m
12.56 m

2.
10 km
31.4 km

3.
6 mi
37.68 mi

4. $d = 7$ hm
21.98 hm

5. $r = 7$ in.
43.96 in.

6. $r = 9$ km
56.52 km

7. $d = 2$ in.
6.28 in.

8. $d = 8$ cm
25.12 cm

9. $d = 6$ yd
18.84 yd

10. Which of the U.S. coins listed in the table have circumferences greater than 68 mm?

Quarter, half-dollar, dollar

Coin	Diameter
Penny	19.05 mm
Nickel	21.21 mm
Dime	17.91 mm
Quarter	24.26 mm
Half-dollar	30.61 mm
Dollar	26.5 mm

For 11 and 12, round the circumference to the nearest hundredth millimeter.

What is the circumference of a

11. penny? **59.82 mm**

12. dime? **56.24 mm**

Test Prep

13. Which pair correctly shows the diameter and circumference of a circle?

   A. $d = 10$ m, $C = 15.7$ m
   B. $d = 10$ m, $C = 31.4$ m
   C. $d = 10$ m, $C = 50$ m
   D. $d = 10$ m, $C = 7.85$ m

14. **Writing in Math** Could you find the circumference of a circle using the exact value for π? Why or why not?

No; Sample answer: There is no exact value for π. It is a decimal that does not end.

© Pearson Education, Inc. 5

Name_____

Finding Circumference

The circumference is the distance around a circle. You can use either of the formulas illustrated below to find the circumference of a circle.

4 ft

7 m

$C = π \times 2 \times r$
$C = 3.14 \times 2 \times 4$
$C = 25.12$

So, the circumference of the circle is 25.12 ft.

$C = π \times d$
$C = 3.14 \times 7$
$C = 21.98$

So, the circumference of the circle is 21.98 m.

Find each circumference. Use 3.14 for π.

1.
11 in.
34.54 in.

2.
9 cm
56.52 cm

3.
2.3 m
7.222 m

4.
4.3 ft
27.004 ft

5.
21 m
65.94 m

6.
115 cm
722.2 cm

© Pearson Education, Inc. 5

Name_____

Around and Around It Goes

1. On the Ferris wheel, the distance from the center of the wheel to one of the passenger cars is 75 ft. Draw and label a Ferris wheel with this measurement.

75 ft

2. Kerry just got into a car to take a ride on the Ferris wheel. How far will she travel in one revolution of the wheel? Write and solve an equation to find this distance.

$C = π \times 2 \times r$, so $C = 3.14 \times 2 \times 75 =$ **471 ft, 1 revolution = 471 ft**

3. Write a word problem that uses the diagram to the right and find the missing information.

$d = 6$ ft; Check students' word problems.

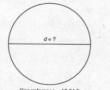
$d = ?$
Circumference = 18.84 ft

© Pearson Education, Inc. 5

Name_____

Finding Circumference

U.S. Coins

Coin	Diameter in Inches	Diameter in Millimeters
Penny	0.8	19.0
Nickel	0.8	21.2
Dime	0.7	17.9
Quarter	1.0	24.3
Half-dollar	1.2	30.6
Dollar	1.0	26.5

Find the circumference of each coin to the nearest tenth of an inch. Use 3.14 for π.

1. nickel **2.5 in.**
2. dime **2.2 in.**
3. quarter **3.1 in.**
4. half-dollar **3.8 in.**

Find the circumference of each coin to the nearest tenth of a millimeter. Use 3.14 for π.

5. half-dollar **96.1 mm**
6. penny **59.7 mm**
7. quarter **76.3 mm**
8. dime **56.2 mm**
9. nickel **66.6 mm**
10. dollar **83.2 mm**

11. **Writing in Math** Explain how to find the circumference of the circle.

9 ft

Sample answer: Use the equation $C = π \times 2 \times r$. Then solve: $C = 3.14 \times 2 \times 9$. So, the circumference is 56.52 ft.

© Pearson Education, Inc. 5

Practice

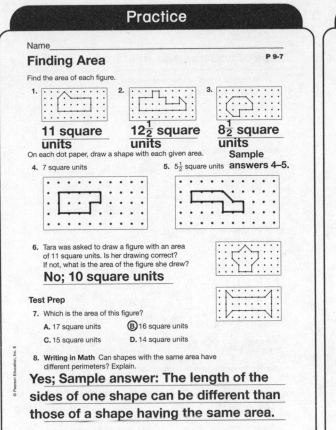

Name_____ P 9-7

Finding Area

Find the area of each figure.

1. **11 square units**

2. **12½ square units**

3. **8½ square units**

On each dot paper, draw a shape with each given area.

Sample answers 4–5.

4. 7 square units

5. 5½ square units

6. Tara was asked to draw a figure with an area of 11 square units. Is her drawing correct? If not, what is the area of the figure she drew?

No; 10 square units

Test Prep

7. Which is the area of this figure?

   A. 17 square units   B. 16 square units
   C. 15 square units   D. 14 square units

8. **Writing in Math** Can shapes with the same area have different perimeters? Explain.

Yes; Sample answer: The length of the sides of one shape can be different than those of a shape having the same area.

© Pearson Education, Inc. 5

Reteaching

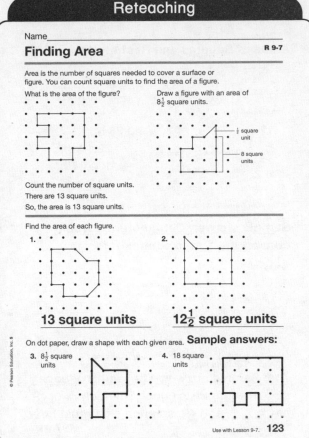

Name_____ R 9-7

Finding Area

Area is the number of squares needed to cover a surface or figure. You can count square units to find the area of a figure.

What is the area of the figure?

Draw a figure with an area of 8½ square units.

½ square unit

8 square units

Count the number of square units.
There are 13 square units.
So, the area is 13 square units.

Find the area of each figure.

1. **13 square units**

2. **12½ square units**

On dot paper, draw a shape with each given area. **Sample answers:**

3. 8½ square units

4. 18 square units

© Pearson Education, Inc. 5

Enrichment

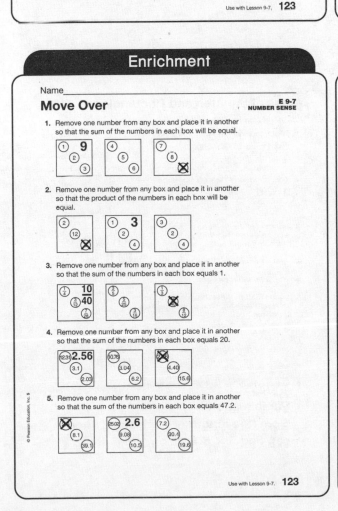

Name_____

Move Over

E 9-7
NUMBER SENSE

1. Remove one number from any box and place it in another so that the sum of the numbers in each box will be equal.

   ① **9** ②③   ④ ⑤⑥   ⑦ ⑧ ⊗

2. Remove one number from any box and place it in another so that the product of the numbers in each box will be equal.

   ② ⑫ ⊗   ① **3** ④   ③ ② ④

3. Remove one number from any box and place it in another so that the sum of the numbers in each box equals 1.

   ¼ **10/40** 3/12   3/5 2/25   ⊗ 8/15 7/15

4. Remove one number from any box and place it in another so that the sum of the numbers in each box equals 20.

   12.31 **2.56** 3.1 2.03   10.76 3.04 6.2   ⊗ 4.40 15.6

5. Remove one number from any box and place it in another so that the sum of the numbers in each box equals 47.2.

   ⊗ 8.1 39.1   25.02 **2.6** 9.08 10.5   7.2 20.4 19.6

© Pearson Education, Inc. 5

Problem Solving

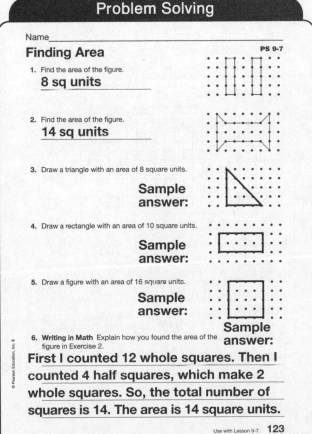

Name_____

Finding Area

PS 9-7

1. Find the area of the figure.

   8 sq units

2. Find the area of the figure.

   14 sq units

3. Draw a triangle with an area of 8 square units.

   Sample answer:

4. Draw a rectangle with an area of 10 square units.

   Sample answer:

5. Draw a figure with an area of 16 square units.

   Sample answer:

6. **Writing in Math** Explain how you found the area of the figure in Exercise 2.

First I counted 12 whole squares. Then I counted 4 half squares, which make 2 whole squares. So, the total number of squares is 14. The area is 14 square units.

© Pearson Education, Inc. 5

Name_____

Areas of Squares and Rectangles
P 9-8

Find the area of each figure.

1.
    l = 4 cm
    w = 3 cm

    12 cm²

2.
    s = 9.5 mi

    90.25 mi²

3. a rectangle with sides 6.5 km and 3.4 km
   22.1 km²

4. a square with a side of 10.2 ft
   104.04 ft²

5. a rectangle with sides 9 m and 9.2 m
   82.8 m²

6. **Number Sense** Which units would you use to measure the area of a rectangle with l = 1 m and w = 34 cm? Explain.

Sample answer: Centimeters; I would convert the 1 m to centimeters.

Test Prep

7. Which of the following shapes has an area of 34 ft²?

   A. A square with s = 8.5 m

   B. A rectangle with l = 15 ft, w = 2 ft

   C. A square with s = 16 ft

   D. A rectangle with l = 17 ft, w = 2 ft

8. **Writing in Math** The area of a square is 49 m². What is the length of one of its sides? Explain how you solved this problem.

7 m; Sample answer: The length of each side of a square is equal. The factors of 49 are 1, 7, 7, and 49, so each side must be 7 m.

124 Use with Lesson 9-8.

© Pearson Education, Inc. 5

Name_____

Areas of Squares and Rectangles
R 9-8

You can use formulas to find the areas of rectangles and squares.

Find the area of the rectangle.

5 m
4 m

Find the area of the square.

42 cm
42 cm
42 cm
42 cm

Use this formula for rectangles:

Area = length × width

$A = l \times w$

$A = 5\,m \times 4\,m$

$A = 20$ square meters = 20 m²

Use this formula for squares:

Area = side × side

$A = 42\,cm \times 42\,cm$

$A = 1,764$ square centimeters = 1,764 cm²

Find the area of each figure.

1. 58 ft
   3,364 ft²

2.
   5.5 in.
   3.2 in.
   17.6 in²

3. a square with a side of 12.4 m
   153.76 m²

4. a rectangle with a length of 9.7 cm and a width of 7.3 cm
   70.81 cm²

5. **Number Sense** If the area of a square is 81 in², what is the length of one side?
   9 in.

6. What is the area of the tennis court?
   195.16 m²

   8.2 m
   23.8 m

124 Use with Lesson 9-8.

© Pearson Education, Inc. 5

Name_____

Out of Stock
E 9-8
VISUAL THINKING

The grass in Mr. Thompson's front yard has died. He has decided to re-sod the entire yard. The total size of the yard is 18 ft × 10 ft. He calls a home improvement store to place his order, but they do not have what he needs.

Mr. Thompson's Front Yard

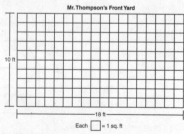

10 ft

18 ft

Each ☐ = 1 sq. ft

1. The home improvement store has 20 pieces of sod that are 1 ft × 2 ft and 20 pieces of sod that are 1 ft × 3 ft. If he wants to begin the work in a square-shaped area, how large a square will he be able to fix? Drawing a picture may help answer the question.

10 ft × 10 ft area

2. Find how many more 1 ft × 2 ft and 1 ft × 3 ft pieces he will still need to order to finish the job. **Sample answer: He will need 10 more 1 ft × 2 ft pieces and 20 more 1 ft × 3 ft pieces.**

3. If the sod costs $2.20 per square foot, how much will it be to sod Mr. Thompson's front yard?

$396.00

124 Use with Lesson 9-8.

© Pearson Education, Inc. 5

Name_____

Areas of Squares and Rectangles
PS 9-8

A diagram of Zachary's garden is shown.

1. What is the perimeter of Zachary's garden?
   54 ft
   9 ft
   18 ft

2. What is the area of Zachary's garden?
   162 ft²
   9 ft
   18 ft

3. Suppose Zachary divides his garden into two equal halves as shown. What are the dimensions of each half?
   9 ft by 9 ft

4. What is the perimeter of each half?
   36 ft

5. What is the area of each half?
   81 ft²

6. Suppose Zachary divides his garden into four equal parts as shown. What are the dimensions of each part?
   9 ft by 4.5 ft
   9 ft
   18 ft

7. What is the perimeter of each part?
   27 ft

8. What is the area of each part?
   40.5 ft²

9. **Writing in Math** The perimeter of a square is 20 cm. Explain how to find the area.

Sample answer: I can find 20 ÷ 4 = 5 cm (the length of each side). Then I can find 5 × 5 = 25 cm² (the area).

124 Use with Lesson 9-8.

© Pearson Education, Inc. 5

Name_____

Areas of Parallelograms

P 9-9

Find the area of each parallelogram.

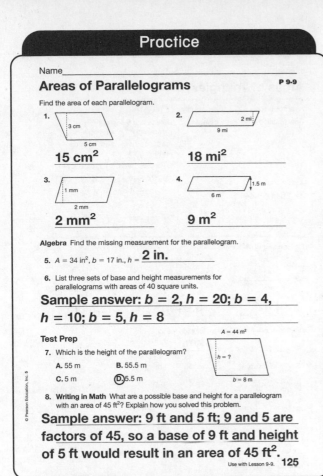

1. 3 cm / 5 cm

15 cm² _____

2. 2 mi / 9 mi

18 mi² _____

3. 1 mm / 2 mm

2 mm² _____

4. 6 m / 1.5 m

9 m² _____

Algebra Find the missing measurement for the parallelogram.

5. $A = 34$ in², $b = 17$ in., $h =$ **2 in.** _____

6. List three sets of base and height measurements for parallelograms with areas of 40 square units.

Sample answer: $b = 2$, $h = 20$; $b = 4$, $h = 10$; $b = 5$, $h = 8$ _____

Test Prep

7. Which is the height of the parallelogram?

$A = 44$ m²

$h = ?$

$b = 8$ m

A. 55 m
B. 55.5 m
C. 5 m
D. 5.5 m

8. **Writing in Math** What are a possible base and height for a parallelogram with an area of 45 ft²? Explain how you solved this problem.

Sample answer: 9 ft and 5 ft; 9 and 5 are factors of 45, so a base of 9 ft and height of 5 ft would result in an area of 45 ft².

Use with Lesson 9-9. 125

Name_____

Areas of Parallelograms

R 9-9

The formula used to find the area of a parallelogram is similar to the one you used to find the area of a rectangle. Instead of using length × width, use base × height.

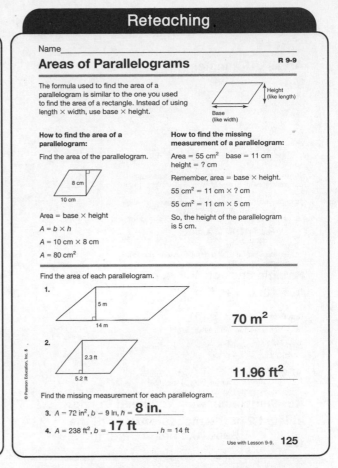

Height (like length)

Base (like width)

How to find the area of a parallelogram:

Find the area of the parallelogram.

8 cm / 10 cm

Area = base × height

$A = b \times h$

$A = 10$ cm × 8 cm

$A = 80$ cm²

How to find the missing measurement of a parallelogram:

Area = 55 cm²   base = 11 cm
height = ? cm

Remember, area = base × height.

55 cm² = 11 cm × ? cm

55 cm² = 11 cm × 5 cm

So, the height of the parallelogram is 5 cm.

Find the area of each parallelogram.

1. 5 m / 14 m

70 m² _____

2. 2.3 ft / 5.2 ft

11.96 ft² _____

Find the missing measurement for each parallelogram.

3. $A = 72$ in², $b = 9$ in, $h =$ **8 in.** _____

4. $A = 238$ ft², $b =$ **17 ft** _____, $h = 14$ ft

Use with Lesson 9-9. 125

Name_____

Equal Areas

E 9-9
NUMBER SENSE

Find and circle the shape on the right that has the same area as the parallelogram on the left.

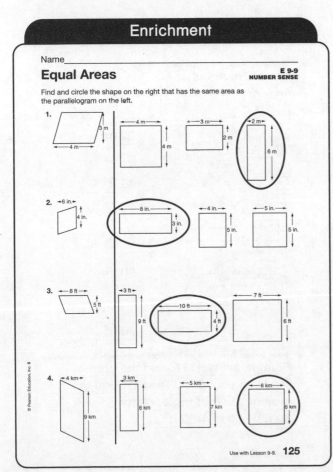

1. 3 m / 4 m
   4 m / 4 m   3 m / 2 m   2 m / 6 m

2. 6 in. / 4 in.
   8 in. / 3 in.   4 in. / 5 in.   5 in. / 5 in.

3. 8 ft / 5 ft
   3 ft / 9 ft   10 ft / 4 ft   7 ft / 6 ft

4. 4 km / 9 km
   3 km / 8 km   5 km / 7 km   6 km / 6 km

Use with Lesson 9-9. 125

Name_____

Areas of Parallelograms

PS 9-9

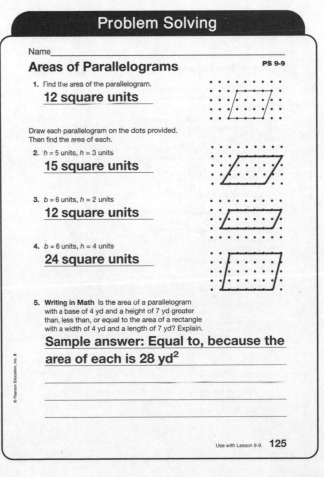

1. Find the area of the parallelogram.

12 square units _____

Draw each parallelogram on the dots provided. Then find the area of each.

2. $b = 5$ units, $h = 3$ units

15 square units _____

3. $b = 6$ units, $h = 2$ units

12 square units _____

4. $b = 6$ units, $h = 4$ units

24 square units _____

5. **Writing in Math** Is the area of a parallelogram with a base of 4 yd and a height of 7 yd greater than, less than, or equal to the area of a rectangle with a width of 4 yd and a length of 7 yd? Explain.

Sample answer: Equal to, because the area of each is 28 yd²

Use with Lesson 9-9. 125

Name_____

Areas of Triangles
P 9-10

Find the area of each triangle.

1.
10 ft
8 ft

40 ft²

2.
3.6 yd
6 yd

10.8 yd²

3.
7 mm
13 mm

45.5 mm²

4. **Number Sense** What is the base measurement of a triangle with an area of 30 m² and a height of 10 m?

6 m

Algebra Find the missing measurement for each triangle.

5. $A = 36$ mi², $b =$ **6 mi** , $h = 12$ mi

6. $A =$ **45 mm²** , $b = 12$ mm, $h = 7.5$ mm

7. List three sets of base and height measurements for triangles with areas of 30 square units.

Sample answer: $b = 4$, $h = 15$; $b = 6$, $h = 10$; $b = 8$, $h = 7.5$

Test Prep

8. Which is the height of the triangle?

A = 27 ft²
12 ft

Ⓐ 4.5 ft   **B.** 6 ft
C. 8 ft   **D.** 9 ft

9. **Writing in Math** Can you find the base and height measurements for a triangle if you know that the area is 22 square units? Explain why or why not.

No; Sample answer: You need to know at least 2 of the measurements of the base, the height, and the area.

© Pearson Education, Inc. 5

Name_____

Areas of Triangles
R 9-10

Area of a triangle = $\frac{1}{2} \times$ base $\times$ height

How to find the area of a triangle:

4 ft
3 ft

$A = \frac{1}{2} \times b \times h$
$A = \frac{1}{2} \times 3$ ft $\times 4$ ft
$A = \frac{1}{2} \times 12$ ft
$A = 6$ ft²

How to find the missing measurement of a triangle:

Area = 100 cm² base = 40 cm
height = ? cm

Remember, Area = $\frac{1}{2} \times$ base $\times$ height.

100 cm² = $\frac{1}{2} \times 40$ cm $\times$? cm
100 cm² = 20 cm $\times$? cm
100 cm² = 20 cm $\times$ 5 cm

So, the height of the triangle is 5 cm.

Find the area of each triangle.

1.
4 in.
7 in.

14 in²

2.
2.2 m
5.4 m

5.94 m²

3.
5 cm
9 cm

22.5 cm²

Find the missing measurement for each triangle.

4. $A = 16$ in², $b = 8$ in., $h =$ **4 in.**

5. $A = 20$ m², $b =$ **10 m** , $h = 4$ m

6. $A =$ **24.32 ft²** , $b = 6.4$ ft, $h = 7.6$ ft

7. $A = 14$ cm², $b = 2$ cm, $h =$ **14 cm**

© Pearson Education, Inc. 5

Name_____

A House for Rover
E 9-10
VISUAL THINKING

David is helping his dad paint the new doghouse. Use the diagrams to help decide how much paint they will need.

The back of the doghouse is made of two shapes, a triangle and a square. Use the diagram to fill in the missing information.

1. The area of the triangle is 3 ft². The height of the triangle is 2 ft and the base of the triangle is **3** ft.

2. One side of the square is **3** ft.
The area of the square is **9** ft².

3. The total area of these two sections of the doghouse is **12** ft².

The sides and roof of the doghouse are made of rectangles. Use the diagram to fill in the missing information.

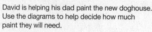
A
B
4 ft

4. The rectangle (B) has a length of 4 ft and a height of 3 ft.
The area of this rectangle is **12** ft².

5. The rectangle (A) on top has an area of 10 ft².
The length of the missing side is **2.5** ft.

6. The total area of these two sections of the doghouse is **22** ft².

7. Using your information in Exercises 3 and 6, how large of an area will David and his dad need to paint? Remember that a doghouse has two sides, a roof, a back, and a front. The front is the same size as the back, except it has a 4 ft² opening for a door.

64 ft²

© Pearson Education, Inc. 5

Name_____

Areas of Triangles
PS 9-10

Use triangles and squares to find the area of each figure.

1.
4 m
3 m

22 m²

2.
6 ft
4 ft

48 ft²

Use triangles and rectangles to find the area of each figure.

3.
3 m
5 m   4 m

21 m²

4.
4 mm
12 mm   6 mm

60 mm²

5.
10 ft
5 ft   6 ft

80 ft²

6. **Writing in Math** Explain how you found the area in Exercise 5.

Sample answer: I found the area of the triangle: 30 ft². Then I found the area of the rectangle: 50 ft².
30 ft² + 50 ft² = 80 ft²

© Pearson Education, Inc. 5

Practice

Name_____

PROBLEM-SOLVING STRATEGY P 9-11
Draw a Picture
Sample answers are given.
Check students' drawings.

Solve. Write the answer in a complete sentence.

1. Erica painted a picture of her dog. The picture has an area of 3,600 cm² and is a square. She has placed the picture in a frame that is 5 cm wide. What is the perimeter of the picture frame?

The perimeter of Erica's picture frame is 280 cm.

2. The new playground at Middledale School will be enclosed by a fence. The playground will be a square and will have an area of 225 yd². The number of yards on each side will be a whole number. What is the least amount of fencing that could be required to enclose the playground?

The amount of fencing needed for the playground is 60 yd.

3. The floor in the back of Karl's truck is 6 ft long and has an area of 24 ft². Karl wants to haul as many boxes on the floor as possible. He cannot stack the boxes or they will fall out as he drives. If each square box is 2 ft long, how many boxes can Karl fit in the back of his truck?

Karl can fit exactly 6 boxes in the back of his truck.

Use with Lesson 9-11. **127**

Reteaching

Name_____

PROBLEM-SOLVING STRATEGY R 9-11
Draw a Picture

Tiles Paula's new room is shaped like a rectangle and has an area of 12 square feet. She has purchased 12 square tiles to place on the floor. Each tile is 1 ft long on each side. Will all 12 of the tiles fit if the room has a perimeter of 16 ft?

[Read and Understand]

Step 1: What do you know?

The room is shaped like a rectangle and has an area of 12 square feet. Paula has 12 tiles that are 1 ft long on each side.

Step 2: What are you trying to find?

If all the tiles will fit on the floor if the room has a perimeter of 16

[Plan and Solve]

Step 3: What strategy will you use?   **Strategy:** Draw a picture

The rectangle has an area of 12 square feet and a perimeter of 16 ft. So Paula's 12 tiles will fit.

[Look Back and Check]

Step 4: Is your answer reasonable?

Yes, I found the area of the rectangle by counting squares, and the perimeter by counting the units on each side. The work is correct.

Solve.

1. Elise wants to plant a garden with an area of 35 ft². What could the length and width of the garden be?

Sample answer: Length could be 7 ft, width could be 5 ft

Use with Lesson 9-11. **127**

Enrichment

Name_____

Follow the Path
E 9-11
NUMBER SENSE

Follow the arrows to get from home to the library.

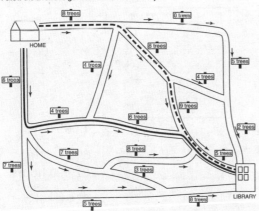

1. Draw a solid line to show the path with the least number of trees.

2. Draw a broken line to show the path with the greatest number of trees.

Use with Lesson 9-11. **127**

Problem Solving

Name_____

PROBLEM-SOLVING STRATEGY PS 9-11
Draw a Picture

Gardening Cara's garden is 12 ft by 8 ft. She wants to plant 4 flowers per square foot. How many flowers will she plant? Draw a picture to solve.

[Read and Understand]

1. What are the dimensions of Cara's garden?

12 ft by 8 ft

2. How many flowers will Cara plant per square foot?

4 flowers per square foot

3. What are you trying to find?

The number of flowers Cara will plant

[Plan and Solve]

4. Draw a picture to help you solve.

8 ft

12 ft

5. What is the area of the garden?

96 ft²

6. How many flowers will Cara plant? Write your answer in a complete sentence.

Cara will plant 384 flowers.

[Look Back and Check]

7. Explain how you can check your answer.

Sample answer: I can divide 384 by 96 to get 4. My answer checks.

Use with Lesson 9-11. **127**

Name_____

Time

Find each equal measure.

1. 96 hr = **4** d
2. 343 d = **49** wk
3. 6 yr 9 d = **2,199** d
4. 1,416 hr = **59** d
5. 12 h 9 min = **43,740** sec
6. 3 yr 5 d = **26,400** hr

7. **Reasoning** Are there more days or weeks in a century? How do you know?

Days; Sample answer: I know because there are 7 days in a week.

Information about the International Space Station is in the table.

Expedition Number	Time from Launching to Landing
Expedition One	138 d, 18 hr, 39 min
Expedition Two	167 d, 6 hr, 4 min

8. Express the length of Expedition One in hours and minutes.

3,330 hr, 39 min

9. Express the length of Expedition Two in weeks, days, hours, and minutes.

23 wk, 6 d, 6 hr, 4 min

Test Prep

10. Which length of time is equivalent to 92 hr?

A. 4 d   B. 331,200 min   **C** 5,520 min   D. 3,200 sec

11. **Writing in Math** How many hours are in 43,200 sec? Explain how you solved this problem.

There are 12 hr. Sample answer: To solve this problem you must divide 43,200 by 60 twice.

Name_____

Time

How to convert from one unit of time to another:

How many days have passed if 96 hr have gone by?

To change from smaller units to larger units, divide.

96 hours = _____ days

Remember, there are 24 hr in one day. So divide 96 by 24.

96 ÷ 24 = 4

So, 4 days passed if 96 hr went by.

Units of Time

60 seconds (sec) = 1 minute (min)
60 minutes = 1 hour (hr)
24 hours = 1 day (d)
7 days = 1 week (wk)
12 months (mo) = 1 year (yr)
52 weeks = 1 year
365 days = 1 year
366 days = 1 leap year
100 years = 1 century

Find each equal measure.

1. 7 min = **420** sec
2. 3 yr = **156** wk
3. 1 century = **36,500** d
4. 4 yr, 15 wk = **1,565** d
5. 216 hr = **9** d
6. 91 d = **13** wk
7. 8 hr = **28,800** sec
8. 6 hr 20 min = **22,800** sec
9. 68 min = **4,080** sec
10. 154 d = **22** wk
11. 336 hr = **14** d
12. 7 yr, 22 wk = **2,709** d

13. **Reasoning** Is 500,000 sec more or less than 1 wk?

Less than

14. The men's Olympic record for running 800 m is 1 min, 43 sec. How many seconds is that?

103 sec

Name_____

Do You Have the Time?

Ken's daily schedule is below. Use the list and times to answer the following.

6:45 A.M.–7:15 A.M.	get dressed, eat breakfast
7:15 A.M.–7:25 A.M.	wash up, brush teeth
7:30 A.M.	catch bus for school
7:58 A.M.	arrive at school
8:10 A.M.	school starts
11:15 A.M.–11:50 A.M.	lunch
2:10 P.M.	school ends
2:40 P.M.	arrive home from school
3:00 P.M.–3:30 P.M.	snack and homework
5:00 P.M.–5:30 P.M.	dinner
8:00	bedtime

1. How many seconds does it take Ken to get dressed and eat breakfast in the morning?

1,800 sec

2. How many minutes is Ken on the bus in the morning? How many seconds is he on the bus?

28 min; 1,680 sec

3. Ken needs to spend 1,200 sec practicing the piano each day. Does he have time to do this before school? Explain.

No, he does not have 20 free minutes before school.

4. Ken practices the piano 1,200 sec a day, 7 days a week. How many minutes will he practice during a week?

140 min

5. How many hours a day does Ken spend at school? Is this more or less than 21,000 sec?

6 hr; more than 21,000 sec

6. If Ken's lunch period includes 900 sec for recess, how many minutes does he have to eat?

20 min

Name_____

Time

The chart shows the average life span of some animals.

Animal	Average Life Span
Mouse	3 years
Kangaroo	7 years
Pig	10 years
Moose	12 years
Lion	15 years
Bald eagle	40 years
Gray whale	70 years

1. What is the average life span of a mouse in days? **1,095 days**

2. What is the average life span of a kangaroo in weeks? **364 weeks**

3. What is the average life span of a pig in hours? **87,600 hours**

4. What is the average life span of a moose in weeks? **624 weeks**

5. What is the average life span of a lion in days? **5,475 days**

6. What is the average life span of a bald eagle in months? **480 months**

7. What is the average life span of a gray whale in centuries? **0.7 or $\frac{7}{10}$ centuries**

8. **Writing in Math** Which is older, a dog that is 83 days old or a cat that is 2,000 hr old? Explain.

Sample answer: The cat is older because the dog is 1,992 hr old.

Practice

Name_____

Elapsed Time

P 9-13

Find each elapsed time.

1. 9:59 P.M. to 10:45 P.M. **46 min**

2. 11:45 A.M. to 3:38 P.M. **3 hr 53 min**

3. **2 hr 51 min**

4. **2 hr 22 min**

Find the start time using the given elapsed time.

5. Start: 3:46 P.M   Elapsed: 2 hr 20 min   **6:06 P.M.**

6. Add.   2 hr 45 min
        + 3 hr 58 min
   6 hr 43 min

7. Add.   6 hr 47 min
        + 5 hr 28 min
   12 hr 15 min

The White House Visitor Center is open from 7:30 A.M. until 4:00 P.M.

8. Tara and Miguel got to the Visitor Center when it opened, and spent 1 hr 20 min there. At what time did they leave?
   8:50 A.M.

9. Jennifer left the Visitor Center at 3:30 P.M. after spending 40 min there. At what time did she arrive?
   2:50 P.M.

Test Prep

10. A football game lasted 2 hr 37 min. It finished at 4:22 P.M. When did it start?
    (A) 1:45 P.M.   B. 1:55 P.M.   C. 2:45 P.M.   D. 2:50 P.M.

11. **Writing in Math** What is 1 hour and 35 minutes before 4:05 P.M.? Explain how you solved this problem.   **Sample answer:**

2:30 P.M.; I solved this problem using subtraction.

Use with Lesson 9-13. 129

Reteaching

Name_____

Elapsed Time

R 9-13

How to find elapsed time:

Iris left her house at 11:15 A.M. and arrived at her grandparents' house at 1:30 P.M. How long did the trip take?

Use a number line to count up.

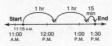

The trip took 2 hr, 15 min.

How to use elapsed time to find when an event began or ended:

Omar and his brothers played floor hockey for 1 hr, 9 min. They finished playing at 6:30 P.M. At what time did they begin playing?

You can subtract to find the start time.

End Time − Elapsed Time = Start Time

```
  6 hr 30 min
− 1 hr  9 min
  5 hr 21 min
```

So, they began playing at 5:21 P.M.

Find each elapsed time.

1. 8:13 P.M. to 10:00 P.M.   **1 hr, 47 min**

2. 11:24 A.M. to 2:47 P.M.   **3 hr, 23 min**

3. 3:35 P.M. to 6:09 P.M.   **2 hr, 34 min**

4. 9:55 P.M. to 11:42 P.M.   **1 hr, 47 min**

Find each start time or end time using the given elapsed time.

5. Start: 8:49 A.M.
   Elapsed: 5 hr, 20 min
   2:09 P.M.

6. End: 8:27 P.M.
   Elapsed: 4 hr, 13 min
   4:14 P.M.

Add or subtract.

7.   6 hr 31 min
   + 7 hr 16 min
   13 hr 47 min

8.   7 hr 12 min
   − 3 hr 30 min
   3 hr 42 min

9.   3 hr 5 min
   + 8 hr 55 min
   12 hr

10.   9 hr 5 min
    − 8 hr 22 min
    43 min

Use with Lesson 9-13. 129

Enrichment

Name_____

Can You Find the Time?

E 9-13
REASONING

Use the table to answer the questions below.

Attraction	Days	Open	Close
Columbus Zoo and Aquarium	Daily	9:00 A.M.	5:00 P.M.
Center of Science and Industry	Mon.–Sat. Sun.	10:00 A.M. 12:00 Noon	5:00 P.M. 6:00 P.M.
Santa Maria	Wed.–Fri. Sat.–Sun.	10:00 A.M. 12:00 Noon	3:00 P.M. 5:00 P.M.
State Capitol	Mon.–Fri. Sat.–Sun.	10:00 A.M. 12:00 Noon	3:00 P.M. 3:00 P.M.

1. How many hours longer is the Center of Science and Industry open on Monday than on Sunday?
   1 hr

2. How many hours is the state capitol open on Sundays?
   3 hr

3. Lance worked at the zoo on Wednesday from opening time until 2:00 P.M. How many hours did he work?
   5 hr

4. The Williams family arrived at the zoo at 10:00 A.M. They stayed for 3 hr and 20 min. What time did they leave the zoo?
   1:20 P.M.

5. Irene is making plans to visit the Santa Maria on Thursday. It takes her 20 min to drive there from her home. If she wants to arrive at opening time, what time should she leave her house?
   9:40 A.M.

6. The fifth-grade class is visiting the Center of Science and Industry. They arrive at opening time and plan on meeting for lunch 2½ hr after they arrive. They will leave 1 hr and 15 min after they start lunch. What time will they eat lunch? What time will they leave?
   Lunch: 12:30 P.M.; leave 1:45 P.M.

Use with Lesson 9-13. 129

Problem Solving

Name_____

Elapsed Time

PS 9-13

Time Zones There is a 2 hr time difference between cities in the Eastern time zone and cities in the Mountain time zone. If it is 8:00 P.M. in the Eastern time zone, it is 6:00 P.M. in the Mountain time zone. Use the chart to find the length of each flight. The arrival time shown is always the local time.

Flight Schedule

From			To		
City	Time Zone	Departure Time	City	Time Zone	Arrival Time
Miami, FL	Eastern	8:00 A.M.	Santa Fe, NM	Mountain	8:30 A.M.
Denver, CO	Mountain	10:30 A.M.	Boston, MA	Eastern	3:45 P.M.
Portland, ME	Eastern	1:00 P.M.	Helena, MT	Mountain	2:45 P.M.
Norfolk, VA	Eastern	3:30 P.M.	Boulder, CO	Mountain	5:00 P.M.

1. Denver to Boston   **3 hr 15 min**

2. Norfolk to Boulder   **3 hr 30 min**

3. Miami to Santa Fe   **2 hr 30 min**

4. Portland to Helena   **3 hr 45 min**

5. Sumi is flying from Miami to Santa Fe and then back to Miami. How long will she be flying?   **5 hr**

6. Hector is flying from Norfolk to Boulder and back. Next week he is flying from Portland to Helena and back. How long will he be flying in all?   **14 hr 30 min**

7. **Writing in Math** If it is 10:00 P.M. in Norfolk, VA, what time is it in Santa Fe, NM? Explain.

8:00 P.M.; Sample answer: Norfolk is in the Eastern time zone and Santa Fe is in the Mountain time zone, so the time is 2 hours earlier.

Use with Lesson 9-13. 129

Name_____

Temperature
P 9-14

Write each temperature in Celsius and Fahrenheit.

1.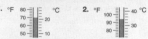
70°F 21°C

2.
94°F 34°C

3.
50°F 10°C

Find each change in temperature.

4. 34°F to 67°F **33°F increase**

5. 12°C to 7°C **5°C decrease**

6. **Number Sense** Which is a smaller increase in temperature: a 5°F increase or a 5°C increase?
5°F is a smaller increase.

Information about the record highest temperatures in four states is shown.

7. What is the difference between the record high temperature in Florida and the record high temperature in Alaska in °C?
5°C

Record High Temperature		
State	°F	°C
Alaska	100	38
Florida	109	43
Michigan	112	44
Hawaii	100	38

8. What is the difference between the record high temperature in Michigan and the record high temperature in Florida in °F?
3°F

Test Prep

9. What is the difference between −6°C and 12°C?
A. 6°C   B. 12°C   C. 18°C   D. 19°C

10. **Writing in Math** Which is warmer, 1°F or 1°C? Explain how you found this answer.
1°C is warmer. Sample answer: You can tell by looking at the thermometers.

130 Use with Lesson 9-14.

© Pearson Education, Inc. 5

Name_____

Temperature
R 9-14

How to read temperature:

Miami's average high temperature in June is 87°F. What is the average high temperature in degrees Celsius?

°F 87   31 °C

Step 1: Find 87° on the Fahrenheit scale.

Step 2: Read across to find the temperature on the Celsius scale.

31°C is the same as 87°F.

How to find changes in temperatures:

Find the change in temperature from 57°F to 18°F.

Step 1: Find the difference between 57°F and 18°F by subtracting. 57°F − 18°F = 39°F

Step 2: Tell if the difference is an increase or decrease. Since the second temperature is less than the first temperature, there was a decrease.

So, the change is a decrease of 39°F.

Write each temperature in Celsius and Fahrenheit.

1.
°F 55   13 °C
55°F ; 13°C

2.
°F 92   33 °C
92°F ; 33°C

Find each change in temperature.

3. 34°F to 89°F **55°F increase**

4. 11°C to 26°C **15°C increase**

5. 86°F to 54°F **32°F decrease**

6. 30°C to 8°C **22°C decrease**

7. 3°F to 81°F **78°F increase**

8. 12°C to 5°C **7°C decrease**

9. **Number Sense** Yesterday's high temperature was 76°F. The difference between the high and low temperature was 33°F. What was yesterday's low temperature?
43°F

130 Use with Lesson 9-14.

© Pearson Education, Inc. 5

Name_____

Just the Right Temperature
E 9-14
DECISION MAKING

1. Snow is falling outside. What might the Fahrenheit temperature read?
Any temperature under 32°F

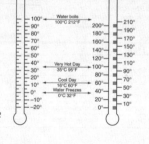

Celsius / Fahrenheit

Water boils 100°C 212°F

Very Hot Day 35°C 95°F

Cool Day 16°C 60°F

Water Freezes 0°C 32°F

2. A thermometer reads about 20°C. Do you need to wear a coat outdoors?
No

3. If the temperature in Exercise 2 rose 4°, what would the temperature read?
24°C

4. The thermometer reads 20°C. Can you go ice skating? Explain.
No, it must be 0°C or 32°F.

Circle the more sensible temperature for each outdoor activity.

5. building a snowman
26°F   56°F

7. snowboarding
10°F   10°C

6. swimming
17°C   **33°C**

8. hiking
80°C   **80°F**

130 Use with Lesson 9-14.

© Pearson Education, Inc. 5

Name_____

Temperature
PS 9-14

Average Highs Veronica kept track of the average high temperature in her city for six months. She recorded the temperatures in degrees Fahrenheit for three months and in degrees Celsius for three months.

Average Temperatures	
Month	Temperature
February	42°F
April	62°F
June	84°F
August	33°C
October	17°C
December	4°C

Use the thermometer to find the approximate average high for each month in Celsius.

1. February **6°C**

2. April **17°C**

3. June **29°C**

4. Find the change in temperature from February to June.
42°F increase

Use the thermometer to find the approximate average high for each month in Fahrenheit.

5. August **92°F**

6. October **63°F**

7. December **39°F**

8. Find the change in temperature from August to December.
29°C decrease

9. **Writing in Math** It is 4°C. Is it above or below freezing? Explain.
Sample answer: It is above freezing because 0°C is the freezing point.

130 Use with Lesson 9-14.

© Pearson Education, Inc. 5

Name_____

PROBLEM-SOLVING SKILL   P 9-15
Writing to Explain   Sample answers are given.

Write to explain.

1. How could you convert a measurement given in millimeters to kilometers?

I would use division to convert a measurement in millimeters to kilometers. You would need to divide by 10 six times in order to convert the measurement.

2. How could you find the perimeter of a brick in this wall?

I would first find the height of one brick ($\frac{1}{2}$ ft). Then I would find the length of one brick (1 ft). Then I would add the lengths of four sides of an individual brick together to find the perimeter: $\frac{1}{2} + \frac{1}{2} + 1 + 1 = 3$ ft.

3. How could you find the height of this triangle?

$A = 30$ in^2

$30 \times 2 = 60$. $60 \div 5$ gives the height of the triangle, 12 in.

Use with Lesson 9-15. **131**

Name_____

PROBLEM-SOLVING SKILL   R 9-15
Writing to Explain

Write and explain how you would find the area of the triangle.

6 ft
10 ft

- Break the process into steps.
- Use pictures and words to explain.
- Tell about things to watch out for and be careful about.
- Use words like *find* and *put* when explaining a process.

1. First, write the formula for finding the area of a triangle. Make sure you have the correct formula.

   $A = \frac{1}{2} \times b \times h$

2. Next, put the numbers for the base and height into the formula.

   $A = \frac{1}{2} \times 10$ ft $\times 6$ ft

3. Multiply. It is usually easier to multiply the base and height first.

   $10 \times 6 = 60$

   Then multiply this amount by $\frac{1}{2}$.

   $\frac{1}{2} \times 60 = 30$ So, the area $= 30$ ft^2.

Sample answer:

1. Explain how you would find the perimeter of the figure to the right.

9 m
2.5 m   2.5 m
12 m   3.5 m

First look at each of the sides. Write down each number and add them up. Make sure you write the units at the end. The perimeter is 29.5 m.

Use with Lesson 9-15. **131**

Name_____

Time Zones   E 9-15
                                           NUMBER SENSE

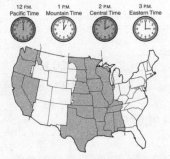

12 P.M. Pacific Time   1 P.M. Mountain Time   2 P.M. Central Time   3 P.M. Eastern Time

As you travel across the United States, you cross into different time zones. Use the map to answer the following questions.

1. Name the time zone that is 2 hr earlier than Eastern Time.

   Mountain Time

2. When it is 10:30 A.M. in Louisiana, what time is it in California?

   8:30 A.M.

3. When it is 1:00 P.M. in Georgia, what time is it in Nevada?

   10:00 A.M.

4. If you live in New York and it is 8:00 A.M., is it a good idea to call your aunt in Washington State? Why or why not?

   No, it is 5 A.M. in Washington, and she is probably still sleeping.

5. If you live in Montana and it is 4 P.M., is it a good idea to call your grandmother in Ohio? Why or why not?

   Yes, it is 6 P.M. in Ohio.

Use with Lesson 9-15. **131**

Name_____

PROBLEM-SOLVING SKILL   PS 9-15
Writing to Explain

Area Find the area of the parallelogram. Explain how you found the area.

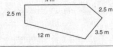
12 cm
18 cm

Read and Understand

1. What is the length of the base?   **18 cm**

2. What is the length of the height?   **12 cm**

3. What are you trying to find?

   The area of the parallelogram

Plan and Solve

4. What is the formula for area?

   $A = b \times h$

5. What is the area of the parallelogram?

   $A = 18 \times 12$; 216 cm^2

6. Explain how you found the area.

   Sample answer: I multiplied the length of the base, 18 cm, by the length of the height, 12 cm. The product was 216, so I wrote the area as 216 cm^2.

Look Back and Check

7. Explain how you can check your answer. **Sample answer: I can use division to check: 216 divided by 12 is 18. My answer checks.**

Use with Lesson 9-15. **131**

Name_____

PROBLEM-SOLVING APPLICATIONS   P 9-16

Summer Parade

The parade-planning committee met to organize the summer parade. Here are some notes from the meeting.

> *Springdale Summer Parade*
>
> Planning Information:
> Date of parade—June 5
> Parade start time—1:30 P.M.
> Maximum size of floats—12 ft x 20 ft
> Parade may be canceled due to rain or temp less than 50°F
> Parade route—5.2 km long

1. On parade day, the conductor of each marching band must check in at least 2 hr before the parade starts. What is the latest time the band conductors can check in?

   11:30 A.M.

2. The floats and marching groups will be judged, and prizes will be awarded. The judge's stand is exactly halfway through the parade route. How many meters from the beginning of the parade is the judge's stand?

   2,600 m

3. If a rectangular parade float is the maximum allowed size, what is the area of the parade float?

   240 ft²

4. The temperature on June 5 is 85°F. How many degrees greater than the minimum temperature for the parade is this?

   35°F

5. The parade-planning committee met 6 weeks before the parade. How many days before the parade was this?

   42 days

132   Use with Lesson 9-16.

© Pearson Education, Inc. 5

Name_____

PROBLEM-SOLVING APPLICATIONS   R 9-16

The Clubhouse

Andrew wants to build a clubhouse in the backyard for his children. He has drawn several different plans for the clubhouse. Which clubhouse will have the greatest perimeter?

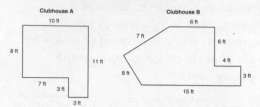

Add up the sides of each clubhouse.

Clubhouse A   Clubhouse B

10 + 11 + 3 + 3 + 7 + 8 = 42 ft   6 + 6 + 4 + 3 + 15 + 8 + 7 = 49 ft

So, Clubhouse B would have the greater perimeter.

1. Andrew is considering building a clubhouse in the shape of a rectangle. His sketch of the clubhouse is to the right. What would the area of this clubhouse be?

   32 ft²

2. On one wall of the clubhouse, Andrew wants to cut a large circular opening to be a window. The circle's radius is 2 ft. What will the circle's circumference be?

   12.56 ft

3. Andrew started to build the clubhouse at 6:15 A.M. He completed the job at 4:30 P.M. He took a ½ hr break for lunch. How long did it take him to build the clubhouse?

   9 hr, 45 min

132   Use with Lesson 9-16.

© Pearson Education, Inc. 5

Name_____

Sales Tax   E 9-16
NUMBER SENSE

Sales tax is an amount of money added to the cost of items we buy. Use the sales tax table to write the total cost including sales tax.

Sales Tax Table 6%

Amount of Sale	Tax
$0.09–$0.24	$0.01
$0.25–$0.41	$0.02
$0.42–$0.58	$0.03
$0.59–$0.74	$0.04
$0.75–$0.91	$0.05
$0.92–$1.08	$0.06
$1.09–$1.24	$0.07
$1.25–$1.41	$0.08
$1.42–$1.58	$0.09
$1.59–$1.74	$0.10
$1.75–$1.91	$0.11
$1.92–$2.08	$0.12
$2.09–$2.24	$0.13
$2.25–$2.41	$0.14
$2.42–$2.58	$0.15
$2.59–$2.74	$0.16
$2.75–$2.91	$0.17
$2.92–$3.08	$0.18
$3.09–$3.24	$0.19
$3.25–$3.41	$0.20
$3.42–$3.58	$0.21
$3.59–$3.74	$0.22

1. Iris bought a pack of gum for $0.40. What will be the total cost including sales tax?

   $0.42

2. Mrs. Barnes bought 2 lb of grapes at $0.56 per pound. What will the total cost be with sales tax?

   $1.19

3. Joe needed to buy a gallon of milk. The regular price was $2.69, but it was on sale for $1.00 off. What will be his total cost after sales tax?

   $1.79

4. Jay needs to buy 9 screws to finish his project. They are $0.25 each. What will be the total cost including sales tax?

   $2.39

5. Hank bought a pack of pens for $1.10 and a pack of paper for $1.25. What was the total cost including sales tax?

   $2.49

6. Chris has $3.00 and wants to buy a new toy car for $1.30 and a new toy truck for $1.59. After the sales tax is added, will he have enough money? Explain.

   No, the total cost is $3.06.

132   Use with Lesson 9-16.

© Pearson Education, Inc. 5

Name_____

PROBLEM-SOLVING APPLICATIONS   PS 9-16

Fence

Magdalena bought 320 ft of fencing material for her yard. If her yard is three times as long as it is wide, what is the length of her yard? Draw a picture to solve.

Read and Understand

1. How much fencing did Magdalena buy?

   320 ft

2. What shape is Magdalena's yard?

   Rectangular

3. What are you trying to find?

   The length of her yard

Plan and Solve

4. Is 320 ft the area or perimeter of Magdalena's yard?

   Perimeter

5. Draw a picture to solve the problem.

   Sample answer:

   120 ft
   40 ft

6. What is the length? Write your answer in a complete sentence.

   The yard is 120 ft long.

Look Back and Check

7. Explain how you can check your answer.

   Sample answer: 120 + 120 + 40 + 40 = 320. My answer checks.

Solve Another Problem

8. Fred's garden is the same width as Frank's but is 2 ft longer. Frank's square garden is 10 ft wide. What is the area of Fred's garden?

   120 ft²

132   Use with Lesson 9-16.

© Pearson Education, Inc. 5

Name_____

Solid Figures

P 10-1

What solid figure does each object resemble?

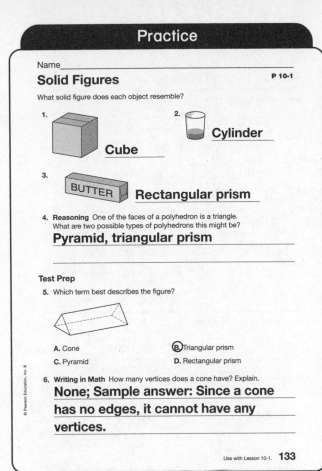

1. **Cube**

2. **Cylinder**

3. **Rectangular prism**

4. **Reasoning** One of the faces of a polyhedron is a triangle. What are two possible types of polyhedrons this might be?
Pyramid, triangular prism

Test Prep

5. Which term best describes the figure?

A. Cone
B. Triangular prism
C. Pyramid
D. Rectangular prism

6. **Writing in Math** How many vertices does a cone have? Explain.
None; Sample answer: Since a cone has no edges, it cannot have any vertices.

Use with Lesson 10-1. **133**

Name_____

Solid Figures

R 10-1

The solid's vertices are: A, B, C, D, E, F, G, and H.
The solid's edges are: $\overline{AC}$, $\overline{AB}$, $\overline{CD}$, $\overline{DB}$, $\overline{AH}$, $\overline{BG}$, $\overline{HG}$, $\overline{HE}$, $\overline{GF}$, $\overline{EF}$, $\overline{CE}$, and $\overline{DF}$.
The solid's faces are: ACEH, BDFG, ABCD, EFGH, CDEF, and ABHG.

Here are some common solid figures:

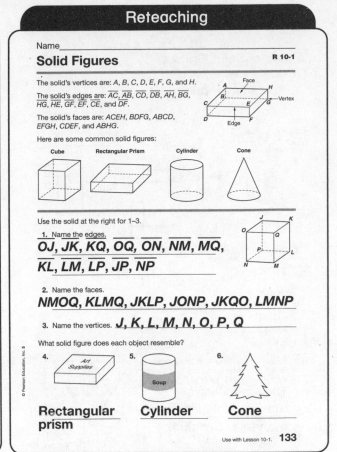

Cube   Rectangular Prism   Cylinder   Cone

Use the solid at the right for 1–3.

1. Name the edges.
$\overline{OJ}$, $\overline{JK}$, $\overline{KQ}$, $\overline{OQ}$, $\overline{ON}$, $\overline{NM}$, $\overline{MQ}$, $\overline{KL}$, $\overline{LM}$, $\overline{LP}$, $\overline{JP}$, $\overline{NP}$

2. Name the faces.
NMOQ, KLMQ, JKLP, JONP, JKQO, LMNP

3. Name the vertices. **J, K, L, M, N, O, P, Q**

What solid figure does each object resemble?

4. **Rectangular prism**

5. **Cylinder**

6. **Cone**

Use with Lesson 10-1. **133**

Name_____

Shape Up!

E 10-1
VISUAL THINKING

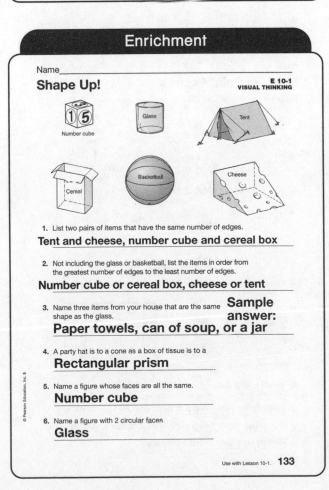

Number cube   Glass   Tent
Cereal   Basketball   Cheese

1. List two pairs of items that have the same number of edges.
Tent and cheese, number cube and cereal box

2. Not including the glass or basketball, list the items in order from the greatest number of edges to the least number of edges.
Number cube or cereal box, cheese or tent

3. Name three items from your house that are the same shape as the glass. **Sample answer:**
Paper towels, can of soup, or a jar

4. A party hat is to a cone as a box of tissue is to a
Rectangular prism

5. Name a figure whose faces are all the same.
Number cube

6. Name a figure with 2 circular faces.
Glass

Use with Lesson 10-1. **133**

Name_____

Solid Figures

PS 10-1

Wrap It Up Jamie wants to help her mother wrap two presents. The two boxes they will be using are shown.

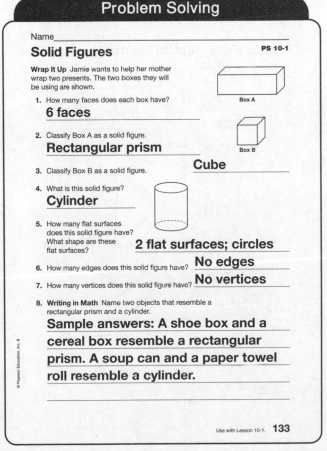

Box A
Box B

1. How many faces does each box have?
6 faces

2. Classify Box A as a solid figure.
Rectangular prism

3. Classify Box B as a solid figure.
Cube

4. What is this solid figure?
Cylinder

5. How many flat surfaces does this solid figure have? What shape are these flat surfaces?
2 flat surfaces; circles

6. How many edges does this solid figure have?
No edges

7. How many vertices does this solid figure have?
No vertices

8. **Writing in Math** Name two objects that resemble a rectangular prism and a cylinder.
Sample answers: A shoe box and a cereal box resemble a rectangular prism. A soup can and a paper towel roll resemble a cylinder.

Use with Lesson 10-1. **133**

© Pearson Education, Inc. 5

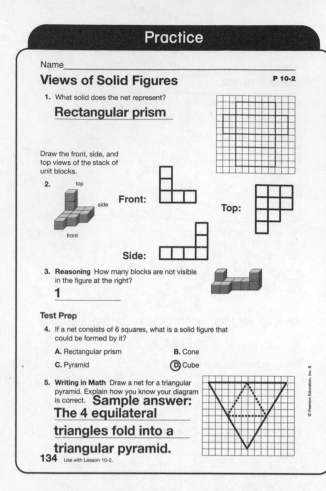

Name_____

Views of Solid Figures
P 10-2

1. What solid does the net represent?

Rectangular prism

Draw the front, side, and top views of the stack of unit blocks.

2.

Front:

Top:

Side:

3. **Reasoning** How many blocks are not visible in the figure at the right?

1

Test Prep

4. If a net consists of 6 squares, what is a solid figure that could be formed by it?

A. Rectangular prism   B. Cone

C. Pyramid   (D) Cube

5. **Writing in Math** Draw a net for a triangular pyramid. Explain how you know your diagram is correct. **Sample answer: The 4 equilateral triangles fold into a triangular pyramid.**

134 Use with Lesson 10-2.

© Pearson Education, Inc. 5

Name_____

Views of Solid Figures
R 10-2

If the net on the left was folded, it would form the figure on the right.

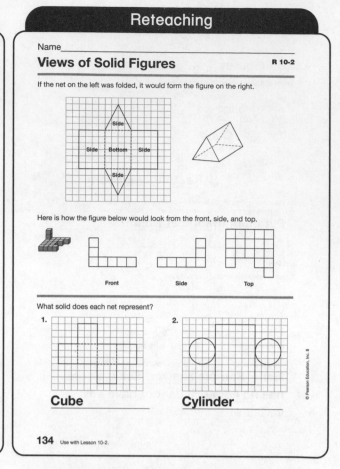

Side
Side | Bottom | Side
Side

Here is how the figure below would look from the front, side, and top.

Front   Side   Top

What solid does each net represent?

1.

2.

Cube   **Cylinder**

134 Use with Lesson 10-2.

© Pearson Education, Inc. 5

Name_____

Folding and Unfolding Figures
E 10-2
VISUAL THINKING

1. Which net does not fold into a cube?

A

A   B   C

2. On a clean sheet of paper, trace, cut out, and assemble the shapes into a net that represents a triangular prism.

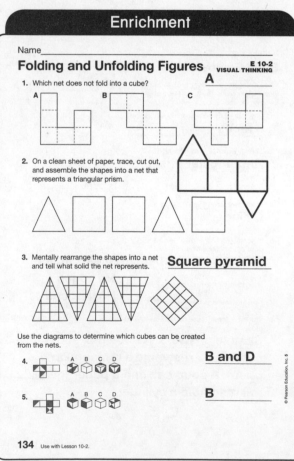

3. Mentally rearrange the shapes into a net and tell what solid the net represents.

Square pyramid

Use the diagrams to determine which cubes can be created from the nets.

4.   A B C D

B and D

5.   A B C D

B

134 Use with Lesson 10-2.

© Pearson Education, Inc. 5

Name_____

Views of Solid Figures
PS 10-2

Net or Not? Tell whether each plane figure is a net and can be folded into a solid figure.

1.   **Net**

2.   **Not a net**

3.   **Not a net**

4.   **Net**

5.   **Net**

6. Make a rough sketch of the city block looking directly down from above.

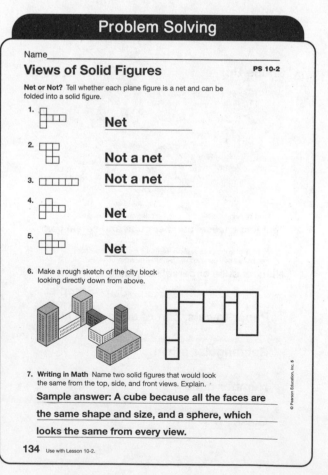

7. **Writing in Math** Name two solid figures that would look the same from the top, side, and front views. Explain.

Sample answer: A cube because all the faces are the same shape and size, and a sphere, which looks the same from every view.

134 Use with Lesson 10-2.

© Pearson Education, Inc. 5

---

134   Use with Chapter 10, Lesson 2

Practice

Name_____

Surface Area

P 10-3

Find the surface area of each rectangular prism.

1.
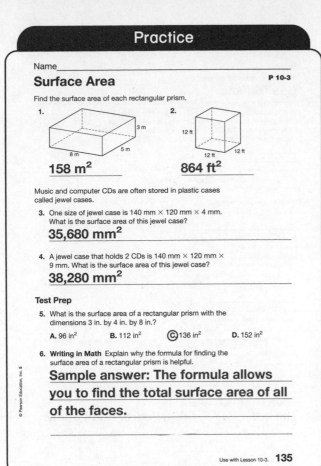
3 m
8 m
5 m

158 m²

2.
12 ft
12 ft
12 ft

864 ft²

Music and computer CDs are often stored in plastic cases called jewel cases.

3. One size of jewel case is 140 mm × 120 mm × 4 mm. What is the surface area of this jewel case?

35,680 mm²

4. A jewel case that holds 2 CDs is 140 mm × 120 mm × 9 mm. What is the surface area of this jewel case?

38,280 mm²

Test Prep

5. What is the surface area of a rectangular prism with the dimensions 3 in. by 4 in. by 8 in.?

A. 96 in²   **B.** 112 in²   **C.** 136 in²   **D.** 152 in²

6. Writing in Math Explain why the formula for finding the surface area of a rectangular prism is helpful.

Sample answer: The formula allows you to find the total surface area of all of the faces.

Reteaching

Name_____

Surface Area

R 10-3

How to find the surface area of a rectangular prism:

The formula for finding the surface area of a rectangular prism is:

$2(l \times w) + 2(l \times h) + 2(w \times h)$

Remember, l = length, w = width, and h = height.

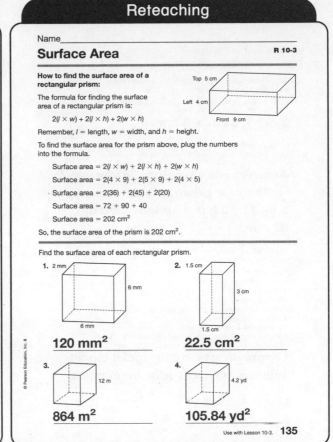
Top 5 cm
Left 4 cm
Front 9 cm

To find the surface area for the prism above, plug the numbers into the formula.

Surface area = $2(l \times w) + 2(l \times h) + 2(w \times h)$

Surface area = $2(4 \times 9) + 2(5 \times 9) + 2(4 \times 5)$

Surface area = $2(36) + 2(45) + 2(20)$

Surface area = $72 + 90 + 40$

Surface area = 202 cm²

So, the surface area of the prism is 202 cm².

Find the surface area of each rectangular prism.

1. 2 mm
6 mm
6 mm

120 mm²

2. 1.5 cm
3 cm
1.5 cm

22.5 cm²

3. 12 m

864 m²

4. 4.2 yd

105.84 yd²

Enrichment

Name_____

Missing Pieces

E 10-3
PATTERNS

You may turn each missing pattern to make it fit.

1. Which pattern is missing in the diagram?   **C** _____

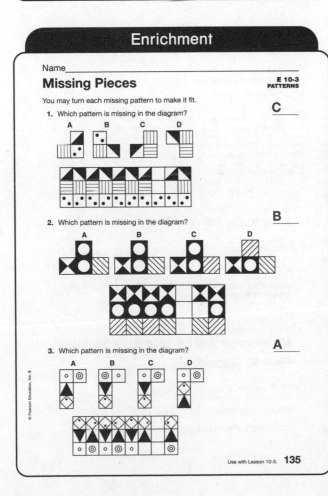
A   B   C   D

2. Which pattern is missing in the diagram?   **B** _____

A   B   C   D

3. Which pattern is missing in the diagram?   **A** _____

A   B   C   D

Problem Solving

Name_____

Surface Area

PS 10-3

Woodworking Peter is building a storage chest in woodworking class. To help him plan the project, Peter made the drawing shown.

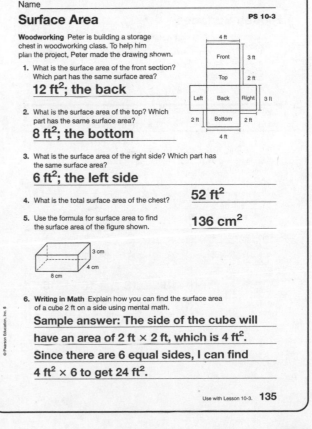
4 ft
Front   3 ft
Top   2 ft
Left   Back   Right   3 ft
Bottom
2 ft   2 ft
4 ft

1. What is the surface area of the front section? Which part has the same surface area?

12 ft²; the back

2. What is the surface area of the top? Which part has the same surface area?

8 ft²; the bottom

3. What is the surface area of the right side? Which part has the same surface area?

6 ft²; the left side

4. What is the total surface area of the chest?   **52 ft²**

5. Use the formula for surface area to find the surface area of the figure shown.   **136 cm²**

3 cm
4 cm
8 cm

6. Writing in Math Explain how you can find the surface area of a cube 2 ft on a side using mental math.

Sample answer: The side of the cube will have an area of 2 ft × 2 ft, which is 4 ft². Since there are 6 equal sides, I can find 4 ft² × 6 to get 24 ft².

© Pearson Education, Inc. 5

Name_____

PROBLEM-SOLVING STRATEGY   P 10-4
Use Objects

Use Centimeter Cubes to Solve a Problem Use centimeter
cubes to find the surface area.

1. Make a model of a cube that has a surface area of 54 cm². What are the measurements of the model?

3 cm × 3 cm × 3 cm

2. Make a model of a rectangular prism that is not a cube and has a surface area of 62 cm². What are the measurements of this rectangular prism?

Answers will vary. Sample answer: A rectangular prism with dimensions of 5 by 2 by 3 has a surface area of 62 cm².

Use Cards to Solve a Problem Write the information on slips
of paper to help solve the problem.

3. Yu-Li takes six classes each day. The classes are math, science, language arts, social studies, music, and physical education. Use the clues to figure out the order of the classes.
   • There is a class before and after social studies.
   • There is no class after music.
   • There is one class before math.
   • There are two classes between social studies and music.
   • Physical education is right after science.

Language arts, math, social studies, science, physical education, music

© Pearson Education, Inc. 5

Name_____

PROBLEM-SOLVING STRATEGY   R 10-4
Use Objects

The Students Six students sit in one row in Mrs. Ussery's class. Vicky sits in the last desk. Tim sits between Pete and Vicky. Frank sits in the second desk, behind Barb and in front of Carrie. What is their order from front to back?

Read and Understand

Step 1: What do you know?

Vicky sits in the last desk. Tim sits between Pete and Vicky. Frank sits in the second desk, behind Barb and in front of Carrie.

Step 2: What are you trying to find?

The order of six students from front to back

Plan and Solve

Step 3: What strategy will you use?

Use note cards with one name on each. Put the cards in the correct order to solve the problem.

| Barb | Frank | Carrie | Pete | Tim | Vicky |

Look Back and Check

Step 4: Is your answer reasonable?

Yes, the order matches the description in the problem.

Write each name on a slip of paper: Greg, Ali, Ruth, Stacy, and Pedro. Put the name cards in the correct order to solve the problem.

1. Five friends are sitting on a park bench. Stacy is sitting on the far right. Ruth is sitting between Pedro and Stacy. Ali is sitting to the left of Greg. Use the clues to determine in what order the friends are seated.

The order is: Ali, Greg, Pedro, Ruth, Stacy.

© Pearson Education, Inc. 5

Name_____

Hidden Surfaces   E 10-4
                                                     ALGEBRA

1. A cube has 6 square faces. Find the pattern and complete the table below.

Length of edge	1	2	3	4	5	6	...	n
Surface area	6 × 1	6 × 4	6 × 9	6×16	6×256	×36	...	6×n×n

2. Complete the table below for the five different ways that four cubes are put together. The edges of the cubes are 4 in. long.

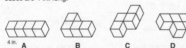

4 in.   A   B   C   D   E

Figure	A	B	C	D	E
Number of hidden surfaces	6	6	6	6	8
Number of visible surfaces	18	18	18	18	16
Surface area	18 × 4 × 4	18 × 4 × 4	18 × 4 × 4	18 × 4 × 4	16 × 4 × 4

© Pearson Education, Inc. 5

Name_____

PROBLEM-SOLVING STRATEGY   PS 10-4
Use Objects

Juice Cans Mr. Hanson wants to make a display of juice cans in his store. He wants to make a single can of juice on the top layer. Every other layer must form a square, with each layer being 1 can wider than the layer above it. The shelf for the juice display is only tall enough for 4 layers of cans. How many cans will be in the display?

Read and Understand

1. How many layers will fit on the shelf? How many cans are on the top layer?

4 layers; 1 can

2. What are you trying to find?

How many cans will be in the display

Plan and Solve

3. What strategy will you use?

Use objects

4. Use centimeter cubes to make a model. **Check students' models. Students should have 16, 9, 4, and 1 can on each successive layer.**

5. Solve the problem. Write the answer in a complete sentence.

Mr. Hanson will be able to fit 30 juice cans in the 4 layers.

Look Back and Check

6. Is your answer reasonable?

Sample answer: Yes. The model I made matches the description in the problem.

© Pearson Education, Inc. 5

Reteaching

Name_____

Volume   P 10-5

Find the volume of each rectangular prism.

1. base area 56 in², height 6 in.   **336 in³**

2. base area 32 cm², height 12 cm   **384 cm³**

3. base area 42 m², height 8 m   **336 m³**

4.   5.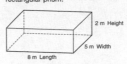
5 yd   8 cm, 10 cm, 2 cm

125 yd³   **160 cm³**

6. **Algebra** What is the height of a solid with a
   volume of 120 m³ and base area of 30 m²?   **4 m**

Michael bought some cereal at the grocery store.

7. What is the base area of the box?
   28 in²

8. What is the volume of the box?
   364 in²

Toasty O's Cereal $3\frac{1}{2}$ 13 in. 8 in.

Test Prep

9. What is the base area of this figure?   V = 320 m³

   A. 3.2 m²   Ⓑ 32 m²   10 m
   C. 320 m²   D. 3,200 m²

10. **Writing in Math** Explain how you would find the base area
    of a rectangular prism if you know the volume and the height.

Sample answer: Divide the volume by the
height to find the base area.   Use with Lesson 10-5. **137**

© Pearson Education, Inc. 5

Name_____

Volume   R 10-5

Find the volume of the
rectangular prism.

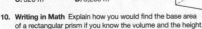
2 m Height, 5 m Width, 8 m Length

$V = (l \times w) \times h$
$V = (8 \times 5) \times 2$
$V = 40 \times 2$
$V = 80$ m³

So, the volume is 80 m³.

Find the volume of the
rectangular prism.

base area: 75 ft²
height: 9 ft

$V = Bh$
$V = 75 \times 9$
$V = 675$ ft³

Use unit cubes, make a drawing, or use the formula to find the
volume of each rectangular prism.

1. base area: 32 cm²   2. base area: 52.4 in²   3. base area: 81 ft²
   height: 4 cm   height: 5 in.   height: 6 ft
   128 cm³   **262 in³**   **486 ft³**

4.   5.
   3 ft, 2 ft, 4 ft   1.2 m, 2.1 m, 4 m

   24 ft³   **10.08 m³**

                                          Use with Lesson 10-5. **137**

© Pearson Education, Inc. 5

Name_____

Who's Right?   E 10-5
                                                    REASONABLENESS

1. The volume of a cube is 216 cubic centimeters. Linda
   says that a rectangular prism with a length of 4, a
   width of 6, and a height of 9 has the same volume.
   Lisa says that she could think of another rectangular
   prism. What could be its measurement?

   12 × 6 × 3

2. Clayton claims that all figures with a volume of 4 cubic
   units have the same surface area. Use the pictures below
   to determine if you agree or not. Explain your conclusion.

   A   B   C

   1 in.   1 in.   1 in.

   No; Surface areas of figures A and C
   are 18 in², surface area of B is 16 in²

3. Akos and Laszlo want to order the figures from greatest
   to least according to the volume. Laszlo said the order
   should be C, A, B. Akos said the order should be C, B, A.
   Who is correct? What is the volume of each?

   A   B   C

   3 in.   2 in.   5 in.
   3 in.   2 in.   5 in.
   3 in.   2 in.   5 in.

   Laszlo is correct. A = 135 in³, B =
   72 in³, C = 250 in³

                                                    Use with Lesson 10-5. **137**

© Pearson Education, Inc. 5

Name_____

Volume   PS 10-5

A maker of cubic number blocks packs a rectangular box so
that there are 8 blocks along one edge, 10 blocks along the
second edge, and 4 blocks along the third edge.

1. How many blocks will be shipped in this box?   **320 blocks**

2. If each block has a side of 1.5 cm,
   what is the volume of the box?   **1,080 cm³**

3. Another maker of number blocks packs a box so
   that there are 6 blocks along one edge, 5 blocks
   along another edge, and 12 blocks along the third
   edge. These blocks are smaller, however. Each has
   a side of 1 cm. What is the volume of this box?   **360 cm³**

Kerry bought a new fish tank. The
drawing shows the dimensions of the tank.

14 in., 16 in., 30 in.

4. What is the volume of the tank?
   6,720 in³

5. If Kerry fills the tank with 10 in. of
   water, how much water is in the tank?
   How much of the tank is empty?
   4,800 in³; 1,920 in³

6. **Writing in Math** Two rectangular prisms have the same
   volume and the same height, even though the length and
   width of each rectangular prism is different. What do you
   know about their bases? Explain.

   Sample answer: Volume equals the
   area of the base times height. Since
   the rectangular prisms have the same
   volume and height, the bases must
   have the same area.

                                                    Use with Lesson 10-5. **137**

© Pearson Education, Inc. 5

Customary Units of Capacity

P 10-6

Complete.

1. 2 qt = **4** pt
2. 5 c = **2** pt **1** c
3. 3 gal = **24** pt
4. 2 fl oz = **12** tsp
5. 4 qt = **16** c
6. 9 pt = **18** c

Write each answer in simplest form.

7.
```
  5 c 4 fl oz
− 4 c 3 fl oz
```
1 c 1 fl oz

8.
```
  7 gal 2 qt
+ 3 gal 1 qt
```
10 gal 3 qt

9.
```
  6 qt 1 pt
+ 2 qt 1 pt
```
9 qt 0 pt

10. **Estimation** Estimate the number of tablespoons in 445 teaspoons.

About 150 tbsp

11. **Reasoning** If you needed only 1 c of milk, what is your best choice at the grocery store—a quart container, a pint container, or a $\frac{1}{2}$ gal container?

A pint container

Test Prep

12. Which of the following is equivalent to 1 c?

A. 4 fl oz   B. 2 pt   C. 48 tsp   D. 32 tbsp

13. **Writing in Math** Explain how you would convert a measurement given in tablespoons into pints.

Sample answer: First, convert the tablespoons to fluid ounces. Then convert to cups, and finally, to pints.

Customary Units of Capacity

R 10-6

Capacity is a measure of an amount of liquid. Many different units can be used to measure capacity.

1 teaspoon (tsp) = $\frac{1}{3}$ tbsp

1 tablespoon (tbsp) = 3 tsp

1 fluid ounce (fl oz) = 2 tbsp

1 cup (c) = 8 fl oz

1 pint (pt) = 2 c

1 quart (qt) = 2 pt

1 gallon (gal) = 4 qt

Changing one unit of capacity to another:

8 pt = _____ c

Think: 1 pt = 2 c

8 × 2 = 16

So, 8 pt = 16 c.

Adding and subtracting units of capacity:

```
  7 qt 2 pt   =   6 qt 4 pt
− 3 qt 3 pt   =  − 3 qt 3 pt
                  3 qt 1 pt
```

Because there are 2 pt in 1 qt, you can rename 7 qt 2 pt to 6 qt 4 pt.

So, 7 qt 2 pt − 3 qt 3 pt = 3 qt 1 pt.

Complete.

1. 16 fl oz = **2** c
2. 8 gal = **32** qt
3. 6 tbsp = **18** tsp
4. 10 c = **5** pt

Write each answer in simplest form.

5.
```
  5 qt 1 pt
+     1 pt
```
6 qt

6.
```
  4 gal 3 qt
− 2 gal 1 qt
```
2 gal 2 qt

7.
```
  6 c 7 fl oz
− 4 c 5 fl oz
```
2 c 2 fl oz

8. **Estimation** Estimate the number of cups in 642 fl oz.

Sample answer: About 80 cups

United Differences

E 10-6
NUMBER SENSE

The United States and the United Kingdom use the same terms for units that measure liquid and dry capacities. However, the actual capacities are different in each case. The U.S. customary unit for a quart is 57.75 in^3 of liquid. The U.K. imperial unit for a quart is 69.355 in^3.

1. What is the difference in cubic inches between the two quarts?

11.605 in^3 more for UK

2. How many cubic inches are in a U.S. gallon and a U.K. gallon?

231 in^3; 277.42 in^3

Sheila lives in Florida and received a recipe from her friend Sarah who lives in London, England, which uses U.K. imperial measurement standards. The U.K. imperial measurement for 1 fl oz is about 1.73 in^3. In the United States, 1 fl oz is about 1.8 in^3.

3. The recipe Sheila received requires 4 oz of milk. What is the measurement in U.S. units and U.K. units?

7.2 in^3 in U.S., 6.92 in^3 in U.K.

4. The recipe requires 2 oz of vanilla. What is the measurement in U.S. units and U.K. units?

3.6 in^3 in U.S., 3.46 in^3 in U.K.

5. The recipe requires 1 c of water. Based on the quart measure, what is the volume in U.S. and U.K. units?

About 14.44 in^3 in U.S., 17.33 in^3 in U.K.

Customary Units of Capacity

PS 10-6

Company Hank has some friends coming over and he wants to serve refreshments. He makes 3 qt of lemonade to serve his guests.

1. How many 12 fl oz glasses will Hank get from this pitcher?

8 glasses

2. If he has 11 guests coming, will everyone be able to have a 12 fl oz glass of lemonade?

No

3. If Hank wants to serve himself and his 11 guests lemonade, what size glasses should he use? Write your answer in cups.

1 c

Birdfeeders Kenneth helps his grandmother care for the birdfeeders and birdbath in her yard.

4. Kenneth puts 2 qt of water in the birdbath each day. How many gallons will he put in the birdbath after 4 days?

2 gal

5. There are 5 birdfeeders in the yard. Each can hold 2 c of birdseed. How many pints of seed will Kenneth need to fill all of the feeders?

5 pt

6. **Writing in Math** If Kenneth bought a 2 qt container of birdseed to fill the feeders, will there be enough? Explain.

No; Sample answer: There are 4 pt in 2 qt, and he needs 5 pt to fill the birdfeeders.

Name_____

Metric Units of Capacity

P 10-7

Complete.

1. 5 L = **5,000** mL
2. 1,298 mL = **1.298** L
3. 3.4 L = **3,400** mL
4. 956 mL = **0.956** L
5. 82 mL = **0.082** L
6. 98 L = **98,000** mL

7. **Estimation** Which capacity is most reasonable for each object?

a. drinking glass
50 mL or 50 L
50 mL

b. swimming pool
80,000 mL or 80,000 L
80,000 L

c. bottle cap
20 mL or 20 L
20 mL

8. Latoya's science fair experiment measured the rate at which the temperature of water changed. She tested four different-sized containers of water: 1 L, 2 L, 4 L, and 5 L. Express these capacities in milliliters.

1,000 mL; 2,000 mL; 4,000 mL; 5,000 mL

Test Prep

9. Which of the following is equivalent to 2 mL?

A. 20 L   B. 0.2 L   C. 0.02 L   D. 0.002 L

10. **Writing in Math** Tell whether you would use multiplication or division to convert milliliters to liters. Explain your answer.

Sample answer: I would divide by 1,000 to convert milliliters to liters, because 1,000 mL = 1 L.

Name_____

Metric Units of Capacity

R 10-7

Milliliters (mL) are used to measure very small amounts of liquid. One milliliter is about 20 drops of water.

Liters (L) are used to measure larger amounts of liquid. You may have seen soda sold in 1 L or 2 L bottles. One liter is a little more than a quart: 1 L = 1,000 mL.

To change from milliliters to liters, divide by 1,000.

780 mL = _____ L

Think: 1,000 mL = 1 L

780 ÷ 1,000 = 0.78

So, 780 mL = 0.78 L.

To change from liters to milliliters, multiply by 1,000.

0.007 L = _____ mL

Think: 1 L = 1,000 mL

0.007 × 1,000 = 7

So, 0.007 L = 7 mL.

Complete.

1. 2,400 mL = **2.4** L
2. 0.9 L = **900** mL
3. 334 mL = **0.334** L
4. 293 L = **293,000** mL
5. 42,000 mL = **42** L
6. 2.118 L = **2,118** mL
7. 3,500 mL = **3.5** L
8. 3.75 L = **3,750** mL
9. 82.4 L = **82,400** mL
10. 93,000 mL = **93** L

11. **Estimation** Which metric unit of capacity is most reasonable for each object?

a. glass of water
150 mL or 1 L
150 mL

b. bucket of water
12 L or 3,500 mL
12 L

Name_____

Liter Lift-Off!

E 10-7
REASONING

Choose the balloon with the correct unit of capacity. Some may be used more than once.

1 L   10 mL   4 L   100 mL

1. 10 mL is to 10 L as 1 mL is to **1 L** .

2. $\frac{1}{2}$ L is to 500 mL as 0.01 L is to **10 mL** .

3. **4 L** is to 400 mL as 4,000 mL is to 400 L.

4. 0.75 L is to 1 L as 75 mL is to **100 mL** .

5. 500 mL is to $\frac{1}{4}$ L as **1 L** is to $\frac{1}{2}$ L.

6. 0.5 L is to **1 L** as 2 L is to 4 L.

7. $\frac{1}{8}$ L is to 2,000 mL as **4 L** is to 64,000 mL.

8. 8 L is to **10 mL** as 18 L is to 22.5 mL.

Name_____

Metric Units of Capacity

PS 10-7

Shopping Natalie went to the store to buy some bottled water. There is a 1 L bottle for $1.99, a 2 L bottle for $2.99, and a pack of 6 bottles that each contain 354 mL of water for $2.99.

1. How many milliliters of water are in the 1 L bottle?
1,000 mL

2. How many milliliters of water are in the 2 L bottle?
2,000 mL

3. How many milliliters of water are in the pack of 6 bottles?
2,124 mL

4. Which purchase would give Natalie the greatest amount of water?
The pack of six bottles

Warming Up The Johnson family is going sledding. They want to take along some hot cocoa in their thermos. The thermos has a capacity of 1.6 L.

5. To make 200 mL of cocoa, you need 2 scoops of cocoa mix. How many scoops will they need to fill the thermos?
16 scoops

6. If it takes 236 mL of cocoa to fill 1 c, about how many cups of cocoa will the family get from the filled thermos?
Sample answer: About 7 c

7. **Writing in Math** Explain how you found your answer to Exercise 6.

Sample answer: I converted 1.6 L to 1,600 mL and then rounded 236 mL to 240 mL, a compatible number. Then I divided 1,600 by 240: $\frac{1600}{240} = \frac{160}{24} = \frac{20}{3} = 6\frac{2}{3}$. So, it holds about 7 cups.

Name_____

Customary Units of Weight

P 10-8

Complete.

1. 200 lb = **0.1** T
2. 56 oz = **3** lb **8** oz
3. 2.5 lb = **40** oz
4. 4,000 lb = **2** T
5. 40 oz = **2** lb **8** oz
6. 90 lb = **1,440** oz

Write each answer in simplest form.

7. 5 lb 12 oz
   − 4 lb 13 oz
   15 oz

8. 7 T 200 lb
   + 1,900 lb
   8 T 100 lb

9. 29 lb 4 oz
   + 11 lb 13 oz
   41 lb 1 oz

10. **Estimation** Estimate the number of ounces of potatoes in a 5 lb bag of potatoes. **About 80 oz**

11. Did you know that there is litter in outer space? Humans exploring space have left behind bags of trash, bolts, gloves, and pieces of satellites. There are currently about 4,000,000 lb of litter in orbit around Earth. About how many tons of space litter is this? **2,000 T**

12. Karla bought 2 lb of red beads, $1\frac{3}{4}$ lb of green beads, and 10 oz of string at the craft store. How much did Karla's supplies weigh altogether? **4 lb 6 oz**

Test Prep

13. Which of the following is equivalent to 92.5 lb?

   A. 1,472 oz   **B.** 1,480 oz   C. 1,479 oz   D. 1,488 oz

14. **Writing in Math** Explain the difference between 1 fl oz and 1 oz.

Sample answer: 1 fl oz measures capacity, and 1 oz measures weight.

Name_____

Customary Units of Weight

R 10-8

Changing from one unit of weight to another:

A blue whale can weigh up to 209 tons (T). How many pounds is that?

209 T = _____ lb

Think: 1 T = 2,000 lb

Multiply to find the weight in pounds.

209 × 2,000 = 418,000

So, 209 T = 418,000 lb.

36 oz = _____ lb

Think: 16 oz = 1 lb

Divide to find the weight in pounds.

36 ÷ 16 = 2 R4

So, 36 oz = 2 lb 4 oz.

Adding and subtracting units of weight:

  5 T 1,750 lb
+ 2 T 1,000 lb
  7 T 2,750 lb

Think: 2,000 lb = 1 T. So, add 1 T to 1 T. 750 are left.

7 T 2,750 lb = 8 T 750 lb

  9 lb 3 oz   =   8 lb 19 oz
− 5 lb 8 oz   = − 5 lb 8 oz
                 3 lb 11 oz

To subtract 8 oz from 3 oz, rename 9 lb 3 oz to 8 lb 19 oz.

Complete.

1. 0.3 T = **600** lb
2. 272 oz = **17** lb
3. 3,200 lb = **1.6** T
4. 0.8 lb = **12.8** oz

Write each answer in simplest form.

5. 4 lb 5 oz
   + 6 lb 12 oz
   11 lb 1 oz

6. 1 T 300 lb
   + 2,500 lb
   2 T 800 lb

7. **Estimation** Estimate the number of pounds in 162 oz.

Sample answer: About 10 lb

Name_____

Tip the Scales

E 10-8
DATA

Animal	Weight
Cow	1,500 lb
Chimpanzee	110 lb
Horse	1.1 T
Moose	880 lb
Polar bear	1,433 lb
Dolphin	573 lb
Raccoon	18 lb
Sheep	220 lb
Walrus	1.35 T

Use the data in the table to compare the weights of the animals. Write >, <, or = in each ◯.

1. 6 sheep **<** 1 horse
2. 1 walrus **>** 10 chimpanzees
3. 3 moose **<** 2 polar bears
4. 30 raccoons **<** 1 dolphin
5. 4 chimpanzees **=** 2 sheep
6. 3 cows **>** 2 horses
7. 5 polar bears **<** 3 walruses
8. 8 sheep **=** 2 moose
9. 1 horse **>** 19 chimpanzees
10. 150 raccoons **=** 1 walrus

Name_____

Customary Units of Weight

PS 10-8

Dinner Hank went to the store and bought 1 lb of hamburger and 2 lb of pasta to make dinner for friends.

1. Hank used 10 oz of hamburger for dinner. How many ounces were left? **6 oz**

2. He also used $1\frac{1}{2}$ lb of pasta for dinner. How many ounces were left? **8 oz**

3. For his next party, Hank ordered a party sandwich. It was 3 ft long and weighed 3 lb. Eleven guests each had a 4 oz piece of the sandwich. How much of the sandwich was left? **4 oz**

Truck Mr. Denny drives a truck for the National Stone Company. His truck weighs $1\frac{1}{2}$ T.

4. How many pounds does Mr. Denny's truck weigh? **3,000 lb**

5. A customer orders 22 T of stone. What is the total weight of the truck after the stone is loaded? Give the weight in tons and pounds. **23 T 1,000 lb**

6. **Writing in Math** Explain how you converted the weight of Mr. Denny's truck from tons to pounds.

Sample answer: I multiplied 1.5 × 2,000.

Name_____

Metric Units of Mass

P 10-9

Complete.

1. 20 kg = **20,000** g
2. 520 g = **0.520** kg
3. 0.189 kg = **189** g
4. 45 g = **45,000** mg
5. 1.45 kg = **1,450** g
6. 1,200 mg = **1.2** g

7. **Number Sense** Which has less mass, 800 g or 8 kg?

800 g

The list shows Jeffrey's grocery list.

1 box of pasta	454 g
1 can of soup	298 g
1 jar of peanut butter	1,130 g
1 box of cereal	432 g

8. Do any items on the list have a mass greater than 400,000 mg? If so, which ones?

Yes; pasta, cereal, peanut butter

9. Do any items on the list have a mass less than 0.3 kg? If so, which ones?

Yes; soup

Test Prep

10. Which of the following is equivalent to 80 mg?

A. 8 g   B. 0.8 g   Ⓒ 0.08 g   D. 0.008 g

11. **Writing in Math** Which do you think is easier to convert, units of customary measurement or units of metric measurement? Explain your answer.

Sample answer: Units of metric measurement; It's easier because they are all multiples of 10.

© Pearson Education, Inc. 5

Name_____

Metric Units of Mass

R 10-9

To change a measurement from one unit to another, multiply or divide by a power of 10.

2.79 kg = _____ g
Think: 1 kg = 1,000 g
Multiply to find the number of grams.
2.79 × 1,000 = 2,790
So, 2.79 kg = 2,790 g.

935 mg = _____ g
Think: 1,000 mg = 1 g
Divide to find the number of grams.
935 ÷ 1,000 = 0.935
So, 935 mg = 0.935 g.

Complete.

1. 25 kg = **25,000** g
2. 0.009 kg = **9** g
3. 425 g = **0.425** kg
4. 2.4 kg = **2,400** g
5. 32.6 mg = **0.0326** g
6. 526 mg = **0.526** g

7. **Number Sense** Which is greater, 5,200 g or 5.6 kg?

5.6 kg

8. What is the mass of a penny in milligrams?

2,500 mg

U.S. Coins	
Coin	**Mass**
Penny	2.5 g
Quarter	5.67 g
Half-dollar	11.34 g

9. What is the mass of a half-dollar in kilograms?

0.01134 kg

10. What is the mass of a quarter in milligrams?

5,670 mg

11. Peter's father has 867 mg of silver. How many grams is that?

0.867 g

© Pearson Education, Inc. 5

Name_____

Island Fun

E 10-9
ALGEBRA

On an imaginary island of Hownow, the standard of weight is a rock called the tuffle. An average man on the island weighs 75 tuffles, an average monkey weighs 30 tuffles, and an average coconut weighs 2 tuffles.

On the island of Wow, the standard of weight is a precious stone called the gemmond. A gemmond weighs twice as much as a tuffle.

1. How many gemmonds would an average monkey from Hownow weigh on Wow?

15 gemmonds

2. How many gemmonds would 50 average coconuts from Hownow weigh on Wow?

50 gemmonds

3. How many gemmonds would 2 average men from Hownow weigh on Wow?

75 gemmonds

4. A cow on Hownow weighs 750 tuffles. How many gemmonds would the same cow weigh on Wow?

375 gemmonds

5. A small wild pig on Wow weighs 15 gemmonds. How much would the same pig weigh on Hownow?

30 tuffles

6. A wild island cat on Wow weighs 6 gemmonds. How much would the same cat weight on Hownow?

12 tuffles

© Pearson Education, Inc. 5

Name_____

Metric Units of Mass

PS 10-9

Coins The table shows the mass of U.S. coins.

Coin	Value	Mass
Penny	$0.01	3 g
Nickel	$0.05	5 g
Dime	$0.10	2 g
Quarter	$0.25	6 g
Half-dollar	$0.50	11 g

1. Joe has 3 coins that have a total value of $0.25. The coins have a total mass of 9 g. What are the coins?

2 dimes, 1 nickel

2. Fran has some coins that have a total value of $0.80. The coins have a total mass of 32 g. What are the coins?

5 pennies, 1 quarter, 1 half dollar

3. Suppose you have some coins that have a total mass of 12 g. What is the greatest value the coins could be? What will the coins be?

$0.60; 6 dimes

Breakfast Mrs. Hanson bought a box of cereal with a mass of 560 g.

4. What is the mass of the box in milligrams? In kilograms?

560,000 mg; 0.56 kg

5. If there are 55,000 mg in 1 serving of cereal, about how many servings will Mrs. Hanson's family get from this box?

About 10 servings

6. **Writing in Math** Explain how you would convert the mass of a dime to milligrams and kilograms.

Sample answer: To convert to milligrams, I would multiply 2 g × 1,000. To convert to kilograms, I would divide by 1,000. The mass of the dime is 2,000 mg and 0.002 kg.

© Pearson Education, Inc. 5

Practice

PROBLEM-SOLVING SKILL   P 10-10

Exact Answer or Estimate

Tell whether an exact answer or an estimate is needed. Then solve each problem and check to see if your answer is reasonable.

1. Paper grocery bags hold between 9 and 10 kg of groceries. If Marie has placed items with a mass of 5.3 kg in a paper grocery bag, about how many more kilograms of groceries can she place in the bag?

Estimate; about 5 kg

2. The water cooler for the cross-country team holds 20 L of water. If each of the 25 runners has had 500 mL of water to drink from the cooler, exactly how much water is left in the cooler?

Exact; 7.5 L

3. A recipe for lemonade calls for about 2 qt of ice water. How many pints of ice water are needed?

Estimate; about 4 pt

4.

4 in.
7 in.   6 in.

The third graders are painting shoe boxes in art class. If it takes Dominic 1 min to paint 4 in², how long will it take him to paint the outside of this box?

Exact; 47 min

142   Use with Lesson 10-10.

Reteaching

PROBLEM-SOLVING SKILL   R 10-10

Exact Answer or Estimate

The Sandbox Erik built a sandbox. He wants to fill the sandbox with as much sand as it can hold. How much sand does he need?

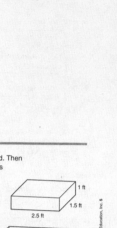
3 ft
3 ft
4 ft

Read and Understand

Step 1: What do you know?
The sandbox is 3 ft by 4 ft by 3 ft.

Step 2: What are you trying to find?
The amount of sand needed

Plan and Solve

Do you need an exact answer or an estimate?
An exact answer

Find the volume of the sandbox.
$V = l \times w \times h$
$V = 3 \text{ ft} \times 4 \text{ ft} \times 3 \text{ ft}$
$V = 36 \text{ ft}^3$

So, Erik needs 36 ft³ of sand.

Tell whether an exact answer or an estimate is needed. Then solve each problem and check to see if your answer is reasonable.

1. James is wrapping a box. How many square feet of wrapping paper will he need?

1 ft
1.5 ft
2.5 ft

Exact answer; 15.5 ft²

2. Hannah is buying mulch for her flower bed. The dimensions of her flower bed are 6 ft by 4 ft by 2 ft. How much mulch does she need to fill the flower bed?

4 ft
2 ft
6 ft

Exact answer; 48 ft³

142   Use with Lesson 10-10.

Enrichment

Matching Measures

E 10-10
ESTIMATION

Match the letter of the estimated measure to the number of people, animals, or insects.

1. **B**    A. 17.5 kg

2. **F**   B. 1,700 kg

3. **C**   C. 8,880 kg

4. **A**   D. 10,000 kg

5. **D**   E. 18 kg

6. **E**   F. 2 g

142   Use with Lesson 10-10.

Problem Solving

PROBLEM-SOLVING SKILL   PS 10-10

Exact Answer or Estimate

Field Trip The first-grade classes are going to a pumpkin patch for a field trip. There are 3 first-grade classes. One class has 17 students, one has 18, and another 19. A bus can hold 60 students. Will one bus be enough to transport the students?

Read and Understand

1. How many classes are there? How many students are in each class?

3 classes; 17, 18, and 19 students

2. How many passengers can one bus transport?

60 passengers

3. What are you trying to find?

If one bus will be enough for the students

Plan and Solve

4. Is an exact answer or estimate needed? Explain.

You can estimate because you only need to know if there will be enough seats on one bus.

5. Solve the problem. Write the answer in a complete sentence.

Sample answer: One bus is enough because $3 \times 20 = 60$, and there are less than 20 students in each of the 3 classes.

Look Back and Check

6. Is your answer reasonable?

Sample answer: Yes; 60 is an overestimate.

142   Use with Lesson 10-10.

© Pearson Education, Inc. 5

Practice

Name_____

PROBLEM-SOLVING APPLICATION　　　　　P 10-11

Tropical Fish

Solve. Write your answer in a complete sentence.

1. Jerome works in a tropical fish store. Every day, he cleans the outside of the fish tanks with glass cleaner. The fish tanks do not have lids, and the bottoms of the fish tanks do not need to be cleaned. What is the total surface area Jerome must clean if there are 50 fish tanks like the one shown here?

Jerome must clean a surface area of 64,800 in².

2. The fish tanks at the tropical fish store hold 20 gal of water each. How many quarts of water are in the 50 fish tanks at the store?

The 50 tanks hold 4,000 qt of water.

3. Jerome's job duties include feeding the fish. There are 5 kinds of fish that he feeds: guppies, zebra danios, betas, platys, and neon tetras. Use the following clues to find the order in which Jerome feeds them.
   - Jerome feeds the guppies third.
   - Jerome does not feed the betas right before or right after the guppies.
   - Jerome feeds the zebra danios last.
   - Jerome feeds the platys after the betas.

Jerome feeds the betas, platys, guppies, neon tetras, and zebra danios in that order.

© Pearson Education, Inc. 5

Use with Lesson 10-11. **143**

Reteaching

Name_____

PROBLEM-SOLVING APPLICATION　　　　　R 10-11

The Trucker

Karen owns 5 trucks, and people pay her to transport things. A local artist has produced a block-shaped sculpture that he needs to have transported to another city. Will the sculpture fit in Karen's truck? Find the volume of the back of the truck as well as the sculpture in order to solve the problem.

Truck:

$V = l \times w \times h$

$V = 40 \times 6 \times 5$

$V = 240 \times 5$

$V = 1{,}200$ ft³

Sculpture:

$V = l \times w \times h$

$V = 8 \times 3 \times 4$

$V = 24 \times 4$

$V = 96$ ft³

So, the sculpture would fit into the truck.

1. Karen is considering buying a larger truck that can carry larger loads. The new truck would have a base area of 450 ft² and a height of 9 ft. What would be the volume of the new truck?

4,050 ft³

2. Karen's smallest truck can carry up to 500 kg. How many grams is that?

500,000 g

3. A construction company needs Karen's truck to deliver 8,000 lb of sand to a work site. How many tons is that?

4 T

4. On Friday, one truck carried 3 T 650 lb of crates. On Saturday the same truck carried 5 T 1,600 lb of crates. How much weight in total did the truck carry?

9 T 250 lb

© Pearson Education, Inc. 5

Use with Lesson 10-11. **143**

Enrichment

Name_____

Painted Faces

E 10-11
DECISION MAKING

Sandra built a 3 × 3 × 3 big cube with 27 smaller cubes.

Then she painted the 6 outside faces of the big cube.

If she now separates the big cube into 27 smaller cubes, how many small cubes would have

1. 3 surfaces painted?　**8**
2. 2 surfaces painted?　**12**
3. 1 surface painted?　**6**
4. 0 surfaces painted?　**1**

5. How did you solve the problem?

Sample answer: I made a chart.

© Pearson Education, Inc. 5

Use with Lesson 10-11. **143**

Problem Solving

Name_____

PROBLEM-SOLVING APPLICATION　　　　　PS 10-11

Roller Coaster

A roller coaster that opened in 2000 consists of 6,595 ft of track. Trains holding 36 passengers each travel at 92 mph. If the ride can handle 1,600 passengers in 1 hr, about how many trains will travel the track during that time?

Read and Understand

1. How many passengers fit in 1 train?

36 passengers

2. How many passengers ride the roller coaster in 1 hr?

1,600 passengers

3. What are you trying to find?

About how many trains will travel the track in 1 hr

Plan and Solve

4. Is an exact answer or estimate needed? Explain.

Estimate, because the problem asks for about how many

5. How can you solve the problem?

Sample answer: I can round 36 up to 40 and then divide 1,600 by 40.

6. Write the answer in a complete sentence.

About 40 trains will travel the track in 1 hr.

Look Back and Check

7. Is your answer reasonable?

Yes. I can check my answer by multiplying 40 and 36, which equals 1,440. This is close to 1,600.

© Pearson Education, Inc. 5

Use with Lesson 10-11. **143**

© Pearson Education, Inc. 5

Name_____

Understanding Ratios

P 11-1

Use the chart below in 1–5 to write each ratio three ways.

Mr. White's 3rd Grade Class (24 Students)

Gender:	Male	8	Female	16		
Eye Color:	Blue	6	Brown	4	Hazel 12	Green 2
Hair Color:	Blond	5	Red	1	Brown 15	Black 3

1. male students to female students **8 to 16, 8:16, $\frac{8}{16}$ (or $\frac{1}{2}$)**

2. female students to male students **16 to 8, 16:8, $\frac{16}{8}$ (or $\frac{2}{1}$)**

3. red-haired students to all students **1 to 24, 1:24, $\frac{1}{24}$**

4. all students to green-eyed students **24 to 2, 24:2, $\frac{24}{2}$ (or $\frac{12}{1}$)**

5. **Reasoning** Is the ratio of male students to female students the same as the ratio of male students to all students? Explain.

No; The number of students that the male students are being compared to is different.

Test Prep

6. George has 2 sons and 1 daughter. What is the ratio of daughters to sons?

A. 2 to 1   (B) 1 to 2   C. 3:1   D. $\frac{2}{1}$

7. **Writing in Math** The ratio of blue beads to white beads in a necklace is 3:8. Nancy says that for every 11 beads, 3 are blue. Do you agree? Explain.

Yes; Sample answer: If there are 3 blue beads to 8 white beads, that is 11 total beads, so 3 are blue.

Name_____

Understanding Ratios

R 11-1

Ratios are written to compare two quantities.

There are 25 students in the class; 13 are boys and 12 are girls.

Write a ratio for the number of boys in the class to the whole class.	Write a ratio for the number of girls in the class to the whole class.	Write a ratio for the number of boys to girls in the class.
13 to 25, 13:25, $\frac{13}{25}$	12 to 25, 12:25, $\frac{12}{25}$	13 to 12, 13:12, $\frac{13}{12}$

Write a ratio for each comparison in three ways.

1. vowel tiles to non-vowel tiles **4 to 5, 4:5, $\frac{4}{5}$**

2. vowel tiles to letter tiles **4 to 9, 4:9, $\frac{4}{9}$**

3. letter A tiles to vowel tiles **2 to 4, 2:4, $\frac{2}{4}$ or $\frac{1}{2}$**

4. non-vowel tiles to letter tiles **5 to 9, 5:9, $\frac{5}{9}$**

5. letter tiles to letter T tiles **9 to 1, 9:1, $\frac{9}{1}$**

6. **Reasoning** Is the ratio of letter A tiles to letter tiles the same as the ratio of letter A tiles to vowel tiles? Explain.

Sample answer. No. Letter A tiles to letter tiles is 2:9, letter A tiles to vowel tiles is 2:4. $\frac{2}{9}$ is not equal to $\frac{2}{4}$.

Name_____

Taste Test

E 11-1
NUMBER SENSE

Healthy Foods Corporation has just completed the taste testing of three new granola bar flavors.

- 84 people tasted the new granola bar flavors.
- $\frac{1}{4}$ tasted honey nut.
- $\frac{2}{3}$ of the people who tasted honey nut liked it.
- $\frac{1}{6}$ tasted crunchy peanut butter.
- $\frac{1}{2}$ of the people who tasted crunchy peanut butter liked it.
- $\frac{7}{12}$ tasted mixed berry.
- $\frac{3}{7}$ of the people who tasted mixed berry liked it.

1. Explain how you would use the information above to find and compare the number of people who liked a new granola bar flavor with the number who did not. **Sample answer:**

First find the number of people who tasted the flavor. For example, $\frac{1}{4}$ of 84 = 21, so 21 people tasted honey nut. Then find the number of people who liked and didn't like honey nut. $\frac{2}{3}$ of 21 = 14, so 14 liked it. 21 − 14 = 7, so 7 didn't like it. Find the same for the other flavors.

2. Complete the report below that shows the results of the taste test.

Honey Nut ___21___ people tasted honey nut. ___14___ people liked it and ___7___ did not. The ratio of people who liked it to those who did not is ___14___ to ___7___.

Crunchy Peanut Butter ___14___ people tasted crunchy peanut butter. ___7___ people liked it and ___7___ did not. The ratio of people who liked it to those who did not is ___7___ to ___7___.

Mixed Berry ___49___ people tasted mixed berry. ___21___ people liked it and ___28___ did not. The ratio of people who liked it to those who did not is ___21___ to ___28___.

Name_____

Understanding Ratios

PS 11-1

U.S. States The chart lists the number of the 50 U.S. states that begin with certain letters of the alphabet.

Number of States That Begin with These Letters			
A	4	N	8
C	3	O	3
I	4	V	2
M	8	W	4

1. What is the ratio of the number of states that start with the letter A to the total number of states? **4:50**

2. What is the ratio that describes the number of states that start with the letter N to the number of states that start with the letter O? **8:3**

3. What is the ratio that describes the number of states that start with the letter V to the number of states that start with the letter M? **2:8**

4. What is the ratio of the number of states that start with the letter I to the number of states that do not start with the letter I? **4:46**

5. What is the ratio of the total number of states to the number of states that start with the letter W? **50:4**

6. **Writing in Math** For Exercise 4, did you write a ratio to compare a part to a part, a part to a whole, or a whole to a part? Explain.

A part to a part; Sample answer: If the ratio compared a part to a whole or a whole to a part it would include 50.

Name_____

Equal Ratios
P 11-2

Write each ratio in simplest form.

1. 9 to 3   **3 to 1**
2. 2:12   **1:6**
3. 20 to 45   **4 to 9**
4. 16:80   **1:5**

Give two other ratios that are equal to each. **Sample answers are given for 5–8.**

5. 1 to 7   **2 to 14, 3 to 21**
6. $\frac{3}{9}$ **$\frac{1}{3}$, $\frac{6}{18}$**
7. 4:3   **8:6, 12:9**
8. 9:24   **3:8, 18:48**

Are the ratios in each pair equal?

9. $\frac{1}{2}$ and $\frac{4}{8}$ **Yes**
10. $\frac{16}{18}$ and $\frac{4}{8}$ **No**
11. $\frac{1}{5}$ and $\frac{5}{30}$ **No**
12. $\frac{10}{34}$ and $\frac{15}{51}$ **Yes**

A cereal company has packaged a movie ticket in some of its cereal boxes. In other boxes, there is either a plastic ring or a puzzle. Out of 50 cereal boxes, there are 21 plastic rings, 28 puzzles, and 1 movie ticket.

13. If 200 boxes of cereal are produced, how many have movie tickets in them?   **4 cereal boxes**

14. What is the ratio of puzzles to total boxes when there are 56 puzzles?   **56:100**

Test Prep

15. Which ratio is equal to 13:26?

   A. 2:1   B. 1:3   (C.) 1:2   D. 1:7

16. **Writing in Math** Use the information from Exercises 13 and 14. Explain how you could find the total number of plastic rings in cereal boxes if there are a total of 3 movie tickets.

Sample answer: The ratio is 1:21, so 21 × 3 = 63 plastic rings.

Name_____

Equal Ratios
R 11-2

How to write ratios in simplest form:

Write 24:30 in simplest form.

First, write the ratio as a fraction. $\frac{24}{30}$

Think: What is the GCF of each number? 6

Divide numerator and denominator by 6.

$\frac{24}{30} = \frac{24 \div 6}{30 \div 6} = \frac{4}{5}$

So, 24:30 in simplest form is $\frac{4}{5}$.

How to write equal ratios:

Write two other ratios equal to $\frac{30}{40}$.

You can use multiplication.

$\frac{30 \times 2}{40 \times 2} = \frac{60}{80}$

So, $\frac{30}{40} = \frac{60}{80}$.

Are the ratios equal?

$\frac{5}{20}$ and $\frac{2}{4}$

First, change each fraction to simplest form. If they are the same, then the ratios are equal.

$\frac{5}{20} = \frac{1}{4}$ and $\frac{2}{4} = \frac{1}{2}$

$\frac{1}{4}$ is not the same as $\frac{1}{2}$, so $\frac{5}{20}$ and $\frac{2}{4}$ are not equal.

You can use division.

$\frac{30 \div 2}{40 \div 2} = \frac{15}{20}$

So, $\frac{30}{40} = \frac{15}{20}$.

Write each ratio in simplest form.

1. 5 to 30   **1 to 6**
2. 60 to 24   **5 to 2**

Give 2 other ratios that are equal to each. **Sample answers:**

3. 6 to 2   **12 to 4, 3 to 1**
4. 14:20   **7:10, 28:40**

Are the ratios in each pair equal?

5. $\frac{4}{5}$ and $\frac{80}{100}$ **Yes**
6. $\frac{16}{4}$ and $\frac{60}{20}$ **No**

7. **Number Sense** The ratio of cats to dogs at a pet shelter is 3 to 2. What equal ratio has the number of dogs as 12?   **18 to 12**

Name_____

Matching Ratios
E 11-2
VISUAL THINKING

Each picture has a ratio of shaded parts to the total number of parts. Match each ratio on the left side to an equal ratio on the right side by drawing a line. Also write the ratios on the lines provided. The first match is done for you.

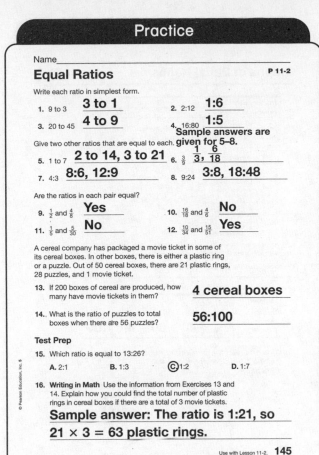

1. $\frac{5}{8}$
2. $\frac{1}{2}$
3. $\frac{3}{7}$
4. $\frac{4}{16}$
5. $\frac{2}{9}$

$\frac{8}{16}$
$\frac{6}{27}$
$\frac{10}{16}$
$\frac{1}{4}$
$\frac{6}{14}$

Name_____

Equal Ratios
PS 11-2

Music Store The owner of a music store kept a record of all of the music CDs she sold in one week. She then listed how many of each type of CD she sold.

Number of CDs Sold	
Classical	75
Jazz	100
Rap	250
Rock	300
Pop	400
Total	1,125

1. Write a ratio to show the number of classical CDs compared to the number of jazz CDs the music store sold in one week. Then write an equivalent ratio.   **75:100; 3:4**

2. The store owner said that for every 15 CDs she sells, one CD is classical music. Is she correct?   **Yes**

3. What is the ratio of rap CDs sold to rock CDs sold in simplest form?   **5:6**

4. For every 15 rock CDs sold, how many pop CDs are sold?   **20**

5. What is the ratio of jazz CDs sold to rock CDs sold in simplest form?   **1:3**

6. **Writing in Math** Use mental math to find two ratios that are equal to 1:5. Explain how you found your answer.

Sample answer: 2:10, 3:15. I multiplied both parts of the ratio by the same number.

Name_____

Graphs of Equal Ratios

P 11-3

1. A square has four angles. Complete this table of equal ratios.

Squares	1	2	3	4	5	6
Angles	4	8	**12**	**16**	**20**	**24**

2. On the grid, graph the ordered pairs from the table. Connect them with a line.

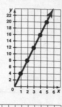

3. If the line in Exercise 2 is extended, would it cross the point (10, 36)? Explain.

No, the point (10, 36) is not in a ratio that is equal to 1:4.

4. Give three equal ratios not shown that would be found on the line of the given graph.

Sample answer: $\frac{6}{3}$, $\frac{10}{5}$, $\frac{14}{7}$

Test Prep

5. Which ordered pair will be found on the graph for the ratio 2:3?

   A. (3, 6)   B. (6, 4)   **C.** (4, 6)   D. (12, 16)

6. **Writing in Math** Does the given graph show a line that is more likely to be for ratios equal to 1:3 or 3:1? Explain.

Sample answer: 1:3; The *y* value is becoming greater more quickly than the *x* value.

Name_____

Graphs of Equal Ratios

R 11-3

Number of birds	1	2	3	4	5
Number of wings	2	4	6	8	10

Plot each ordered pair from the table on the graph. Then connect each of the points using a straight line.

Notice that when the line is extended, it will give you values for other ratios that are equal to the ones that you found.

The line crosses the point (6, 12). The ratio $\frac{6}{12} = \frac{1}{2}$.

1. A block weighs 20 lb. Complete the table of equal ratios.

Number of blocks	1	2	3	4	5
Weight in pounds	20	**40**	**60**	**80**	**100**

2. On the grid, graph the ordered pairs from the table. Connect the ordered pairs with a straight line.

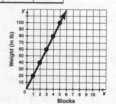

Name_____

Soccer League

E 11-3
NUMBER SENSE

A new youth soccer league has been formed. Each team will have 12 youths and 15 soccer balls to use for games and practices. There will be 12 teams based on the number of youths who want to play in the league. Use this information to complete the tables below. **Sample answers given.**

Number of players	12	24	36	**48**	**60**	**72**	**84**	**96**	**108**	**120**	**132**	**144**
Number of teams	1	2	3	4	5	6	7	8	9	10	11	12

Number of soccer balls	15	30	45	**60**	**75**	**90**	**105**	**120**	**135**	**150**	**165**	**180**
Number of teams	1	2	3	4	5	6	7	8	9	10	11	12

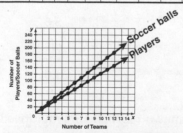

1. Graph each ordered pair from the completed tables on the grid above and draw a line through the points. Use a different color for each table. Do these lines represent a graph of equal ratios? Explain.

Yes; Because the ordered pairs make a straight line.

Name_____

Graphs of Equal Ratios

PS 11-3

Running Laps In physical education class, each student was required to run 3 laps around the track.

1. Complete the table to show the total number of laps run by 1, 2, 3, and 4 students.

Number of students	1	2	3	4
Total number of laps	**3**	**6**	**9**	**12**

2. Graph the ordered pairs from the completed table. Then draw a line to connect the ordered pairs.

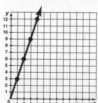

3. If the line on your graph were extended, would the point for (15, 30) be on it? Explain.

No; Sample answer: 15:30 in simplest form is 1:2, and the rest of the ordered pairs on the line are 1:3 in simplest form.

4. **Writing in Math** Explain how you can use the graph of a straight line to make a list of equal ratios.

Sample answer: The *x* and *y* values of various points are equal ratios.

Practice

Name_____

Rates
P 11-4

Tell the two quantities being compared in each.

1. 32 mi per hour

2. $16.00 each hour

3. 32 cents per mile

Miles, hours

Dollars, hours

Cents, miles

Write each rate as a unit rate.

4. 18 mi in 2 hr

5. $60.00 for 5 blankets

6. 300 beats in 2 min

9 mi/hour

$12.00/blanket

150 beats/minute

7. At a carnival for the school, you can purchase booth tickets in groups of 4 or 25. Four tickets cost $1, and 25 tickets cost $5. Which is a better buy? Use the unit rate to explain.

25 tickets for $5; Sample answer: Because the unit rate is 5:1, which is greater than 4:1.

Test Prep

8. Which rate is the best buy?

A. $19 for 3 lb   B. $12 for 2 lb   C. $55 for 10 lb   D. $350 for 50 lb

9. **Writing in Math** Sharon says that she changed jobs because she gets paid a better rate now. Her old job paid her $8 per hour. Her new job pays her $300 per week. Sharon has worked 40 hr per week in each job. Does Sharon get paid a better rate for her new job? Explain.

No; Sample answer: The old job paid $320.00 for 40 hr, so the rate is greater.

Use with Lesson 11-4. **147**

Reteaching

Name_____

Rates
R 11-4

A rate is a ratio that compares unlike quantities, like feet per second, miles per hour, dollars per hour, or miles per gallon.

56 ft in 6 sec

In the ratio above, feet and seconds are compared.

When a rate is written to compare one unit, the rate is called the unit rate.

If you are paid $27 for 3 hr, the rate is written as $\frac{$27}{3 \text{ hr}}$. The unit rate is found by finding an equal ratio with a unit of 1 in the hour's place.

$$27 \div \frac{3}{3} \div 3 = \frac{9}{1}$$

The unit rate is $\frac{$9}{h}$.

Tell the two quantities that are being compared in each rate.

1. $3.29 per gallon

2. 42 ft in 6 min

3. 3 cans per lb

Dollars and gallons

Feet and minutes

Cans and pounds

Write each rate as a unit rate.

4. $25 for 2 hr work

5. 195 mi in 3 hr

6. $1.20 for 4 bags of lima beans

7. 96 m in 10 sec

8. 54 words in 3 lines

9. 160 pencils for 40 students

$\dfrac{$12.50}{\text{hour}}$

$\dfrac{65 \text{ mi}}{\text{hr}}$

$\dfrac{$0.30}{\text{bag}}$

$\dfrac{9.6 \text{ m}}{\text{sec}}$

$\dfrac{18 \text{ words}}{\text{line}}$

$\dfrac{4 \text{ pencils}}{\text{student}}$

10. A normal housefly can fly at a rate of $\frac{8 \text{ km}}{\text{hr}}$. How many kilometers can a housefly travel in 5 hr?

40 km in 5 hr

Use with Lesson 11-4. **147**

Enrichment

Name_____

Sports Statistics
E 11-4
ALGEBRA

John Rogers had a spectacular year playing football for the university. In 12 games he had the statistics shown at the right.

John Rogers	
Rushing yards	1,740
Receiving yards	520
Rushing touchdowns	16
Receiving touchdowns	8
Total rushing carries	310

1. How many rushing yards did John have per game?

145 rushing yards per game

2. How many receiving yards did John have per game?

$43\frac{1}{3}$ receiving yards per game

3. How many rushing yards did John have per carry?

5.61 yd per carry

4. How many rushing touchdowns did John have per carry? Does this make sense? Explain.

0.05 rushing touchdowns per carry; Sample answer: Yes, this makes sense because he is not going to score a touchdown every time he carries the ball.

5. Was John more valuable running the ball or catching the ball? Explain.

Sample answer: John had 108.75 rushing yards for every rushing touchdown and 65 receiving yards for every receiving touchdown. He is more valuable rushing.

Use with Lesson 11-4. **147**

Problem Solving

Name_____

Rates
PS 11-4

The Heart of the Matter The typical heart rate of a teenager is 70 to 80 beats per minute. The rate is lower during sleep and is higher during exercise.

1. Raul's heart rate went up to 95 beats per minute in physical education class. If he maintained this heart rate for 12 min, how many times did his heart beat in this period?

1,140 times

2. If a student counts 300 heartbeats in 4 min, what is his or her heart rate per minute?

75 beats per minute

Newspaper Delivery Jeff and his sister Lynn work together on a paper route.

3. Each day Jeff delivers 30 newspapers in 1 hr 30 min. Describe the rate at which Jeff delivers newspapers in newspapers per hour.

20 newspapers per hour

4. Lynn delivers newspapers at a rate of 45 newspapers per hour. How many newspapers did she deliver today if she worked for 40 min?

30 newspapers

5. If Jeff and Lynn ride their bikes on their paper route, they can deliver newspapers at a rate of 50 newspapers per hour. Jeff rode his bike and delivered newspapers for 30 min and Lynn rode her bike and delivered newspapers for 1 hr 30 min. How many newspapers did they deliver altogether?

100 newspapers

6. **Writing in Math** Write a sentence that explains why rates always use two different units.

Sample answer: A rate is a comparison of two different quantities, so there must be two units.

Use with Lesson 11-4. **147**

Name_____

PROBLEM-SOLVING STRATEGY P 11-5

Make a Table

Solve. Write the answer in a complete sentence.

1. Brenda is making bracelets that each use three 6 in. strips of leather. She wants to make 6 bracelets. How many strips of leather does Brenda need?

Brenda needs 18 strips of leather to make 6 bracelets.

2. Charles can type 72 words per minute. He needs to type a paper with 432 words. How many minutes will it take Charles to type the paper?

Charles can type the document in six minutes.

3. Samuel is building a brick wall. Each row has 15 bricks. Samuel has 75 bricks. How many rows of bricks can he build?

Samuel can build the wall 5 rows high.

4. Maggie is taking her cats into the vet for their shots. The vet charges $18 for one shot and $16 for each shot after that. How much will it cost Maggie to get shots for all of her 6 cats?

It will cost Maggie $98 to get shots for her 6 cats.

5. A baseball team is ordering equipment for their practice sessions. For every 2 bats they order, they also order 9 balls. The coach decides to order 12 new baseball bats. How many balls did he order?

The coach ordered 54 new balls.

Name_____

PROBLEM-SOLVING STRATEGY R 11-5

Make a Table

Cleaners A cleaning company divides into groups of 7 cleaners, 2 dusters for every 5 sweepers. There are 45 sweepers. How many dusters are needed?

Read and Understand

Step 1: What do you know?

For every 5 sweepers, 2 dusters are needed in a group.

Step 2: What are you trying to find?

The number of dusters needed when there are 45 sweepers.

Plan and Solve

Step 3: What strategy will you use?   Strategy: Make a table

First, set up a table with correct labels, and enter the known data in the table. Then find a pattern and extend the table.

Number of Groups	1	2	3	4	5	6	7	8	9	10
Number of Dusters	2	4	6	8	10	12	14	16	18	20
Number of Sweepers	5	10	15	20	25	30	35	40	45	50

Answer: When there are 45 sweepers, there are 18 dusters. 18 dusters are needed.

Look Back and Check

Step 4: Is your work correct?

Yes, each group has 2 more dusters and 5 more sweepers.

1. Every week Catherine receives $4.50 in allowance. If she saves the entire amount, how many weeks will it take her to save $22.50?

Number of Weeks	1	**2**	**3**	**4**	**5**
Total Dollars Saved	4.50	**9.00**	**13.50**	**18.00**	**22.50**

5 weeks

Name_____

Fun Fair

E 11-5
NUMBER SENSE

The student council at Truman School has decided to organize a fun fair to raise money for the drama club.

1. Tricia is in charge of buying the prizes that will be needed. Large prizes cost $2.00, medium prizes cost $1.00, and small prizes cost $0.50. She wants to buy as many of the large prizes as possible and at least 1 of each of the other types of prizes. She can spend $10.00. Complete the table to show the possibilities.

Large Prize ($2.00)		Medium Prize ($1.00)		Small Prize ($0.50)	
Number	Cost	Number	Cost	Number	Cost
1	$2.00	7	$7.00	2	$1.00
2	$4.00	5	$5.00	2	$1.00
3	$6.00	3	$3.00	2	$1.00
4	$8.00	1	$1.00	2	$1.00

2. How many of each type of prize should Tricia order?

4 large prizes, 1 medium prize, and 2 small prizes

3. One day after school Tricia spent 45 min making posters for the fun fair, 20 min organizing games, 25 min planning decorations, and 30 min talking on the phone with other members of the student council. If she started at 3:45 P.M. and did not take any breaks, what time did she complete her tasks?

5:45 P.M.

4. Tricia made 56 posters to advertise the fun fair. If she made three times as many small posters as large posters, how many of each size did she make?

42 small posters and 14 large posters

Name_____

PROBLEM-SOLVING STRATEGY PS 11-5

Make a Table

Snack Mix Students are preparing a snack mix to take on a hike. In addition to cereal and nuts, the recipe includes 4 tsp of raisins and 3 tsp of sunflower seeds for every 2 servings. The students used 32 tsp of raisins. How many teaspoons of sunflower seeds did they use?

Read and Understand

1. How many teaspoons of raisins are used to prepare 2 servings? How many teaspoons of sunflower seeds?

4 tsp of raisins; 3 tsp of sunflower seeds

2. What are you trying to find?

The total amount of sunflower seeds

Plan and Solve

3. Complete the table to help solve the problem.

Servings	2	4	6	8	10	12	14	16
Raisins	4 tsp	8 tsp	12 tsp	16 tsp	20 tsp	24 tsp	28 tsp	32 tsp
Sunflower Seeds	3 tsp	6 tsp	9 tsp	12 tsp	15 tsp	18 tsp	21 tsp	24 tsp

4. Write your answer in a complete sentence.

They used 24 tsp of sunflower seeds.

Look Back and Check

5. Is your answer reasonable?

Sample answer: Yes, the ratio of raisins to sunflower seeds should be 4:3.

Practice

Practice

Name_____

Scale Drawings

P 11-6

Refer to this scale drawing of a park.

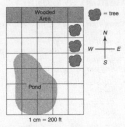

1 cm = 200 ft

1. What is the actual length of the pond from the north end to the south end?

800 ft

2. What is the actual width, from west to east, of the wooded area?

1,000 ft

3. A common highway map scale is 1 cm = 5 mi. If you were going to make a map that covered a distance of 900 mi wide, how wide would your map need to be?

180 cm wide

4. A garden plot is drawn to scale. The actual garden is 60 ft long and 20 ft wide. If you have a paper that is 1 ft long, what scale can you use to draw the plot as large as possible on the paper?

1 in. = 5 ft

Test Prep

5. In a scale drawing of a house that uses a scale of 5 mm = 3 ft, how tall will a house that is 27 ft tall appear on the drawing?

A. 9 mm   B. 27 mm   C. 30 mm   D. 45 mm

6. **Writing in Math** David drew a scale drawing of an airplane. The actual airplane was 32 ft long and David's drawing was 8 in. long. Find the scale and explain.

Sample answer: The scale David used is 1 in. = 4 ft. I found it by finding the unit rate for 8 to 32.

Reteaching

Name_____

Scale Drawings

R 11-6

Ralph made a scale drawing of his living room and the furniture in it. The scale he has chosen is 1 cm:2 ft, or 1 cm = 2 ft.

What is the actual length of the living room? Remember, each square centimeter in the drawing is equal to 2 ft. By counting the squares, you can see that the room is 9 cm long.

Multiply: $9 \times 2 = 18$

So, the living room is 18 ft long.

What is the actual width of the living room?

The room is 6 cm wide.

Multiply: $6 \times 2 = 12$

So, the living room is 12 ft wide.

Refer to the scale drawing of the garden.

1 cm : 4 ft

1. What is the actual length of the garden?   **24 ft**

2. What is the actual width of the garden?   **16 ft**

3. **Number Sense** Darrel says the actual length of the potato section of the garden is 20 ft. Is he correct? How do you know?

Sample answer: No. Since the section is 4 cm long, and $4 \times 4 = 16$, its actual length would be 16 ft long.

Enrichment

Name_____

Ratios for Redecorating

E 11-6
NUMBER SENSE

Karl has decided to have new curtains made for every room in his house. Use ratios to help him figure out how much fabric he needs for each room.

1. Karl wants 20 in. of fabric to cover each foot of window in the living room. If there are 3 windows in the living room that each measure 36 in. wide, how many inches of fabric does Karl need for each window? for the entire room?

60 in.; 180 in.

2. In the dining room, Karl wants 45 in. of fabric to cover each foot of window. If there are 5 windows in the dining room that each measure 24 in. wide, how many inches of fabric does Karl need for each window? for the entire room?

90 in.; 450 in.

3. For the master bedroom, Karl wants 24 in. of fabric to cover each foot of window. If there are 2 windows in the bedroom that each measure 48 in. wide, how many inches of fabric does Karl need for each window? for the entire room?

96 in.; 192 in.

4. Karl wants 18 in. of fabric to cover each foot of window in the guest bedroom. If there are 3 windows in the guest bedroom that each measure 30 in. wide, how many inches of fabric does Karl need for each window? for the entire room?

45 in.; 135 in.

5. In the bathroom, Karl wants 14 in. of fabric to cover each foot of window. If there are 2 windows in the bathroom that each measure 30 in. wide, how many inches of fabric does Karl need for each window? for the entire room?

35 in.; 70 in.

6. For the kitchen, Karl wants 38 in. of fabric to cover each foot of window. If there are 3 windows in the kitchen that each measure 42 in. wide, how many inches of fabric does Karl need for each window? for the entire room?

133 in.; 399 in.

Problem Solving

Name_____

Scale Drawings

PS 11-6

Leaf Study Each member of a fifth-grade class found a leaf to study and draw to scale.

1. One student used a scale of 1 cm = 3 cm for his drawing. If the drawing was 4 cm tall, how tall was the leaf?

12 cm tall

2. A student found a leaf that was 7 in. long. He wanted his scale drawing to be at least 2 in. long but not more than 4 in. long. What scale could he use for his drawing?

Sample answer: 1 in. = 3 in.

The Eiffel Tower The Eiffel Tower is in Paris, France. It is 986 ft high.

3. If you drew a scale drawing of the Eiffel Tower with a scale of 1 in. = 100 ft, how many inches tall would your drawing be?

9.86 in.

4. Evan needed to draw a scale drawing of the Eiffel Tower that was no more than 4 in. high. What scale could he use to make his drawing?

Sample answer: 1 in. = 300 ft

5. If you drew a scale drawing of the Eiffel Tower with a scale of 1 cm = 9.86 ft, how many centimeters tall would your scale drawing be?

100 cm

6. **Writing in Math** Explain how you found your answer to Exercise 4.

Sample answer: I tried different scales until I found one that worked.

Name_____

PROBLEM-SOLVING SKILL   P 11-7

Writing to Explain

Write to explain.

Sample answers are given.

1. Use the juice prices to predict how much a 64 oz container of juice will cost.

JUICE 8 oz $0.40   JUICE 32 oz $1.60

A 64 oz juice will cost $3.20, because the unit rate is $0.05 per ounce.

2. Isabel took 20 min to run around the track 6 times. John took 3 min to run around the track once. Which student was running faster?

John; John's rate is 3 min per lap. Isabel's rate is $3\frac{1}{3}$ min per lap.

3. Nancy is saving $2 from her allowance every week. Marco is saving $1 the first week, $2 the second week, $3 the third week, and so on. At the end of 10 weeks, who will have saved more money? How much more?

Marco; Marco will have saved $35 more than Nancy ($55 − $20 = $35).

4. **Reasonableness** For every 3 cans of vegetables purchased, you get 1 free can. Tessie went home with 32 cans of vegetables, but only had to pay for 16. Is this correct? Explain.

No; For every 4 cans, you must purchase 3. So if Tessie wants 32 cans of vegetables, she will have to pay for 24.

Name_____

PROBLEM-SOLVING SKILL   R 11-7

Writing to Explain

Times Brendan ran 4 laps around the track on Tuesday. It took him 16 min. On Wednesday he ran 6 laps around the track and it took him 24 min. If he runs 8 laps on Thursday, how long do you think it will take him? Write and explain how you made your prediction.

Writing a Math Explanation

- Make sure your prediction is clearly stated.

- Use steps to make your explanation clear.

- Show and explain carefully how you used the numbers to make your prediction.

Example

I predict it will take him 32 min. Below is how I made my prediction.

1. *I looked at how long it took him to run 4 laps, which was 16 min. That means it took him 4 min to run each lap, because 16 ÷ 4 = 4.*

2. *I did the same for how long it took him to run 6 laps. I saw that it also took him 4 min per lap. I saw the pattern.*

3. *Since it always takes him 4 min to run 1 lap, I multiplied 8 × 4 = 32.*

Write to explain. Write the answer in a complete sentence.

1. The football team is playing a game away. There are 22 players on the team and 8 cheerleaders. The band will be playing a show at halftime. There are 16 band members. There will be 6 adults that will be riding on buses with the students. The school is using buses that can each carry 16 people. How many buses will the school need?

Sample answer: There are a total of 52 people who need to ride on the buses. 52 ÷ 16 = 3 R4. Since those 4 people must also ride on a bus, the school needs 4 buses.

Name_____

Mashed Potatoes

E 11-7   REASONING

Katy is making mashed potatoes for a family gathering. The recipe calls for 6 Idaho potatoes. Katy looks through the grocery store ads and finds the coupons shown.

Al's Market $0.50 each — Idaho Potatoes — Buy 2, get 1 free

John's Grocery $0.46 each — Idaho Potatoes — Buy 1, get 2nd 50% off

1. What would be the price for each of the 6 potatoes at the different stores?

Al's Market: 6 potatoes for $2.00; John's Grocery: 6 potatoes for $2.07

2. Which store has the better deal?

Al's Market

3. If Katy had to drive 20 more miles roundtrip to shop at Al's Market than to shop at John's Grocery, would this affect her decision? Why or why not?

Sample answer: Yes. She would pay more for the 6 potatoes at John's Grocery, but she would save money on gas.

Name_____

PROBLEM-SOLVING SKILL   PS 11-7

Writing to Explain

Apples A grocery store counted the number of apples it sold over three time periods. In 20 min it sold 12 apples, in 50 min it sold 25 apples, and in 30 min it sold 13 apples. Predict how many apples the grocery store sells each hour it is open.

Read and Understand

1. How many apples were sold during each time period?

20 min: 12 apples; 50 min: 25 apples; 30 min: 13 apples

2. What are you trying to find?

A prediction for the number of apples sold per hour

Plan and Solve

3. How can you solve the problem?

I can find the ratio of apples sold per minute and then change the ratio to hours.

4. Make a prediction. Write your answer in a complete sentence.

The store will sell about 30 apples in 1 hr.

Look Back and Check

5. Is your answer reasonable?

Sample answer: Yes, the final answer matches the numbers in the problem.

Name_____

Understanding Percent

P 11-8

Write the fraction in lowest terms and the percent that represents the shaded part of each figure.

1.

$\frac{9}{25}$, 36%

2.

$\frac{13}{25}$, 52%

3. In the square, if part A is $\frac{1}{4}$ of the square and part C is $\frac{1}{10}$ of the square, what percent of the square is part B?

65%

4. In Russia, $\frac{1}{4}$ of the land is covered by forests. What percent of Russia is covered by forest? What percent of Russia is not covered by forest?

25%, 75%

5. In the United States, $\frac{3}{10}$ of the land is forests and woodland. What percent of the United States is forest and woodland?

30%

Test Prep

6. If $\frac{2}{5}$ of a figure is shaded, what percent is not shaded?

A. 20%   B. 30%   C. 50%   (D) 60%

7. **Writing in Math** Explain how a decimal is related to a percent.

Sample answer: A percent is a decimal with the decimal point moved two places to the right.

Name_____

Understanding Percent

R 11-8

What fraction of the grid is shaded?

Since 32 of the hundred units are shaded, the fraction is $\frac{32}{100}$. In simplest form that is $\frac{8}{25}$.

What percent of the grid is shaded?

32 of the hundred units are shaded.

$\frac{32}{100} = 32\%$

It may be helpful to think of the percent sign (%) as having the same meaning as "out of 100."

Write a fraction in lowest terms and the percent that represents the shaded part of each figure.

1.

$\frac{1}{4}$, 25%

2.

$\frac{1}{5}$, 20%

3.

$\frac{21}{25}$, 84%

4.

$\frac{7}{10}$, 70%

5. **Number Sense** What is "eighty-two percent" written as a fraction in simplest form?

$\frac{41}{50}$

Name_____

Number Cards

E 11-8
NUMBER SENSE

Use the number cards below to answer the questions.

A

8	3	78	51	16	7	6	93	57	64
17	34	27	45	69	22	57	26	79	9
72	43	01	96	37	15	4	39	50	13
81	12	25	1	58	71	65	99	23	36
10	31	82	20	19	47	33	48	55	2

B

3	42	34	22
21	65	54	91
53	38	64	45
11	27	16	72
96	14	9	31

C

99	4	30	17	1	50
20	39	85	54	15	2
51	8	23	10	41	72
70	63	74	43	5	90

D

73	81	22	65	92	13	14	79	3	55	88	31
4	43	7	34	85	8	39	56	71	22	65	74
15	6	99	12	28	47	64	27	16	43	18	53
9	63	32	1	77	53	89	5	2	19	25	17

1. Write the fraction of the numbers on Card A that are evenly divisible by 4. Simplify, if necessary.

$\frac{1}{5}$

2. Write the percent of the numbers on Card B that have a 3 in the tens place.

15%

3. Write the ratio comparing the numbers on Card C that contain a zero to the total of the numbers on the card.

6 to 24

4. Write the fraction of the numbers on Card D that have a 1 in the ones place. Simplify, if necessary.

$\frac{1}{12}$

5. On which 2 cards are $\frac{1}{2}$ of the numbers even and $\frac{1}{2}$ of the numbers odd?

Card B and Card C

Name_____

Understanding Percent

PS 11-8

Garden Tina planted a garden in her backyard. The drawing shows the types of plants in the garden and the amount of space each type of plant takes up.

Tina's Garden

1. Which type of plant takes up 30% of Tina's garden?

Tomatoes

2. Which type of plant takes up less than 15% of Tina's garden?

Beans

3. What percent of the garden has either tomatoes or lettuce?

54%

4. What percent of the garden is peas?

16%

5. What percent of the garden is lettuce?

24%

6. **Writing in Math** Tim said that 50% of the fifth graders and 40% of the sixth graders at his school ride the bus, so he knows that more fifth graders than sixth graders ride the bus. Is he correct? Explain.

No; Sample answer: Percents do not tell actual numbers.

Mental Math: Finding a Percent of a Number

P 11-9

Find each using mental math.

1. 20% of 60 **12**

2. 30% of 500 **150**

3. 25% of 88 **22**

4. 70% of 30 **21**

5. **Reasoning** Order these numbers from least to greatest.
0.85, $\frac{1}{4}$, 72%, $\frac{5}{8}$, 20%, 0.3

20%, $\frac{1}{4}$, 0.3, $\frac{5}{8}$, 72%, 0.85

	Rural	Urban
Bermuda	0%	100%
Cuba	25%	75%
Guatemala	60%	40%

The table shows the percent of the population that live in rural and urban areas of each country.

6. Out of every 300 people in Cuba, how many of them live in a rural area? **75**

7. Out of every 1,000 people in Guatemala, how many live in urban areas? **400**

Test Prep

8. What is 40% of 240?

A. 48 **B** 96 C. 128 D. 960

9. **Writing in Math** If there are 1,241,356 people who live in Bermuda, how many residents of Bermuda live in urban areas? How many live in rural areas? Explain your answer.

1,241,356 in urban; 0 in rural; Sample answer: If 100% are in urban areas, then 0% are in rural areas.

© Pearson Education, Inc. 5

Mental Math: Finding a Percent of a Number

R 11-9

You can use the table below to help you find the percent of a number mentally.

Percent	10%	20%	25%	33$\frac{1}{3}$%	40%	50%	60%	66$\frac{2}{3}$%	75%	80%
Fraction	$\frac{1}{10}$	$\frac{1}{5}$	$\frac{1}{4}$	$\frac{1}{3}$	$\frac{2}{5}$	$\frac{1}{2}$	$\frac{3}{5}$	$\frac{2}{3}$	$\frac{3}{4}$	$\frac{4}{5}$
Decimal	0.1	0.2	0.25	0.33$\frac{1}{3}$	0.4	0.5	0.6	0.66$\frac{2}{3}$	0.75	0.8

How to find a percent of a number:

Find 66$\frac{2}{3}$% of 33.

66$\frac{2}{3}$% × 33 = $\frac{2}{3}$ × 33

$\frac{2}{3}$ × 33 = 22

So, 66$\frac{2}{3}$% of 33 is 22.

Find 40% of 25.

40% is the same as $\frac{2}{5}$ or 0.4.

$\frac{2}{5}$ × 25 = 10

So, 40% of 25 is 10.

Find each using mental math.

1. 25% of 200 **50**

2. 50% of 16 **8**

3. 30% of 60 **18**

4. 10% of 370 **37**

5. **Reasoning** Order these numbers from least to greatest.
$\frac{3}{4}$, 0.91, 50%, $\frac{2}{5}$, 0.3

0.3, $\frac{2}{5}$, 50%, $\frac{3}{4}$, 0.91

6. To be labeled a juice drink, only 10% of a drink must be real fruit juice. How many ounces of a 64 oz juice drink must be real juice?

6.4 oz must be fruit juice.

© Pearson Education, Inc. 5

Mental Match

E 11-9
MENTAL MATH

Without using pencil and paper or a calculator, solve the problems on the left and match them with the answers on the right. Write the correct letters on the lines. You will not need to use one of the answers.

1. 50% of $\frac{1}{2}$ **m**

2. Another name for $\frac{7}{42}$ **h**

3. 30% of 160 **l**

4. Another name for $\frac{42}{14}$ **g**

5. 75% of 20 **i**

6. 16% of 150 **k**

7. Another name for $\frac{12}{16}$ **b**

8. Another name for $\frac{3}{5}$ **d**

9. 80% of 40 **n**

10. 28% of 75 **f**

11. Another name for $\frac{3}{17}$ **a**

12. 20% of 45 **j**

13. Another name for $\frac{5}{0}$ **o**

14. Another name for $\frac{96}{12}$ **c**

a. $\frac{18}{102}$

b. $\frac{3}{4}$

c. 8

d. $\frac{21}{35}$

e. 2

f. 21

g. 3

h. $\frac{1}{6}$

i. 15

j. 9

k. 24

l. 48

m. $\frac{1}{4}$

n. 32

o. $\frac{15}{27}$

© Pearson Education, Inc. 5

Mental Math: Finding a Percent of a Number

PS 11-9

State Populations The chart shows information about the populations of the 50 U.S. states.

Population	Percent of U.S. States
Greater than 10,000,000	14%
5,000,000 to 10,000,000	24%
1,000,000 to 4,999,999	46%
Less than 1,000,000	16%

1. How many states have a population greater than 10,000,000? **7 states**

2. How many states have a population less than 5,000,000? **31 states**

3. How many states have a population between 5,000,000 and 10,000,000? **12 states**

Field Trip There were 120 fifth graders who went on a field trip to the science museum.

4. If 10% of the students took part in the insect identification activity, how many students took part? **12 students**

5. If 50% of the students took part in the electricity activity, how many students took part? **60 students**

6. **Writing in Math** Explain how you would use mental math to find 25% of 40.

Sample answer: 25% is $\frac{1}{4}$, which is the same as $\frac{10}{40}$, so the answer is 10.

© Pearson Education, Inc. 5

Practice

Estimating Percents   P 11-10

Estimates may vary.

Estimate.

1. 52% of 420 **210**   2. 68% of 70 **49**   3. 11% of 120 **12**

4. 76% of 81 **60**   5. 39% of 31 **12**   6. 27% of 24 **6**

7. 9% of 72 **7**   8. 58% of 492 **300**   9. 18% of 402 **80**

10. **Algebra** Use estimation to find the value of *x*
    when 25% of *x* is about 30.   ***x* = 120**

A group of students were surveyed on what
they like to do after school. There were 200
students surveyed, and the results were
graphed.

11. Estimate the number of students who
    prefer to play a sport after school.

    About 50 students

12. Do more than or fewer than 40 students prefer to read after school?

    Fewer than 40 students

Test Prep

13. Which is the best estimation for 31% of 68?

    A. 20   **B.** 21   C. 25   D. 27

14. **Writing in Math** Linda says that 42 is a reasonable estimate
    for 34% of 119. Is she correct? Explain why or why not.

    **Yes; Sample answer: 34% is close to
    35% and 119 is close to 120. 30% of
    120 is 36 and 5% is 6, so 36 + 6 = 42.**

Reteaching

Estimating Percents   R 11-10

There are some percents that are easy to find mentally, such as
25%, 10%, 20%, 50%, 75%, and 100%.

To find an estimate for a percent of a number, you can change
the percent and the number to compatible numbers.

Find 62% of 190.

62% is close to 60% and 190 is close
to 200.

62% of 190 is about 60% of 200.

$60\% \text{ of } 200 = \frac{6}{10} \times 200$

$= 6 \times 20$

$= 120$

So, 62% of 190 is about 120.

Find 47% of 617.

47% is close to 50% and 617 is close
to 600.

47% of 617 is about 50% of 600.

$50\% \text{ of } 600 = \frac{1}{2} \times 600$

$= 300$

So, 47% of 617 is about 300.

Estimate.

1. 81% of 196 **About 160**   2. 38% of 62 **About 24**

3. 34% of 13 **About 4**   4. 76% of 84 **About 63**

5. 98% of 19 **About 19**   6. 53% of 23 **About 11**

7. 9% of 73 **About 7**   8. 77% of 63 **About 45**

9. **Estimation** Estimate 53% of 71. Is your estimate an
   underestimate or an overestimate? Explain.

   **Sample answer: About 35. It is an
   underestimate. I changed 53% to
   50%, so I lowered the percent, and I
   changed 71 to 70, so I also lowered
   the actual number.**

Enrichment

Back-to-School Shopping   E 11-10
                                     DECISION MAKING

Your mother gives you $200.00 to spend on school clothes.
When you get to the store, you find out it has a 20% off sale.
Choose a combination of clothes for less than $200.00. You can
buy more than one of any item. (Hint: Round to the nearest
dollar before estimating the discount.)

Clothes:

**Sample answer: 1 turtleneck, 2 pairs
of jeans, 1 pair of shorts, 2 pairs of
socks, 1 belt, 3 T-shirts, 1 pair of
casual pants, and 1 pair of tennis shoes**

Turtleneck: $24.95   Jeans: $29.95   Shorts: $19.95   Socks: $4.95

Bolt: $19.95

Tennis shoes: $49.95

Dress shirt: $34.95   T-shirt: $9.95   Casual pants: $34.95   Skirt: $34.95   Sandals: $31.95

Problem Solving

Estimating Percents   PS 11-10

Sample answers are given for 1–6.

Favorite Fruit Students were surveyed
about their favorite fruit. The results are
shown in the circle graph. There were
192 students surveyed.

Favorite Fruit

Bananas 7%   Other 3%

Apples 47%   Oranges 32%

Pears 11%

1. About how many students surveyed
   liked oranges the best?

   About 60 students

2. About how many students surveyed
   liked apples the best?

   About 100 students

3. Estimate the number of students who liked either bananas
   or pears the best.

   About 40 students

4. About how much greater is the number of students who
   liked apples the best than the number of students who
   liked pears the best?

   About 80 students

5. Estimate the number of students who liked either apples or
   oranges the best.

   About 160 students

6. **Writing in Math** Use compatible numbers to estimate
   39% of 103. Explain how you found your answer.

   **About 40; Sample answer: I used the
   compatible numbers 40% of 100 to
   estimate.**

Name_____

A Pack of Percents

Solve. Write your answer to each in a complete sentence.

1. A bookstore charges 12% of your purchase price to cover sales tax and shipping and handling. About how much will be added to your purchase price if your order totals $216?

About $22 will be added to the price.

2. In Derreck's class, 3 out of every 7 students are girls. If there are 16 boys in Derreck's class, how many of the students are girls?

There are 12 girls in Derreck's class.

3. Complete the table to help you find how many blocks are needed if a tower is built of blocks where each row has one less block than the one below it. The tower is 8 rows high, and the bottom row has 20 blocks in it.

Rows	1	2	3	4	5	6	7	8
Blocks Needed	20	39	57	74	90	103	119	132

In a tower 8 rows high, there are 132 blocks used.

4. Kinsey ran 3 laps around the track in 12 min yesterday. Today she ran 5 laps, and it took her 19 min 20 sec. Which day did Kinsey run faster?

Kinsey ran faster today than yesterday.

5. It costs $0.89 for 1 L of spring water, and a 5 L jug of spring water costs $4.95. Which is the better buy?

It is a better buy to buy the 1 L container of spring water, because the unit rate for the 5 L jug is $0.99/L.

Name_____

The Rug Maker

Kung designs rugs and carpets. Two of her latest designs are shown below. Which rug has a higher percentage of squares shaded?

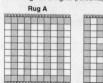

Rug A   Rug B

Rug A has $\frac{52}{100}$ squares shaded. That is 52% or $\frac{13}{25}$ shaded.

Rug B has $\frac{44}{100}$ squares shaded. That is 44% or $\frac{11}{25}$ shaded.

So, Rug A has a higher percentage of squares shaded.

1. Kung recently made the rug at the right. Write the fraction in lowest terms and the percent that represents the shaded part of the rug.

$\frac{21}{50}$; 42%

2. If Kung made 12 rugs in 6 months, what is the unit rate?

2 rugs in 1 month

3. What is the ratio of triangles to squares? Write the ratio in three ways.

Sample answer:
5:9, $\frac{5}{9}$, 5 to 9

Name_____

Nutrition Facts

Your school's head cook is deciding on menus for school lunches. Right now she is focusing on protein and wants to offer a variety of protein sources. Look at the Key Food Facts chart and answer the questions.

Key Food Facts

Food	Amount	Protein
Almonds	$\frac{1}{2}$ c	14 g
Lima beans	$\frac{1}{2}$ c	6 g
Beef chow mein	1 c	10 g
Cornbread	1 piece	4 g
American cheese	2 oz	13 g
Chicken salad	3 oz	10 g
Grapefruit	1 medium	1 g
Macaroni and cheese	1 c	7 g
Milk (2%)	1 c	8 g
Raisins, seedless	$\frac{1}{2}$ c	2 g

1. One piece of cornbread would contain what percent of the protein in $\frac{1}{2}$ c of lima beans?   **67%**

2. If you have $\frac{1}{2}$ c of almonds on your plate along with 2 c of beef chow mein, what is the ratio of the amount of protein in almonds to that in beef chow mein?

14:20, or 7:10

3. Say you want to eat 20 g of protein today. What combination of foods might you choose?

Sample answer: 1 c of milk, 1 piece of cornbread, $\frac{1}{2}$ c of lima beans, and $\frac{1}{2}$ c of raisins

4. If you are supposed to eat 20 g of protein per day, what percent of that amount will you be eating if you have 1 c of macaroni and cheese?   **35%**

Name_____

Piano Practice

Stephanie practices playing piano each day. On Mondays she practices 25 min, on Tuesday 32 min, on Wednesday 29 min, and on Thursday 22 min. Predict how many minutes Stephanie will practice in 14 days.

Read and Understand

1. How many minutes does Stephanie practice on each of the 4 days?

Mon: 25 min; Tues: 32 min; Wed: 29 min; Thurs: 22 min

2. What are you trying to find?

A prediction for how many minutes she will practice in 14 days

Plan and Solve

3. How can you solve the problem?

I can find the ratio for the number of minutes practiced per day.

4. Make a prediction. Write your answer in a complete sentence.

She will practice for about 378 min in 14 days.

Look Back and Check

5. Is your answer reasonable?

Sample answer: Yes, the ratio of 27 min per day is reasonable.

Properties of Equality
P 12-1

What property of equality is illustrated by each pair of equations?

1. $12 \times 2 = 24$
So, $(12 \times 2) \div 6 = 24 \div 6$. **Division**

2. $19 - 4 = 15$
So, $(19 - 4) + 6 = 15 + 6$. **Addition**

3. $21 + 7 = 28$
So, $(21 + 7) - 18 = 28 - 18$. **Subtraction**

Tell what inverse operation and what number you would use to get n alone.

4. $n - 9$ **Add 9**   **5.** $14 + n$ **Subtract 14**

6. $n \times 17$ **Divide by 17**   **7.** $n \div 3$ **Multiply by 3**

8. $41n$ **Divide by 41**   **9.** $n + 7$ **Subtract 7**

10. Jerry has a paper route on Sundays. He started with 64 deliveries, but lost 6 accounts. Then he got 6 new accounts. How many papers does Jerry now deliver on Sundays?

64 newspapers

Test Prep

11. Which operation should be used to get y alone in $16y$?

A. Add 16   **B.** Subtract 16   **C.** Multiply by 16   **D.** Divide by 16

12. Writing in Math Explain how to get j alone in $12j$.

Sample answer: j is being multiplied by 12, so I would use the inverse operation of multiplication and divide by 12.

Properties of Equality
R 12-1

Property

Addition: You can add the same number to both sides of an equation and the sides remain equal.	Subtraction: You can subtract the same number from both sides of an equation and the sides remain equal.	Multiplication: You can multiply both sides of an equation by the same number and the sides remain equal.	Division: You can divide both sides of an equation by the same number (except 0) and the sides remain equal.
Example: $4 + 8 = 8 + 4$ $2 + 4 + 8 = 8 + 4 + 2$	Example: $12 + 6 = 18$ $(12 + 6) - 3 = 18 - 3$	Example: $3 \times 8 = 4 \times 6$ $3 \times 8 \times 4 = 4 \times 6 \times 4$	Example: $14 + 10 = 24$ $(14 + 10) \div 3 = 24 \div 3$

You can use inverse operations to solve equations.

Subtraction can undo addition.	Addition can undo subtraction.	Division can undo multiplication.	Multiplication can undo division.
$(6 + 8) - 8 = 6$ $14 - 8 = 6$ $6 = 6$	$(7 - 3) + 3 = 7$ $4 + 3 = 7$ $7 = 7$	$(12 \times 3) \div 3 = 12$ $36 \div 3 = 12$ $12 = 12$	$(56 \div 8) \times 8 = 56$ $7 \times 8 = 56$ $56 = 56$

Which property of equality is illustrated by each pair of equations?

1. $30 - 6 = 24$
So, $(30 - 6) + 2 = 24 + 2$. **Addition**

2. $21 \div 7 = 3$
So, $(21 \div 7) \times 2 = 3 \times 2$. **Multiplication**

Tell what inverse operation and what number must be used to get n alone.

3. $n \div 2$ **Multiply by 2**   **4.** $14 + n$ **Subtract 14**

Evaluate each expression.

5. $6 \times 10 = (2 + 4) \times \bigcirc$ **10**   **6.** $(15 - 5) \div 2 = 10 \div \bigcirc$ **2**

Exploring Relationships
E 12-1
ALGEBRA

Match each expression on the left side with the equivalent expression on the right side. Write the correct letters on the lines.

1. $15 + 8 - 3$ **d**   **a.** $52 - 18$

2. $(6 \times 7) + 5$ **g**   **b.** $9 \div 3$

3. $37 + 15 - 18$ **a**   **c.** $21 - 2$

4. $(24 \div 3) \times 4$ **h**   **d.** $23 - 3$

5. $(18 \times 2) \div 4$ **f**   **e.** $5 + 6$

6. $(2 + 3 + 4) \div 3$ **b**   **f.** $(2 \times 18) \div 4$

7. $6 \div 3 \times 9$ **j**   **g.** $42 + 5$

8. $8 + 2 - 4$ **i**   **h.** 8×4

9. $3 \times 7 - 2$ **c**   **i.** $10 - 4$

10. $(40 \div 8) + 6$ **e**   **j.** 2×9

Properties of Equality
PS 12-1

Write the missing number that makes each number sentence true.

1. $(2 \times 4) \div 1 = (4 \times 2) \div \square$ **1**

2. $(10 \div 5) \times 3 = \square \times 3$ **2**

3. $\square + (9 - 3) = 7 + (9 - 3)$ **7**

4. $(20 \div 4) - 2 = \square - 2$ **5**

5. $(8 \times 6) - 10 = (6 \times 8) - \square$ **10**

6. $16 - x = (10 + 6) - \square$ **x**

Using the rule given, complete each table.

7.

Rule: Add 25	
34	59
45	70
52	77
66	**91**

8.

Rule: Multiply by 7	
13	91
20	140
26	**182**
31	217

9. Writing in Math Tina said that if $(3 \times 3) - 5 = (3 \times 3) - n$, then n must equal 3×3. Is she correct? Explain.

No; Sample answer: Each (3×3) cancels the other out, so $n = 5$.

Name_____

Solving Addition and Subtraction Equations

Solve and check each equation.

1. $x + 4 = 16$ $x = 12$
2. $t - 8 = 15$ $t = 23$
3. $m - 9 = 81$ $m = 90$
4. $7 + y = 19$ $y = 12$
5. $k - 10 = 25$ $k = 35$
6. $15 + b = 50$ $b = 35$
7. $f + 18 = 20$ $f = 2$
8. $w - 99 = 100$ $w = 199$
9. $75 + n = 100$ $n = 25$
10. $p - 40 = 0$ $p = 40$

11. Jennifer has $14. She sold a notebook and pen, and now she has $18. Solve the equation $14 + m = 18$ to find how much money Jennifer received by selling the notebook and pen.   **$4**

12. Kit Carson was born in 1809. He died in 1868. Use the equation $1,809 + x = 1,868$ to find how many years Kit Carson lived.   **59 years**

Test Prep

13. Which is the solution for y when $y - 6 = 19$?
   A. 13   **B.** 15   **C.** 23   **(D)** 25

14. **Writing in Math** Nellie solved $y - 3 = 16$. Is her answer correct? Explain and find the correct answer if she is incorrect.

$y - 3 = 16$	
$y = 13$	Subtract 3

   No; Sample answer: Nellie used the wrong operation. She needed to use addition to get the variable alone. The correct answer is $y = 19$.

Name_____

Solving Addition and Subtraction Equations

You can use inverse operations to solve addition and subtraction equations.

$n - 8 = 6$

8 has been subtracted from n. The inverse of subtraction is addition, so you can add 8 to both sides of the equation.

$n - 8 + 8 = 6 + 8$

$n = 6 + 8$ The + 8 undoes the − 8.

$n = 14$

Check your solution by substituting it into the original equation.

$n - 8 = 6$ Replace the n with 14.

$14 - 8 = 6$

$6 = 6$ The solution checks.

$n + 13 = 40$

13 has been added to n. The inverse of addition is subtraction, so you can subtract 13 from both sides of the equation.

$n + 13 - 13 = 40 - 13$

$n = 40 - 13$ The − 13 undoes the + 13.

$n = 27$

Check your solution by substituting it into the original equation.

$n + 13 = 40$ Replace the n with 27.

$27 + 13 = 40$

$40 = 40$ The solution checks.

Solve and check each equation.

1. $x + 14 = 21$ **7**
2. $b - 7 = 13$ **20**
3. $22 + m = 39$ **17**
4. $21 = r - 4$ **25**

5. Mary's sister is 4 years older than Mary. Her sister is 12. Use the equation $m + 4 = 12$ to find Mary's age.   **8 years old**

6. Stephanie had a box of pencils. She gave 13 to her sister and mother. Now she has 23 pencils. Use the equation $p - 13 = 23$ to find out how many pencils were in the box.   **36 pencils**

Name_____

Number Patterns

For 1–5, complete each pattern. Then write each rule.

1. 4, 8, 12, 16, **20**   Rule: **Add 4**
2. 3, 10, 17, 24, **31**   Rule: **Add 7**
3. 38, 33, 28, 23, **18**   Rule: **Subtract 5**
4. 2, 6, 18, 54, **162**   Rule: **Multiply by 3**
5. 1,024; 256; 64; 16; **4**   Rule: **Divide by 4**

For 6–10, use two operations to complete each pattern. Then write each rule.

6. 3, 7, 15, 31, **63**   Rule: **Multiply by 2 and add 1**

7. 4, 9, 24, 69, **204**   Rule: **Subtract 1 and multiply by 3**

8. 5, 13, 37, 109, **325**   Rule: **Multiply by 3 and subtract 2**

9. 5, 12, 33, 96, **285**   Rule: **Subtract 1 and multiply by 3**

10. 4, 13, 31, 67, **139**   Rule: **Multiply by 2 and add 5**

Name_____

Solving Addition and Subtraction Equations

Use mental math to solve each equation.

1. $a + 18 = 32$ $a = 14$
2. $y - 24 = 33$ $y = 57$
3. $270 = b + 120$ $b = 150$
4. $42 - g = 25$ $g = 17$
5. $x + 32 = 75$ $x = 43$

6. Altogether, Angela, Toby, and Brian have 508 baseball cards. If Angela has 162 cards and Toby has 139 cards, how many cards does Brian have?   **207 cards**

7. Michael needs to raise $562 for his trip to Washington, D.C. He earned $275 working at the movie theater. Then he earned $168 selling magazine subscriptions. How much more money does he need?   **$119 more**

8. Lisa had some CDs. She got 4 more for her birthday. Now she has 36 CDs. How many CDs did Lisa have to begin with?   **32 CDs**

9. **Writing in Math** Jorge had 18 pinecones. He gave some of the pinecones to Martin. Jorge had 11 pinecones left. Explain how to write and solve an equation to find how many pinecones Jorge gave to Martin.

   Sample answer: I can write the equation $18 - x = 11$. He gave 7 pinecones to Martin.

Name_____

Solving Multiplication and Division Equations

P 12-3

Solve and check each equation. Remember $\frac{n}{5}$ means $n \div 5$.

1. $\frac{x}{7} = 14$ $x = 98$

2. $15p = 75$ $p = 5$

3. $108 = 4 \times b$ $b = 27$

4. $t \div 12 = 18$ $t = 216$

5. $222 = 3a$ $a = 74$

6. $\frac{y}{3} = 18$ $y = 54$

Reasoning Use mental math to solve each equation.

7. $4j = 400$ $j = 100$

8. $n \div 9 = 1$ $n = 9$

9. Each member of a rescue team can carry 40 lb of equipment in his or her backpack. How many team members are needed to carry 280 lb of equipment? Use the equation $40x = 280$ to solve the problem.

7 rescue team members

10. A box of granola bars is divided between 3 boys. If each boy gets 6 granola bars, how many bars are in the box? Use the equation $\frac{b}{3} = 6$ to solve the problem.

18 granola bars

Test Prep

11. Which property should you use to solve the equation for n when $\frac{n}{2} = 16$?

A. Addition Property of Equality   B. Subtraction Property of Equality

C. Multiplication Property of Equality   D. Division Property of Equality

12. **Writing in Math** Explain why you use division to solve a multiplication problem and multiplication to solve a division problem.

Sample answer: Division and multiplication are inverse operations. In order to get a variable alone, you need to do the inverse operation. Use with Lesson 12-3. **157**

Name_____

Solving Multiplication and Division Equations

R 12-3

You can use inverse operations to solve multiplication and division equations.

$n \times 5 = 35$

The variable n has been multiplied by 5. The inverse of multiplication is division, so you can divide both sides of the equation by 5.

$n \times 5 \div 5 = 35 \div 5$

$n = 35 \div 5$ The $\div 5$ undoes the $\times 5$.

$n = 7$

Check your solution by substituting it into the original equation.

$n \times 5 = 35$ Replace the n with 7.

$7 \times 5 = 35$

$35 = 35$ The solution checks.

$\frac{n}{7} = 8$

The variable n has been divided by 7. The inverse of division is multiplication, so you can multiply both sides of the equation by 7.

$\frac{n}{7} \times 7 = 8 \times 7$

$n = 8 \times 7$ The $\times 7$ undoes the $\div 7$.

$n = 56$

Check your solution by substituting it into the original equation.

$\frac{n}{7} = 8$ Replace the n with 56.

$56 \div 7 = 8$

$8 = 8$ The solution checks.

Solve and check each equation.

1. $\frac{n}{5} = 3$ $n = 15$

2. $7t = 84$ $t = 12$

3. $x \div 9 = 18$ $x = 162$

4. $66 = 6u$ $u = 11$

5. $\frac{y}{10} = 200$ $y = 2,000$

6. $7t = 49$ $t = 7$

7. $160 = 16x$ $x = 10$

8. $r \div 25 = 6$ $r = 150$

9. **Number Sense** A carton of eggs is on sale for $0.49. Use the equation $\$0.49x = \$2.45$ to find how many cartons of eggs you can purchase for $2.45.

You can buy 5 cartons of eggs for $2.45.

Use with Lesson 12-3. **157**

Name_____

Variable Choices

E 12-3
NUMBER SENSE

The values of variables are listed below. For 1–8, choose the variable that will make each equation true. Write the correct variables on the lines.

$a = 3$

$b = 2$

$c = 4$

$d = 10$

$e = 15$

$f = 1$

$g = 5$

$h = 20$

1. $\frac{c}{2} = 2$

2. $150 \times f = 150$

3. $80 \div g = 16$

4. $15 \times a = 45$

5. $\frac{60}{e} = 4$

6. $73 \times b = 146$

7. $h \div 5 = 4$

8. $18 \times d = 180$

Use with Lesson 12-3. **157**

Name_____

Solving Multiplication and Division Equations

PS 12-3

Use mental math to solve each equation.

1. $\frac{n}{2} = 8$ $n = 16$

2. $\frac{x}{5} = 5$ $x = 25$

3. $\frac{y}{4} = 15$ $y = 60$

4. $\frac{b}{10} = 9$ $b = 90$

Distance The chart shows the distance each animal could travel in 5 hr if that animal could maintain its top speed.

Cheetah	325 mi
Giraffe	160 mi
Lion	250 mi
Rabbit	175 mi

Find how far each animal can travel in 1 hr.

5. Giraffe   **32 mi**

6. Cheetah   **65 mi**

7. Rabbit   **35 mi**

8. **Writing in Math** Explain how to find how far a lion could travel in 2 hr.

Sample answer: Divide 250 by 5 to find the distance in 1 hr. Then multiply 50 by 2 to find the distance in 2 hr, which is 100 mi.

Use with Lesson 12-3. **157**

Name_____

PROBLEM-SOLVING STRATEGY   P 12-4
Write an Equation

Solve each problem. Draw a picture to show the main idea for each problem. Then write an equation and solve it. Write the answer in a complete sentence.

Check students' pictures.

1. Bobby has 3 times as many model spaceships as his friend Sylvester does. Bobby has 21 spaceships. How many model spaceships does Sylvester have?

$3m = 21$; $m = 7$; Sylvester has 7 model spaceships.

2. Dan saved $463 over the 12 weeks of summer break. He saved $297 of it during the last 4 weeks. How much did he save during the first 8 weeks?

$d + 297 = 463$; $d = 166$; Dan saved $166 during the first 8 weeks of summer.

3. A box of peanut butter crackers was divided between 6 children. Each child got 9 crackers. How many crackers were in the box?

$\frac{c}{6} = 9$; $c = 54$; There were 54 crackers in the box.

Name_____

PROBLEM-SOLVING STRATEGY   R 12-4
Write an Equation

Buttons Matilda decided to put her buttons into 7 jars. Each jar had 14 buttons in it. How many buttons did Matilda have?

Read and Understand

Step 1: What do you know?

There were a bunch of buttons that were put into 7 jars. Each jar ended up with 14 buttons.

Step 2: What are you trying to find?

How many buttons Matilda has

Plan and Solve

Step 3: What strategy will you use?

Strategy: Write an equation

Draw a picture to help you see the main idea.

Use a letter or variable to show what you are trying to find. Let j = the number of jars.

Write a number sentence using the variable.

$j \div 7 = 14$

Solve the number sentence.

$j \div 7 \times 7 = 14 \times 7$

$j = 98$

Look Back and Check

Step 4: Is your answer reasonable?

Yes, $98 \div 7 = 14$.

Complete the picture to show the main idea for this problem. Then write an equation and solve it.

1. A total of 54 students are going on a field trip, and 36 of the students are girls. How many of the students are boys?

	54	
36		?

$36 + b = 54$, $b = 18$; 18 boys

Name_____

Favorite Sandwiches   E 12-4
                                                    DECISION MAKING

Twenty students completed a survey about their favorite sandwiches. The students were asked to name their favorite sandwich and their second-favorite sandwich from five choices. The tally charts show the results.

Favorite Sandwich	
Ham	II
Vegetable	IIII
Turkey	IIII I
Peanut butter and jelly	IIII II
Cheese	I

Second-Favorite Sandwich	
Ham	IIII I
Vegetable	IIII I
Turkey	IIII I
Peanut butter and jelly	IIII
Cheese	II

1. The school needs to choose two types of sandwiches to be served on a field trip. Which two sandwiches would you suggest? Explain.

Sample answer: The school should choose turkey and peanut butter and jelly, because they got the most votes for favorite sandwich.

2. If the school needed to choose only one type of sandwich to be served on a field trip, which sandwich would you suggest? Explain.

Sample answer: They should choose turkey because it got the most votes combined.

3. Five more students were surveyed. They all chose vegetable as their favorite and second-favorite sandwich. Would this change your suggestion in Question 1? Question 2? Explain.

Sample answer: Yes, because vegetable would have the most votes for favorite and second-favorite sandwich. I would choose vegetable and peanut butter and jelly for Question 1 and vegetable for Question 2.

Name_____

PROBLEM-SOLVING STRATEGY   PS 12-4
Write an Equation

How Far? Angelica lives 27 mi from the lake. If Angelica lives 3 times farther from the lake than Monica, how far does Monica live from the lake?

Read and Understand

1. How far does Angelica live from the lake? How much farther does Angelica live from the lake than Monica?

27 mi; 3 times farther

2. What are you trying to find?

How far Monica lives from the lake

Plan and Solve

3. Write an equation for the problem.   **$3d = 27$**

4. Solve the problem. Write your answer in a complete sentence.

Monica lives 9 mi from the lake.

Look Back and Check

5. Is your answer reasonable?

Sample answer: Yes, because 9 times 3 equals 27

Solve Another Problem

6. Vance bikes 6 mi per day. How many days will it take him to bike 72 mi? Write an equation to solve the problem.

$6x = 72$; 12 days

Practice

Name_____

Understanding Integers

P 12-5

Write an integer for each word description.

1. a withdrawal of $50   **2.** a temperature rise of 14°   **3.** 10° below zero

-50 $+14$ -10

Use the number line for 4–7. Write the integer for each point.

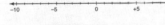

4. A _-8_   **5.** B _$+1$_   **6.** C _-2_   **7.** D _$+7$_

Compare. Use >, <, or = for each ◯.

8. -5 ⊘ -9 **9.** $+8$ ⊘ -12 **10.** $+21$ ⊘ -26

Write in order from least to greatest.

11. $-4, +11, -11, +4$ -11 -4 $+4$ $+11$

12. $-6, +6, 0, -14$ -14 -6 0 $+6$

13. $+11, -8, +7, -4$ -8 -4 $+7$ $+11$

Test Prep

14. Which point is farthest to the right on a number line?

A. -6 **B.** -2 **C.** 0 **D** 2

15. Writing in Math In Fenland, U.K., the elevation from sea level is -4 m. In San Diego, U.S., it is $+40$ ft. The elevations are given in different units. Explain how to tell which location has a greater elevation.

Sample answer: The elevation of Fenland is below sea level, and the elevation of San Diego is above sea level, so San Diego's elevation is greater.

Use with Lesson 12-5. **159**

Reteaching

Name_____

Understanding Integers

R 12-5

You can write integers for word descriptions.

Word Description	Integer
A gain of 15 yd	$+15$
8 steps backward	-8

You can use a number line to compare and order integers.

Compare -2 ◯ -5.

The integer -5 is farther to the left on the number line than the integer -2.

So, $-5 < -2$.

Write an integer for each word description.

1. 84 ft below sea level -84 **2.** A gain of 500 points $+500$

Use the number line for 3–5. Write the integer for each point.

3. Q _-7_   **4.** R _$+3$_   **5.** S _-4_

Compare. Use >, <, or = for each ◯.

6. -1 ⊘ $+1$ **7.** $+8$ ⊘ $+3$

8. -2 ⊘ -16 **9.** $+6$ ⊘ -8

Write in order from least to greatest.

10. $+6, -6, 0, -12$ $-12, -6, 0, +6$

11. $+4, -6, -5, +2$ $-6, -5, +2, +4$

12. Number Sense Which is less, -9 or -4? -9

Use with Lesson 12-5. **159**

Enrichment

Name_____

Integer Patterns

E 12-5
PATTERNS

Use the number line to complete each pattern.

1. $-12, -9, -6,$ _-3_

2. $+4, +2, 0,$ _-2_

3. $-10, -5, 0,$ _$+5$_

4. $+2, -1, -4,$ _-7_

5. $-9, -5, -1,$ _$+3$_

6. $+8, +3, -2,$ _-7_

7. $-3, +1, +5,$ _$+9$_

8. $+3, 0, -3,$ _-6_

9. $-6, -2, +2,$ _$+6$_

10. $+7, +4, +1,$ _-2_

Use with Lesson 12-5. **159**

Problem Solving

Name_____

Understanding Integers

PS 12-5

Temperature The chart shows the temperatures for part of one day.

1. Write the integer that shows the temperature at 6 A.M.

-4

2. At what time was the temperature one degree below zero?

10:00 A.M.

3. At what time was the temperature two degrees above zero?

2:00 P.M.

4. Was it warmer at 10:00 A.M. or 6:00 P.M.?

6:00 P.M.

5. Was it warmer at 8:00 A.M. or 2:00 P.M.?

2:00 P.M.

6. Gerard had $13. He gave $5 to a friend and spent $3 on a snack. He then found a $5 bill. Order the numbers $+13$, -5, -3, and $+5$ from greatest to least.

$+13, +5, -3, -5$

7. Writing in Math Explain how you found the answer to 6.

Sample answer: I graphed them on a number line and then read them from right to left.

Use with Lesson 12-5. **159**

Name_____

Adding Integers

Add. Use a number line.

1. $+1 + +3 =$ **+4**   2. $+4 + -7 =$ **-3**   3. $-4 + -2 =$ **-6**

4. $-3 + +1 =$ **-2**   5. $+6 + -6 =$ **0**   6. $-1 + -4 =$ **-5**

7. $+9 + -7 =$ **+2**   8. $-6 + +12 =$ **+6**   9. $-3 + -8 =$ **-11**

In a word tile game, you score one positive point for each letter tile that you use and one negative point for each tile that you have left.

10. During one round, Shelley used 14 tiles and could not use 6. What was her score for that round?　　**+8 points**

11. Pete used 4 tiles, but he could not use 8. What was his score that round?　　**-4 points**

12. **Reasoning** In the game, if you have 18 tiles and you cannot use 3 of them, what will your score be for that round? Explain how you found the answer.

My score is $+15 + (-3) = +12$ points.

Test Prep

13. Which is the sum of $-8 + +5$?

A. -13 Ⓑ -3 C. $+3$ D. $+13$

14. **Writing in Math** During a week at camp, Tom started with a zero balance in his account at the camp store. On Monday he deposited $15. He withdrew $6 on Tuesday and $3 on Thursday. What was his account balance after Thursday's withdrawal? Explain.

Sample answer: There was a deposit and two withdrawals, so $+15 + -6 + -3 = +6$, for a balance of $6.

Name_____

Adding Integers

Rules for adding integers on the number line:

Always start at 0 and face the positive integers. Walk forward for positive integers and backward for negative integers. The number you stop at is the answer.

Find $-1 + (-4)$.

Start at 0 and face the positive integers. Move backward 1 unit. Then move backward 4 more units.

So, $-1 + (-4) = -5$

Find $+3 + (-5)$.

Start at 0 and face the positive integers. Move forward 3 units. Then move backward 5 units.

So, $+3 + (-5) = -2$

Add. Use a number line.

1. $-3 + (-3) =$ **-6**   2. $-1 + (+4) =$ **+3**

3. $-7 + (+7) =$ **0**   4. $+4 + (-9) =$ **-5**

5. $-5 + (-4) =$ **-9**   6. $+9 + (-2) =$ **+7**

7. $-11 + (+12) =$ **+1**   8. $-2 + (-4) =$ **-6**

9. **Mental Math** What is the sum of $+5 + (-3) + (-5)$? Explain how you found your answer.

Sample answer: -3; The +5 and -5 cancel each other out, and there is only a -3 left.

Name_____

Board Game

Jenny and Tim are playing their favorite board game. Each player spins the spinner and moves the number of spaces the arrow points to. If the spinner lands on a positive number, the player moves forward. If the spinner lands on a negative number, the player moves backward. The chart shows each player's turns for the game.

Turn	Jenny	Tim
1	+3	+2
2	+4	-1
3	-2	+3
4	+1	-2
5	-3	+4
6	+3	+4

1. What space was Tim on after his second turn?　**+1**

2. What space was Jenny on after her third turn?　**+5**

3. What space was Tim on after his fourth turn?　**+2**

4. What space was Jenny on after her fifth turn?　**+3**

5. What space was Tim on after his sixth turn?　**+10**

6. What space was Jenny on after her sixth turn?　**+6**

7. Who won the game?

Tim

8. If the game had ended after 3 turns, who would have won?

Jenny

Name_____

Adding Integers

Scores Six friends are playing a game using cards. Each time you cannot play at least one card, you score negative points. Right now Paulo has -4 points, Gina $+3$, Marcus $+2$, Ivy -1, Xavier $+1$, and Holly -3. Use the number line for 1–6.

1. If Paulo gets $+2$ points on his next turn, what will his new score be?　**-2**

2. If Gina gets -4 points on her next turn, what will her new score be?　**-1**

3. If Marcus gets -3 points on his next turn, what will his new score be?　**-1**

4. If Ivy gets $+5$ points on her next turn, what will her new score be?　**+4**

5. If Xavier gets -6 points on his next turn, what will his new score be?　**-5**

6. If Holly gets $+6$ points on her next turn, what will her new score be?　**+3**

7. **Writing in Math** Suppose that Paulo and Gina are partners, Marcus and Ivy are partners, and Xavier and Holly are partners. Which pair has the highest combined score? Explain.

Marcus and Ivy; Sample answer: Paulo and Gina have -1, Marcus and Ivy have +1, and Xavier and Holly have -2. Only Marcus and Ivy have a positive score.

Name_____

Subtracting Integers

P 12-7

Rewrite each subtraction using addition. Then find the answer.
Use a number line to check.

1. $^-9 - {^+1}$

$$-9 + -1 = -10$$

2. $^+6 - {^-3}$

$$+6 + +3 = +9$$

3. $^+8 - {^+4}$

$$+8 + -4 = +4$$

4. $^-11 - {^-16}$

$$-11 + +16 = +5$$

5. $^-6 - {^-1}$

$$-6 + +1 = -5$$

6. $^-3 - {^+4}$

$$-3 + -4 = -7$$

	High Temperature	Low Temperature
January 1	$-1°F$	$-16°F$
February 1	$27°F$	$18°F$
March 1	$51°F$	$42°F$

7. How much greater was the high temperature than the low temperature on January 1?

$$+15°F$$

8. How much less was the low temperature on January 1 than the low temperature on February 1?

$$-34°F$$

9. How much greater was the high temperature than the low temperature on March 1?

$$+9°F$$

Test Prep

10. Which of the following is the same as $^+4 - {^-9}$?

A. $^-4 + {^-9}$ B. $^+4 - {^-9}$ C. $^-4 - {^-9}$ **D.** $^+4 + {^+9}$

11. Writing in Math Use the information from Exercises 7–9. Which date had the greatest difference between the high and low temperatures? Explain.

January 1; Sample answer: The difference was 15°F. The differences on February 1 and March 1 were both 9°F.

Name_____

Subtracting Integers

R 12-7

As when adding, always start at 0 and face the positive integers. Walk forward for positive integers and backward for negative integers. The subtraction sign signals you to turn around and face the negative integers. The number you stop at is the answer.

Find $-1 - (-4)$.

Start at 0 and face the positive integers. Move backward 1 unit. Then turn around and move backward 4 units.

So, $-1 - (-4) = +3$.

Find $+3 - (+5)$.

Start at 0 and face the positive integers. Move forward 3 units. Then turn around and move forward 5 units.

So, $+3 - (+5) = -2$.

Subtracting an integer is the same as adding its opposite. So, $-10 - (-2)$ can be written as $-10 + (+2)$.

Rewrite each subtraction using addition. Then find the answer.
Use a number line to check.

1. $-16 - (+2)$

$$-16 + (-2) = -18$$

2. $+4 - (-4)$

$$+4 + (+4) = +8$$

3. $+8 - (+9)$

$$+8 + (-9) = -1$$

4. $-13 - (-6)$

$$-13 + (+6) = -7$$

5. $+5 - (+11)$

$$+5 + (-11) = -6$$

6. $-2 - (-4)$

$$-2 + (+4) = +2$$

7. $+6 - (-13)$

$$+6 + (+13) = +19$$

8. Reasoning Which is greater, $+6 - (-3)$ or $+6 + (-3)$?

$$+6 - (-3)$$

Name_____

One Doesn't Belong

E 12-7
REASONING

In each of the tables below, one pair of numbers does not belong. Identify the rule that was used to change the number in Column A to the number in Column B. Each rule involves either adding or subtracting a negative number. Then choose the pair that does not belong.

1. Rule: **Add −2**

Which pair does not belong? **−1 and −6**

A	B
−2	−4
−1	−6
0	−2
+1	−1

2. Rule: **Subtract −4**

Which pair does not belong? **−2 and +1**

A	B
−6	−2
−4	0
−2	+1
0	+4

3. Rule: **Add −5**

Which pair does not belong? **−5 and −9**

A	B
+4	−1
+1	−4
−2	−7
−5	−9

4. Rule: **Subtract −3**

Which pair does not belong? **−10 and −15**

A	B
−10	−15
−8	−5
−6	−3
−4	−1

Name_____

Subtracting Integers

PS 12-7

It's Freezing Out Use what you know about subtracting integers to answer 1–7.

1. The temperature is $-5°F$. What will the temperature be if it drops $10°F$?

$$-15°F$$

2. When Paulette woke up, the temperature was $-1°C$. At noon, the temperature was $+8°C$. How much did the temperature rise?

$$+9°C$$

3. It was $+10°F$. The temperature dropped $12°F$. What is the temperature now?

$$-2°F$$

4. At 2:00 P.M. the temperature was $+14°F$. At 8:00 P.M. the temperature was $-4°F$. How much did the temperature drop?

$$-18°F$$

5. At 6:00 P.M. the temperature was $+2°C$. By 10:00 P.M. the temperature had dropped $5°C$. What was the temperature at 10:00 P.M.?

$$-3°C$$

6. Alice and Craig were building a snowman. When they started, the temperature was $-2°C$. By the time they finished, the temperature had dropped $3°C$. What was the temperature when they finished building the snowman?

$$-5°C$$

7. The temperature is $+4°C$. What will the temperature be if it drops $7°C$?

$$-3°C$$

8. Writing in Math Petra said that any negative integer minus itself equals zero. Is she correct? Explain.

Yes; Sample answer: Because subtracting a negative number is like adding its opposite, Petra is correct. For example, $-7 - {-7} = -7 + {+7}$, which is zero.

Practice

Name_____

PROBLEM-SOLVING SKILL   P 12-8

Writing to Explain   Sample answers are given.

Write to explain.

1. In a game, you score points for each space you move your token. Complete the table and use the pattern to extend it to 7 spaces.

Number of spaces	1	2	3	**4**	**5**	**6**	**7**
Number of points	1	3	5	**7**	**9**	**11**	**13**

Explain how the number of points scored changes as the number of spaces moved changes.

As the number of spaces moved increases by 1, the number of points scored increases by 2.

2. A 4 oz jar of olives costs $1.40. An 8 oz jar of olives costs $2.50. A 16 oz jar of olives costs $3.60. Predict how much a 32 oz jar of olives will cost. Explain your prediction.

As the number of ounces in each jar doubles, the price increases by $1.10. So, the price of a 32 oz jar will be $4.70.

3. Explain how the figures are alike and different.

The figures have five sides, so they are pentagons. The pentagons have different sides and angles.

162 Use with Lesson 12-8.

Reteaching

Name_____

PROBLEM-SOLVING SKILL   R 12-8

Writing to Explain

Backpackers A group of backpackers is hiking a trail that is 10 mi long. The table below shows how the amount of time it takes to hike each mile changes as the hikers continue on the trail.

Number of miles hiked	2	4	6	8	10
Minutes to hike each mile	10	12	14	16	18

Explain how the amount of time it takes to hike each mile changes as the number of miles hiked changes.

Writing a Math Explanation

- Identify the quantities shown in the table.

- Tell how one quantity changes as the other quantity changes. Be specific. This is an explanation of the pattern.

Example

The table shows how many miles the backpackers hiked and how long it took them to hike each mile.

As the number of miles hiked increases by 2, the number of minutes it takes to hike each mile increases by 2. This means that it takes longer and longer for the backpackers to hike the trail.

1. At a banquet, each table received 80 oz of water. Different numbers of people sat at the tables. Use the pattern to complete the table for 16 diners.

Number of diners	1	2	4	8	16
Ounces per diner	80	40	20	**10**	**5**

Explain how the number of ounces per diner changes as the number of diners changes.

Sample answer: As the number of diners doubles, the number of ounces per diner decreases by half.

162 Use with Lesson 12-8.

Enrichment

Name_____

Which Is Next?

                                    E 12-8
                                    VISUAL THINKING

Circle the letter of the figure that completes the pattern shown.

1.

a.   b.   ©

2.

a.   b.   ©

3.
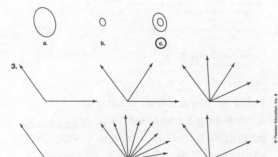

a.   b.   c.

162 Use with Lesson 12-8.

Problem Solving

Name_____

PROBLEM-SOLVING SKILL   PS 12-8

Writing to Explain

Baby-sitting Hannah earns money by baby-sitting. She earns $7 an hour. For 3 hr of baby-sitting she earns $21, for 4 hr $28, for 5 hr $35, and for 6 hr $42. Explain how the amount of money earned by Hannah changes as the number of hours changes.

Read and Understand

1. How much money does Hannah earn for 1 hr, 3 hr, 4 hr, 5 hr, and 6 hr of baby-sitting?

1 hr: $7; 3 hr: $21; 4 hr: $28; 5 hr: $35; 6 hr: $42

2. What are you trying to find?

How the amount earned by Hannah changes

Plan and Solve

3. Identify the quantities shown in the problem.

Hannah earns $7 an hour for baby-sitting.

4. Tell how one quantity changes and the other quantity changes. Write your explanation in a complete sentence.

For every extra hour Hannah baby-sits, she earns 7 more dollars.

Look Back and Check

5. Is your answer reasonable?

Sample answer:

Yes, my explanation fits the quantities shown in the problem.

162 Use with Lesson 12-8.

Practice

Name_____

The Coordinate Plane

P 12-9

Write the ordered pair for each point.

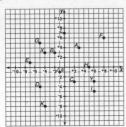

1. A **(3, 4)**
2. B **(−2, 3)**
3. C **(2, −3)**
4. D **(−5, −4)**
5. E **(−7, 1)**
6. F **(8, 6)**

Name the point for each ordered pair.

7. (+5, 0) **H**   8. (−1, −1) **J**   9. (0, +7) **L**

10. (+6, −5) **I**   11. (−4, −8) **K**   12. (−5, +5) **G**

13. If a taxi cab were to start at the point (0, 0) and drive 6 units left, 3 units down, 1 unit right, and 9 units up, what ordered pair would name the point the cab would finish at?   **(−5, 6)**

Test Prep

14. Use the coordinate graph above. Which is the y-coordinate for point X?

    A. +6   **B** +3   C. −3   D. −6

15. **Writing in Math** Explain how to graph the ordered pair (−2, +3).

Sample answer: Begin at the origin point and move 2 places to the left for the x-value of −2. Then move 3 spaces up for the y-value of 3.

Use with Lesson 12-9. **163**

Reteaching

Name_____

The Coordinate Plane

R 12-9

Naming a point:

The ordered pair for point A is (+2, +4). It is 2 units to the right of the origin (0, 0) and 4 units above the origin.

The ordered pair for point B is (−3, −2), which means 3 units to the left of the origin and 2 units below the origin.

Point C is at (+5, 0). Point D is at (+1, −4).

Graphing a point:

To graph a point when you are given an ordered pair, always begin at the origin. Move left for negative x-values and right for positive x-values. Move down for negative y-values and up for positive y-values.

Graph point L at (−2, +3).

Move 2 units to the left and then 3 units up.

Write the ordered pair for each point.

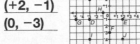

1. A **(+5, +5)**   2. B **(+4, +3)**
3. D **(−3, −1)**   4. E **(+2, −1)**
5. C **(−4, +4)**   6. F **(0, −3)**

Name the point for each ordered pair.

7. (+2, −4) **J**   8. (+1, +3) **L**   9. (−5, −1) **G**

10. (−3, −4) **I**   11. (−1, 0) **H**   12. (−3, +2) **K**

13. **Representation** What is the ordered pair for the origin?   **(0, 0)**

Use with Lesson 12-9. **163**

Enrichment

Name_____

Connect the Points

E 12-9
REASONING

Graph ordered pairs and connect them with lines to form each shape. List the ordered pairs. **Sample answers are given.**

1. Rectangle

(−3, +4), (+4, +4), (+4, −2), (−3, −2)

2. Right triangle

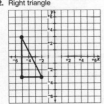

(−5, +3), (−2, −3), (−5, −3)

3. Square

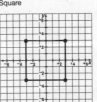

(−3, +3), (+3, +3), (−3, −3), (+3, −3)

4. Trapezoid

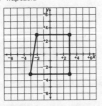

(−2, +3), (+3, +3), (−3, −3), (+3, −3)

Use with Lesson 12-9. **163**

Problem Solving

Name_____

The Coordinate Plane

PS 12-9

Map A coordinate grid illustrating Jake's neighborhood is shown below. Use the map for 1–5.

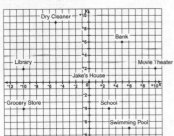

1. What is located at (+3, −4)?   **School**

2. What is the ordered pair for the location of the grocery store?   **(−10, −4)**

3. What is located at (−10, +2)?   **Library**

4. What is located at (+6, −7)?   **Swimming pool**

5. What is the ordered pair for the location of the movie theater?   **(+10, +2)**

6. **Writing in Math** Explain how to find the ordered pair for the location of the bank.

Sample answer: Count five units to the right on the x-axis. Then count six units up on the y-axis. The coordinates are (+5, +6).

Use with Lesson 12-9. **163**

Name_____

Graphing Equations

For each equation, find the values of y when $x = -1$, when $x = 0$, and when $x = +1$. Then name the ordered pairs.

1. $y = x - 1$ $(-1, -2)$ $(0, -1)$ $(1, 0)$

2. $y = 3x$ $(-1, -3)$ $(0, 0)$ $(1, 3)$

3. $y = x + -2$ $(-1, -3)$ $(0, -2)$ $(1, -1)$

Graph the equation. First, make a table using x-values of 0, +1, and +2.

4. $y = x + 4$

x	y
0	4
1	5
2	6

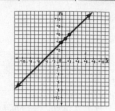

Bob earns $4 every week he takes out the trash. Use $y = 4x$, where x is the number of times Bob takes out the trash, to find how much Bob makes for taking out the trash.

5. How much will Bob have earned when he takes out the trash for 6 weeks?   **$24**

Test Prep

6. Which ordered pair is a solution to the equation $y = 6x$?

  A (0, 0)   **B.** (+6, +1)   **C.** (+2, +6)   **D.** (+6, 0)

7. **Writing in Math** Jolene says that the point $(-2, -1)$ is on the same line as the points (0, 0) and (+2, −1). Is she correct? Explain.

No; Sample answer: The points (0, 0) and (2, −1) are connected by a line, but that line has a y-value of −1 when x has a value of 2, not −2.

Name_____

Graphing Equations

Find the values for y when $x = -2$, 0, and 2.

Put -2 where the x is in the equation.

$y = x + +2$
$y = (-2) + +2$
$y = 0$

The ordered pair, then, is $(-2, 0)$.

The other ordered pairs would be $(0, +2)$ and $(+2, +4)$.

Now you can plot each of the points and connect the points with a solid line. The line formed is the graph of the equation, and all of the points on the line are solutions to the equation.

Find the values of y when $x = -2$, $x = 0$, and $x = +2$, then name the ordered pairs.

1. $y = x$ $-2, 0, +2; (-2, -2), (0, 0), (+2, +2)$

Complete the table using x-values of -2, 0, and $+2$. Graph the equation using your table.

2. $y = x - (-3)$

x	y
−2	+1
0	+3
+2	+5

Name_____

Find the Equation

The coordinate graph shows three lines labeled A, B, and C. Find the equations for these lines. Complete the tables by finding the correct x- and y-values from the graph. Then write the equations once you have discovered them.

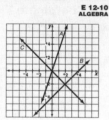

1. **Line A**   Line A equation: **$y = 3x$**

x	y
−1	−3
0	0
+1	+3
+2	+6

2. **Line B**   Line B equation: **$y = x - 4$**

x	y
−1	−5
0	−4
+1	−3
+2	−2

3. **Line C**   Line C equation: **$y = -x$**

x	y
+1	−1
+2	−2
+3	−3
+4	−4

Name_____

Graphing Equations

Art Supplies Bonnie and Hector are buying supplies for the art room. Paint brushes cost $2 each, easels cost $9 each, and paint palettes cost $6 each.

Use $y = 2x$, where x is the number of paint brushes and y is the cost, to find

1. the cost of 3 paint brushes.   **$6**

2. the cost of 12 paint brushes.   **$24**

3. the cost of 40 paint brushes.   **$80**

Use $y = 9x$, where x is the number of easels and y is the cost, to find

4. the cost of 2 easels.   **$18**

5. the cost of 13 easels.   **$117**

6. the cost of 100 easels.   **$900**

Use $y = 6x$, where x is the number of paint palettes and y is the cost, to find

7. the cost of 4 paint palettes.   **$24**

8. the cost of 15 paint palettes.   **$90**

9. the cost of 50 paint palettes.   **$300**

10. **Writing in Math** Irene has $95. How many easels can she buy? Explain.

10 easels; Sample answer: y = $99 when x = 11, and y = $90 when x = 10. With $95 she cannot buy more than 10.

Name_____

PROBLEM-SOLVING APPLICATION   P 12-11

Equations and Graphs

Solve.

1. Today's high temperature was +15°F, and the low temperature was x degrees lower. If the low temperature was −5°F, how much less was the low temperature than the high temperature? Write an equation and solve it to find the answer.

$15 - x = -5$; $x = 20$;

The low temperature was 20°F less.

2. Solve the problem $5x = 125$. Explain which property you needed to use.

$x = 25$; Sample answer: Because it is a multiplication problem, I needed to use the inverse of multiplication, which is division. So, I used the Division Property of Equality and divided both sides by 5.

3. Graph the points with ordered pairs $A(0, +3)$, $B(+3, -3)$, and $C(-3, -3)$. Connect the points and tell what type of figure is formed.

triangle

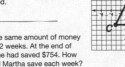

4. Martha saved the same amount of money every week for 52 weeks. At the end of the 52 weeks, she had saved $754. How much money did Martha save each week? Draw a picture and write an equation to solve.

Check students' drawings; $52x = 754$; $x = 14.50$; Martha saved $14.50 each week.

Name_____

PROBLEM-SOLVING APPLICATION   R 12-11

Weather in Romantown

Winter in Romantown is often cold. On December 12, the temperature at 10 A.M. was +8°F. A cold front came through, and the temperature dropped throughout the day. By 3 P.M. the temperature was 19°F lower than it was at 10 A.M. What was the temperature at 3 P.M.?

The temperature at 10 A.M. + the change in temperature = the temperature at 3 P.M.

$+8 + (-19) = n$

$+8 + (-19) = -11$

So, the temperature at 3 P.M. was −11°F.

1. On January 4, the temperature was −6°F in the early morning. By 4:00 P.M. that afternoon, the temperature had risen 31°F. What was the temperature at 4:00 P.M.?   **+25°F**

2. In mid-January, members of a Romantown fire station attempted to build an ice skating rink at a local park. In the afternoon, when the temperature was +35°F, the firemen sprayed hundreds of gallons of water on the field. By how many degrees would the temperature have to drop for the water to turn to ice?   **+3°F**

The month of March in Romantown can be very wintry and cold but can also have some warmer, springlike days. Below are word descriptions for the temperatures on several days in March. Write an integer for each description.

3. 7 degrees below zero   **−7**

4. 49 degrees above zero   **+49**

5. 2 degrees below zero   **−2**

6. 51 degrees above zero   **+51**

Name_____

Graphing Shapes   E 12-11
                                   VISUAL THINKING

By combining some of the skills you have learned in this chapter and looking at the graph below, answer the following questions.

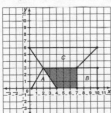

1. Name the shapes labeled A, B, and C.

A is a triangle, B is a square, and C is a trapezoid.

2. Write the ordered pairs for each point of each shape.

A: (0, 0), (+2, +3), (+4, 0); B: (+7, 0), (+7, +3), (+10, +3), (+10, 0); C: (+2, +3), (0, +6), (+10, +6), (+7, +3)

3. Do the shapes share ordered pairs? If so, which ordered pairs are shared?

Yes; (+2, +3) and (+7, +3)

4. Have you noticed that the x-axis and the three lines connecting shapes A, B, and C make another shape? Shade it and write the name of the shape.

Trapezoid

Name_____

PROBLEM-SOLVING APPLICATION   PS 12-11

Correct!

Jimmy answered 95 math questions correctly. He answered 5 times more questions correctly than Bernie. How many questions did Bernie answer correctly?

Read and Understand

1. How many questions did Jimmy answer correctly? How many more did Jimmy answer correctly than Bernie?

95 questions; 5 times more

2. What are you trying to find?

How many questions Bernie answered correctly

Plan and Solve

3. Write an equation for the problem.

$5n = 95$

4. Solve the problem. Write your answer in a complete sentence.

Bernie answered 19 questions correctly.

Look Back and Check

5. Is your answer reasonable?

Sample answer: Yes, because $19 \times 5 = 95$